OBSESSED WITH™
HOLLYWOOD

OBSESSED WITH™
HOLLYWOOD

TEST YOUR KNOWLEDGE OF THE SILVER SCREEN

 by Andrew J. Rausch

Library of Congress Control Number: 2006940411

ISBN: 978-1-932855-92-0

Printed in China

Cover Photographs:
Left: 1971 Paramount
Center: 1960 Paramount
Right: © 1997 20th Century Fox

Design: Paul Barrett
Editorial: Kjersti Egerdahl, Kate Perry, Ali Basye
Image Research: Lisa Metzger
Production Coordination: Leah Finger, Nick Boone-Lutz
Product Development: Peter Schumacher

10 9 8 7 6 5 4 3 2 1

Chronicle Books
680 Second Street
San Francisco, CA 94107

www.chroniclebooks.com

This edition printed specifically for Books Are Fun, Ltd.

Previous Spread: Humphrey Bogart and
Ingrid Bergman in *Casablanca*, 1942.

CONTENTS

HOW TO USE THE MODULE

To turn on the module, press the ENTER (**E**) button.

CHOOSING THE GAME MODE

The module will automatically start in **Random Question** mode. To switch between the **Random Question** and **Question Select** game modes, press **E** and **D** together. The module will ask you to SELECT THE GAME MODE. Press **B** for **Question Select**, or **C** for **Random Question** mode.

• In **Random Question** mode, a question number will appear automatically. Turn to that question in the book and read it. The module will ask you to CHOOSE THE ANSWER.

Select your answer by pressing the corresponding button beneath **A**, **B**, **C**, or **D**. The display window and accompanying sound will notify you whether you are CORRECT or INCORRECT. If you are incorrect, the module will display the correct answer.

The module will then randomly select another question.

• In **Question Select** mode, press **E** to accept the question number displayed, or enter the number of the question you wish to answer by pressing **A** for each 1,000 digit, **B** for each 100, **C** for each 10 and **D** for the single digit. For example, if you would like to answer question number 2,138, you would press **A** twice, **B** once, **C** three times, and **D** eight times.

Press **E** to enter the question. The module will ask you to CHOOSE THE ANSWER. If you are incorrect, the module will display the correct answer.

The module will then automatically advance to the next question in sequence. To accept that question, press **E**. To answer a different question, enter the corresponding question number using the **A**, **B**, **C**, and **D** buttons as above.

CHOOSING THE NUMBER OF PLAYERS

After you choose the game mode, the module will then ask you to SELECT THE NUMBER OF PLAYERS. Press **A** for a 1-PLAYER, or **D** for a 2-PLAYER game. For 2 PLAYER mode, each player will alternate selecting and answering questions as above, according to the game mode. PLAYER 1 or PLAYER 2 will flash to signal which player's turn it is.

SCORING

• In **One-Player** mode, after each question is answered, the module will flash the number of CORRECT answers in the left window, OUT OF the total number of QUESTIONS answered in the right window, followed by the percentage correct in the right window.

• In **Two-Player** mode, the left window **F** displays PLAYER 1's number of CORRECT questions OUT OF the total number of questions, and the resulting percentage correct. PLAYER 2's score appears in the right window **G**.

ADDITIONAL FUCTIONS

The module will go to sleep after forty-five seconds idle, but can be awakened by pressing any button.

To manually turn off the module, hold down the **E** button for three seconds. The module also will turn off after sitting idle for several minutes.

To mute the sound effects, hold down **E** and press **A**. An icon will signal whether the speaker is on ◁ or off ⬨.

BATTERIES

The module includes three AG-13 button-cell batteries. If the module does not turn on, you may need to replace the batteries through the compartment door on the back of the book.

CHAPTER ONE:
THE ICONS

1. What is the name of the studio founded by Sidney Poitier, Barbra Streisand, and Paul Newman in 1969?
   - **A.** Tri-Star
   - **B.** United Artists
   - **C.** First Artists
   - **D.** SNP Pictures

2. From 1950 to 1967, James Stewart rode the same trusty steed in every single western in which he appeared. What was this horse's name?
   - **A.** Dusty
   - **B.** Pie
   - **C.** Smiley
   - **D.** Happy Jack

3. Legendary bombshell Lana Turner was known for the sex appeal she exuded in such films as *The Postman Always Rings Twice*, and *The Bad and the Beautiful*. How many times was Lana Turner married?
   - **A.** Eight
   - **B.** Seven
   - **C.** Ten
   - **D.** Nine

4. Spencer Tracy and Mickey Rooney both portrayed the same real-life person in separate films released in 1940. Who was this?
   - **A.** Louis Pasteur
   - **B.** Abraham Lincoln
   - **C.** Thomas Edison
   - **D.** Christopher Columbus

5. What was Lauren Bacall's birth name?
   - **A.** Harriet Belinda Hubbel
   - **B.** May Markham
   - **C.** Betty Joan Perske
   - **D.** Vivian Sternwood Rutledge

6. In a career that spanned nearly sixty years, Bette Davis appeared in more than a hundred films. In what film did she give her final performance?
   - **A.** *The Whales of August*
   - **B.** *As Summers Die*
   - **C.** *Wicked Stepmother*
   - **D.** *Right of Way*

7. Screen legend and sex goddess Marilyn Monroe was married three times. To which of the following men was she *not* married?
   - **A.** Arthur Miller
   - **B.** Joe DiMaggio
   - **C.** James Dougherty
   - **D.** Yves Montand

OPPOSITE Publicity still of Bette Davis in *All About Eve*, 1950

8. Sean Connery's first name isn't really "Sean." What is it?

A. Joseph
B. Thomas
C. Francis
D. Marion

9. Marlon Brando appeared in more than forty films, but he only directed one. What is the title of Brando's sole directorial effort?

A. *Sayonara*
B. *Burn!*
C. *One-Eyed Jacks*
D. *Candy*

10.

11. Renaissance man Charles Chaplin not only wrote, directed, acted, and scored many films, but he also penned four books. Which of the following books was written by Chaplin?

A. *Getting It Right*
B. *Being Me*
C. *My Trip Abroad*
D. *Looking Back*

12. Three of the four collaborative efforts between Gary Cooper and Clara Bow were released in 1927. Which of these is *not* one of them?

A. *It*
B. *Wings*
C. *Children of Divorce*
D. *Get Your Man*

13. Like most actors and actresses of her era, Claudette Colbert used a stage name. What was her real name?

A. Marsha Fay Whitlock
B. Lily Claudette Chauchoin
C. Coretta Jane Douglas
D. Claudette Ella Mayfeather

14. The late, great Marlon Brando penned an autobiography that was released in 1994. What was the title of his memoir?

A. *Contender*
B. *Occupation: Actor*
C. *Songs My Mother Taught Me*
D. *The Road Less Travelled*

15. Julie Andrews later reteamed with Robert Wise, who'd directed her previously in *The Sound of Music*. What was their second collaboration?

A. *West Side Story*
B. *Mary Poppins*
C. *Star!*
D. *Little Miss Marker*

16. Lauren Bacall has appeared in more than sixty films during her long, productive career. In which of these films did she make her screen debut?

A. *The Big Sleep*
B. *To Have and Have Not*
C. *Dark Passage*
D. *How to Marry a Millionaire*

10.

In the early 1960s, a soon-to-be legendary group of entertainers started going by "The Rat Pack." The central members—Frank Sinatra, Dean Martin, Sammy Davis Jr., Peter Lawford, and Joey Bishop—partied together, performed on stage together, recorded together, and collaborated on a handful of films, including *Sergeants 3*, *Ocean's Eleven*, *4 for Texas*, and *Robin and the 7 Hoods*. Sinatra and Martin, who remained friends until their deaths, appear together in ten films. What was the first film that featured both of them?

A. *Pepe*
B. *Robin and the 7 Hoods*
C. *Some Came Running*
D. *The Road to Hong Kong*

17. Screen team Fred Astaire and Ginger Rogers danced their way through nine RKO films together. What film was their first collaboration?

A. Top Hat   **C.** Carefree

B. Flying Down to Rio Castle   **D.** The Story of Vernon and Irene

18. Paul Newman has played a wide variety of characters, from bank robbers to evil tycoons. In what film does he play a crime boss named John Rooney?

A. The Sting   **C.** Road to Perdition

B. Message in a Bottle   **D.** Slap Shot

19. Underrated helmer Monte Hellman has directed actor Jack Nicholson in five films. Which of these is *not* one of them?

A. The Shooting   **C.** The Raven

B. Back Door to Hell   **D.** Ride in the Whirlwind

20. Legendary thespian Laurence Olivier once said he couldn't breathe without something. What was it?

A. Movies   **C.** Theatre

B. His wife, Vivien Leigh   **D.** Acting

21. Which of George C. Scott's films has been released under the alternate title *One Born Every Minute*?

A. The Hustler   **C.** The Hospital

B. The Flim-Flam Man   **D.** The Formula

22. There are nine *Pink Panther* films in the original series. All but two of them feature Peter Sellers in the lead role. Which of these does not?

A. A Shot in the Dark   **C.** Inspector Clouseau

B. The Return of the Pink Panther   **D.** The Pink Panther Strikes Again

23. Can you name the actress who was born Virginia Katherine McMath, but is better known by her stage name?

A. Jean Harlow   **C.** Ginger Rogers

B. Bette Davis   **D.** Katharine Hepburn

24. Iconic tough guys Humphrey Bogart and Edward G. Robinson appear in five films together. Which of these marks their first collaboration?

A. The Amazing Dr. Clitterhouse   **C.** Bullets or Ballots

B. Kid Galahad   **D.** Brother Orchid

25. What does Julia Roberts say she believes to be the biggest misconception about her?

A. That she's a "bitch"

B. That she dislikes serious roles

C. That she's an "airhead"

D. That she can't act

26. Funnyman Robin Williams appears in more than seventy films. In what film did he make his screen debut?

A. *The World According to Garp*

B. *Can I Do It 'Till I Need Glasses?*

C. *Popeye*

D. *Moscow on the Hudson*

27.

28. In what film does Natalie Wood play a character named Debbie Edwards?

A. *Rebel Without a Cause*

B. *West Side Story*

C. *The Searchers*

D. *Splendor in the Grass*

29. Lauren Bacall was married just twice, but she was also briefly engaged to a popular singer in the late 1950s. Which one?

A. Dean Martin

B. Bill Haley

C. Frank Sinatra

D. Bing Crosby

30. Which of these iconic actresses was the first woman to be president of the Academy of Motion Picture Arts and Sciences?

A. Elizabeth Taylor

B. Barbara Stanwyck

C. Lauren Bacall

D. Bette Davis

31. Marilyn Monroe died as the result of an apparent suicide attempt on August 5, 1962. How old would this make her at the time of her death?

A. 30

B. 24

C. 36

D. 28

32. Humphrey Bogart named one of his children after another actor. Who was it?

A. Leslie Caron

B. Leslie Townes "Bob" Hope

C. Leslie Howard

D. Leslie Nielsen

33. In the brief period of his life during which James Dean was a star, his love life was of national interest. With whom did he have a well-publicized love affair?

A. Elizabeth Taylor

B. Sal Mineo

C. Natalie Wood

D. Pier Angeli

27.

Heaven Can Wait, the story of a dead NFL quarterback who is given a second shot at life (written by Elaine May and Hollywood icon Warren Beatty), is the 1978 remake of the film *Here Comes Mr. Jordan*, which was based on a play by Harry Segall. The film was produced and co-directed by Beatty (who also appeared in the lead role) and received an impressive nine Academy Award nominations, taking home one for art direction. By the time Beatty's 1981 film *Reds* was awarded its third Oscar, he had proven himself as an actor, producer, screenwriter, and director—a true quadruple threat.

With whom did Warren Beatty co-direct *Heaven Can Wait*?

A. Charles Grodin

B. Arthur Penn

C. Robert Towne

D. Buck Henry

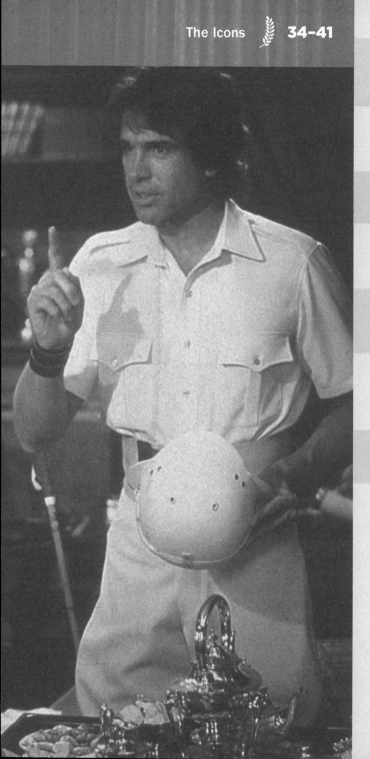

34. Legendary tough guys James Cagney and Edward G. Robinson appear in only one film together. Can you name it?

   A. *G Men*   **C.** *Smart Money*

   B. *A Bullet for Joey*   **D.** *The Public Enemy*

35. What health problem kept Spencer Tracy from attending the premiere for *Guess Who's Coming to Dinner*?

   A. Pneumonia   **C.** Death

   B. Cancer   **D.** Emphysema

36. What legendary actress was nicknamed "The Face"?

   A. Ingrid Bergman   **C.** Greta Garbo

   B. Elizabeth Taylor   **D.** Myrna Loy

37. Which legendary actor's filmography includes *Sunset Boulevard, Network,* and *The Wild Bunch*?

   A. Cary Grant   **C.** Kirk Douglas

   B. Jack Lemmon   **D.** William Holden

38. The character who kills John Wayne in *The Cowboys* is played by which of these actors?

   A. Robert Duvall   **C.** James Caan

   B. Bruce Dern   **D.** Dennis Hopper

39. For what crime was Robert Mitchum arrested on August 31, 1948 (and later jailed)?

   A. Being drunk and disorderly   **C.** Firing a handgun in a public place

   B. Possession of marijuana   **D.** Possession of a controlled substance

40. Who was the first actor to appear on the cover of *Time* magazine?

   A. Rudolph Valentino   **C.** Clark Gable

   B. Frank Sinatra   **D.** Charles Chaplin

41. Which screen siren was awarded "Sexiest Woman of the Century" honors by *People* magazine in 1999?

   A. Marilyn Monroe   **C.** Raquel Welch

   B. Julia Roberts   **D.** Sophia Loren

42. Natalie Wood drowned on November 29, 1981. What film was she making at the time of her death?

A. *The Last Married Couple in America*

B. *The Memory of Eva Ryker*

C. *Meteor*

D. *Brainstorm*

43. Popular myth says this actress was discovered at Schwab's Drug Store in Los Angeles. However, she was actually discovered while purchasing a drink at Top's Café. Who is she?

A. Raquel Welch

B. Judy Garland

C. Lana Turner

D. Gene Tierney

44.

45. What did Spencer Tracy say he looked for in a film script?

A. "A good role"

B. "Lots of words and punctuation marks"

C. "Days off"

D. "Something inexplicably magical"

46. What actress married real-life prince Aly Khan in 1949?

A. Grace Kelly

B. Ingrid Bergman

C. Rita Hayworth

D. Jean Harlow

47. Humphrey Bogart's son wrote a memoir about his father. What is its title?

A. *Humphrey Bogart: My Father*

B. *Bogart: In Search of My Father*

C. *Bogie: In My Father's Eyes*

D. *Sins of the Father: A Humphrey Bogart Story*

48. What magazine is credited with discovering ingenue Clara Bow in 1921?

A. *Starstruck*

B. *Life*

C. *Photoplay*

D. *Motion Picture Magazine*

49. What actor referred to screen legend Lee Marvin as "Lee Moron"?

A. James Coburn

B. Marlon Brando

C. Frank Sinatra

D. Jane Fonda

50. James Cagney portrayed a real-life person in *Man of a Thousand Faces*. Can you name this person?

A. P.T. Barnum

B. Lon Chaney

C. Max Factor

D. Rudolph Valentino

44.

Woody Allen began performing as a stand-up comic and writing for stars like Sid Caesar when he was only sixteen years old. He studied film at New York University and City College of New York and began writing for a number of television shows including *The Tonight Show* and *The Ed Sullivan Show* while still a teenager. He penned short stories, plays, and screenplays and in 1966, at thirty-one, directed his first film, *What's Up, Tiger Lily?* A successful acting career followed, underscored by Oscar nominations for acting, directing, and writing. Today Allen continues to work as a respected filmmaker and satirist with nearly fifty films to his credit.

How has he said he wants to achieve immortality?

A. By being cryogenically frozen

B. Through his work

C. By not dying

D. By marrying his stepdaughter

51. Sean Connery claims to hate which of his characters?

A. Professor Henry Jones   C. James Bond

B. Allan Quatermain   D. Sir August de Wynter

52. Fred Astaire penned his autobiography in 1959. What is the title of this book?

A. *Cheek to Cheek*   C. *Steps in Time*

B. *To a Different Drummer*   D. *The Music in My Heart*

53. Linda Darnell was brought to Hollywood by a talent scout, but lied about her age and was sent back home. How old was Darnell when she began appearing in films?

A. Eleven   C. Sixteen

B. Thirteen   D. Twenty

54. Jack Nicholson stars in a film whose title comes from a song by the Plastic Ono Band. What is this film?

A. *The Two Jakes*   C. *The Shining*

B. *The Witches of Eastwick*   D. *As Good As It Gets*

55. Robert Redford wore his jacket from the baseball film *The Natural* in another of his films years later. What is this film?

A. *Spy Game*   C. *Sneakers*

B. *Indecent Proposal*   D. *Havana*

56. What is the only film in which Julia Roberts has appeared with her brother, Eric Roberts?

A. *I Love Trouble*   C. *Blood Red*

B. *The Player*   D. *Mystic Pizza*

57. How many children did Anthony Quinn father?

A. Ten   C. Twelve

B. Thirteen   D. Eleven

58. Name the film in which Sidney Poitier's character befriends a blind white girl.

A. *No Way Out*   C. *A Patch of Blue*

B. *Lilies of the Field*   D. *Little Nikita*

59. What did Mary Pickford become the first actress ever to do in 1912's *Friends*?

A. Kiss on screen   C. Appear in a close-up

B. Undress on screen   D. Kill someone

60. Prolific actor Al Pacino appears in more than forty films. In which one does he play a character named Ricky Roma?

- **A.** *Gigli*
- **B.** *Heat*
- **C.** *Glengarry Glen Ross*
- **D.** *Scent of a Woman*

61. Any time Gregory Peck was asked which of his many great films was his favorite, he always gave the same answer. What was this?

- **A.** *Roman Holiday*
- **B.** *Twelve O'Clock High*
- **C.** *To Kill a Mockingbird*
- **D.** *The Boys from Brazil*

62. Which of these 1942 films does *not* feature both Humphrey Bogart and Sydney Greenstreet?

- **A.** *Across the Pacific*
- **B.** *The Big Shot*
- **C.** *Casablanca*
- **D.** *In This Our Life*

63. Who did novelist Eleanor Glyn dub the "It" girl?

- **A.** Jean Harlow
- **B.** Myrna Loy
- **C.** Clara Bow
- **D.** Mae West

64. What NBA team's games are famously frequented by Jack Nicholson?

- **A.** Sacramento Kings
- **B.** Los Angeles Lakers
- **C.** New Jersey Nets
- **D.** Los Angeles Clippers

65. Like a great number of her peers, screen icon Marilyn Monroe used a stage name. What was her real name?

- **A.** Norma Jean Morgenstern
- **B.** Norma Jean Mortensen
- **C.** Norma Jeane Monroe
- **D.** Norma Jean Morrison

66. James Dean was about to begin work on a fourth film with a starring role when he was killed. What was the film?

- **A.** *Raintree County*
- **B.** *Somebody Up There Likes Me*
- **C.** *Baby Doll*
- **D.** *High Society*

67. Whose wife discovered Lauren Bacall at the age of nineteen?

- **A.** John Ford
- **B.** Humphrey Bogart
- **C.** King Vidor
- **D.** Howard Hawks

70.

The son of a New York surgeon, Humphrey Bogart was dismissed from prep school and joined the Naval Reserve before being bitten by the acting bug. He began performing onstage in 1921, toiling for more than a decade playing small bit parts. In 1934, Bogart finally found success on Broadway as Duke Mantee in *The Petrified Forest*, and became a Hollywood player when Warner Bros. adapted the play into a film two years later. He then appeared in a string of forgettable films, playing mostly generic tough guys, before finally landing a breakout role in Raoul Walsh's *High Sierra* (1941). From then on, there was no stopping him. Best known for films such as *Casablanca*, *Treasure of the Sierra Madre*, and *The African Queen*, "Bogie" remains cemented as one of Tinseltown's greatest stars.

Although Bogart's most popular nickname was "Bogie," he was also referred to as "the Last Century Man." Why is this?

A. He spoke abruptly, like a caveman
B. He was considered old fashioned
C. He was born on Christmas Day, 1899
D. He openly believed the world would end soon

68. Bette Davis married one of her *All About Eve* costars. Which one?
A. George Sanders
B. Hugh Marlowe
C. Gary Merrill
D. Addison De Witt

69. What actress said of Humphrey Bogart, "I kissed him, but I never knew him"?
A. Ingrid Bergman
B. Katharine Hepburn
C. Lauren Bacall
D. Audrey Hepburn

70.

71. Can you name the 1971 film in which Robert De Niro plays a taxi driver?
A. *Taxi Driver*
B. *Jennifer on My Mind*
C. *The Wedding Party*
D. *Greetings*

72. In what film does Doris Day sing "*Que Sera Sera*"?
A. *Pillow Talk*
B. *Please Don't Eat the Daisies*
C. *The Man Who Knew Too Much*
D. *Calamity Jane*

73. James Dean worked on a game show before succeeding as an actor. What is this game show?
A. "Twenty One"
B. "Beat the Clock"
C. "The Price Is Right"
D. "What's My Line?"

74. Only one Steven Spielberg film features the great Audrey Hepburn. Which one is this?
A. *Hook*
B. *The Sugarland Express*
C. *Always*
D. *Duel*

75. Whose autobiography is titled *An Actor's Life*?
A. Glenn Ford
B. Charlton Heston
C. Spencer Tracy
D. William Holden

76. Who did Mae West say climbed the ladder of success "wrong by wrong"?
A. Marilyn Monroe
B. Clara Bow
C. Jean Harlow
D. Carole Lombard

77. In what film does Tom Hanks play a character named Sherman McCoy?

A. Philadelphia   **C.** The Man with One Red Shoe

B. Volunteers   **D.** Bonfire of the Vanities

78. What was the first film on which Rita Hayworth and Glenn Ford collaborated?

A. Gilda   **C.** The Lady in Question

B. Affair in Trinidad   **D.** The Money Trap

79. Legendary actress Olivia de Havilland appears in 55 films. Do you know where this screen great was born?

A. Tokyo, Japan   **C.** Paris, France

B. Des Moines, Iowa   **D.** London, England

80. Julie Andrews appears in only one film directed by Alfred Hitchcock. What is it?

A. Suspicion   **C.** Torn Curtain

B. Marnie   **D.** Family Plot

81. This legendary actor's life was depicted in the 1985 TV movie My Wicked, Wicked Ways. Can you name him?

A. Rudolph Valentino   **C.** Clark Gable

B. Errol Flynn   **D.** James Dean

82.

83. Anne Bancroft, best remembered for the films The Miracle Worker and The Graduate, was married to which notable Mel?

A. Mel Ferrer   **C.** Mel Tormé

B. Mel Brooks   **D.** Mel Blanc

84. Warren Beatty's sister is also a famous actress. What is her name?

A. Faye Dunaway   **C.** Shirley MacLaine

B. Shelly Long   **D.** Annette Bening

85. Three of Glenn Ford's four wives were actresses. To which of these actresses was he *not* married?

A. Eleanor Powell   **C.** Jean Rogers

B. Kathryn Hays   **D.** Cynthia Hayward

82.

John Wayne is one of the most undisputed iconic figures in the history of cinema, but things weren't always that way. Wayne began working in film as a prop manager, earning a meager (by Hollywood standards) $35 a week. In 1930, the former USC football player landed his first starring role in *The Big Trail*, doubling his salary. However, it wasn't until his unforgettable turn in John Ford's *Stagecoach* nearly a decade later that Wayne became a superstar. He would ultimately appear in nearly 250 films, including such gems as *The Searchers*, *Rio Bravo*, *True Grit*, *The Quiet Man*, and *The Shootist*.

Can you name the film that features Wayne's final leading role?

A. The Cowboys

B. The Shootist

C. Brannigan

D. McQ

86. What actress does Julia Roberts refer to as her role model?
- **A.** Jessica Lange
- **B.** Faye Dunaway
- **C.** Susan Sarandon
- **D.** Shirley MacLaine

87. Who said the problem with Humphrey Bogart was that "he thinks he's Bogart"?
- **A.** Ingrid Bergman
- **B.** John Huston
- **C.** Frank Sinatra
- **D.** Michael Curtiz

88. What was James Dean's middle name?
- **A.** William
- **B.** Byron
- **C.** Calvin
- **D.** Blake

89. What film marked Robert De Niro's second appearance in a Martin Scorsese picture?
- **A.** *New York, New York*
- **B.** *Taxi Driver*
- **C.** *The King of Comedy*
- **D.** *Raging Bull*

90. Which of these gangsters has *not* been portrayed by Dustin Hoffman?
- **A.** Meyer Lansky
- **B.** Lucky Luciano
- **C.** Dutch Shultz
- **D.** Hoffman has never played any of them

91. Sylvester Stallone made his directorial debut with what film?
- **A.** *Rocky II*
- **B.** *The Lords of Flatbush*
- **C.** *F.I.S.T.*
- **D.** *Paradise Alley*

92. What was Audrey Hepburn's real last name?
- **A.** Keller
- **B.** Ruston
- **C.** Bartel
- **D.** Yamin

93. Charlton Heston appears in a number of films directed by his son, Fraser Clarke Heston. In which of the following did he *not* appear?
- **A.** *Alaska*
- **B.** *Treasure Island*
- **C.** *Needful Things*
- **D.** *The Crucifer of Blood*

94. Jean Harlow wrote a novel that was published nearly thirty years after her death. What was its title?

A. *Platinum Blonde*
B. *Flora Finds a Man*
C. *Today Is Tonight*
D. *When I Close My Eyes*

95. Charles Vidor directed the great Rita Hayworth in four films. Which of these is *not* one of them?

A. *Affair in Trinidad*
B. *Gilda*
C. *Cover Girl*
D. *The Loves of Carmen*

96. The late Glenn Ford appears in more than a hundred films. What was his last theatrically released film?

A. *Final Verdict*
B. *Raw Nerve*
C. *Happy Birthday to Me*
D. *Border Shootout*

97. In what film does Anne Bancroft sing "Sweet Georgia Brown" in Polish?

A. *The Pumpkin Eater*
B. *The Miracle Worker*
C. *The Turning Point*
D. *To Be or Not to Be*

98. In how many films did Humphrey Bogart and Lauren Bacall appear together?

A. Three
B. Four
C. Five
D. Six

99. What actress claims in her book *Dizzy and Jimmy* to have been secretly engaged to James Dean?

A. Natalie Wood
B. Pier Angeli
C. Liz Sheridan
D. Mercedes McCambridge

100. On one film, Marilyn Monroe reportedly needed forty-seven takes to correctly deliver a line of dialogue containing only three words. What film was this?

A. *Bus Stop*
B. *Some Like It Hot*
C. *The Seven Year Itch*
D. *Gentlemen Prefer Blondes*

101. Who divorced his wife in 1980 and married their babysitter nine days later?

A. Jack Nicholson
B. Warren Beatty
C. Robert Redford
D. Dustin Hoffman

102. John Wayne is a household name around the globe, yet it wasn't the actor's real name. What name was he born with?

A. Michael Morris Wayne
B. Morris Marion Winstead
C. John Marion Michaels
D. Marion Robert Morrison

103.

What is the name of Joan Crawford's abused daughter who penned the bestseller *Mommie Dearest*?

A. Kristen

B. Crissy

C. Crista

D. Christina

104.

Which of the four elderly performers from 1987's *The Whales of August* was the oldest?

A. Vincent Price

B. Lillian Gish

C. Bette Davis

D. Ann Sothern

105.

On how many films was James Cagney credited as "Jimmy" Cagney?

A. He was always credited as Jimmy Cagney

B. One

C. 112

D. None

106.

Few Hollywood performers hold as prominent a place in the nation's collective heart as Marilyn Monroe. In spite of her controversial death nearly half a century ago, Monroe has become the singular personification of sensuality. She remains a true American icon, and despite the not-quite-wholesome life she led, she has become an idealized symbol of what is perceived as a more innocent era. In death, Monroe has become larger than life. While her acting ability was sometimes questioned while she was alive, she is recognized today as one of the greatest stars in the history of Hollywood. As with Elvis, she can be identified solely by her first name, even to those who cannot name a single film in which she appears.

When Monroe died on August 5, 1962, she was midway through shooting a new film. What was this film?

A. *Blonde Ambition*

B. *The Misfits*

C. *Something's Got to Give*

D. *All That Glitters*

107.

What iconic actor makes an appearance as a blind man in *Young Frankenstein*?

A. Richard Burton

B. Robert Duvall

C. Gene Hackman

D. Rod Steiger

108.

What is Ingrid Bergman's relation to director Ingmar Bergman?

A. Niece

B. Daughter

C. No relation

D. Stepdaughter

109.

Screen siren Clara Bow appears in fifty-six feature films. Which of the following was her first film to include sound?

A. *The Wild Party*

B. *The It Girl*

C. *Grit*

D. *Maytime*

110.

There was only one film made under the Marilyn Monroe Productions banner. What is this film?

A. *The Seven Year Itch*

B. *The Prince and the Showgirl*

C. *Gentlemen Prefer Blondes*

D. *The Misfits*

111. Which of these actors was born on the same day as Doris Day?

A. Rock Hudson
B. Cary Grant
C. Rod Taylor
D. Marlon Brando

112. What long-deceased icon appeared posthumously in a Coors beer commercial in 1996?

A. Elvis Presley
B. Clark Gable
C. John Wayne
D. Groucho Marx

113. To which of his four wives was Humphrey Bogart married at the time of his death in 1957?

A. Mayo Methot
B. Lauren Bacall
C. Mary Philips
D. Helen Menken

114. What was the name of the movie studio established by Charles Chaplin, Douglas Fairbanks, Mary Pickford, and D.W. Griffith?

A. Screen Gems
B. United Artists
C. Tri-Star Pictures
D. Four Star Pictures

115.

116. In 1960, what fellow singer and actor did Sandra Dee marry?

A. Richard Egan
B. Bobby Darin
C. James Darren
D. Frankie Avalon

117. What actor portrayed legendary writer-director-actor Charles Chaplin in the Peter Bogdanovich film *Cat's Meow*?

A. Robert Downey, Jr.
B. Ed Harris
C. Eddie Izzard
D. Chick Wango

118. What iconic Hollywood actor established TriBeCa Productions in 1989?

A. George Clooney
B. Sean Penn
C. Harrison Ford
D. Robert De Niro

115.

Cary Grant is perhaps the definitive example of an elegant and debonair leading man. Throughout his career, the charming and witty Englishman was thought to be the ladies' man he personified on-screen. This image was called into question, however, when rumors circulated that Grant and roommate Randolph Scott were lovers. In the years since, numerous books have been published asserting that Grant was gay, including William J. Mann's *Behind the Screen: How Gays and Lesbians Shaped Hollywood*, and in *Brando Unzipped*, Darwin Porter alleges a homosexual love affair between Marlon Brando and Grant. In Boze Hadleigh's book *Hollywood Gays*, openly homosexual director George Cukor confirms Grant's homosexuality. Grant, however, denied such claims until his death in 1986.

Fed up with being the butt of countless jokes, Grant once successfully sued a comic who referred to him as a "homo" on national television. Who was the comedian?

A. Bill Murray
B. Chevy Chase
C. George Carlin
D. Richard Pryor

119. Whose birth name was Doris Mary Ann von Kappelhoff?
- **A.** Barbara Stanwyck
- **B.** Greta Garbo
- **C.** Doris Day
- **D.** Marlene Dietrich

120. How many of the AFI's 1998 list of the one hundred greatest films in the history of American cinema feature Robert Duvall?
- **A.** Seven
- **B.** Three
- **C.** Six
- **D.** Four

121. What is the title of Marlene Dietrich's autobiography?
- **A.** *Life . . . For Better or Worse*
- **B.** *Call Me Marlene*
- **C.** *Marlene*
- **D.** *All of Me*

122. What was the first film to feature both Burt Lancaster and Kirk Douglas?
- **A.** *Tough Guys*
- **B.** *Gunfight at the O.K. Corral*
- **C.** *The Devil's Disciple*
- **D.** *I Walk Alone*

123. One of these films was initially developed as a vehicle for Kevin Costner—however, because of his busy schedule, Costner was forced to turn the role over to Harrison Ford. Can you name the film?
- **A.** *What Lies Beneath*
- **B.** *The Fugitive*
- **C.** *Firewall*
- **D.** *Air Force One*

124. In a case of icon-on-icon crime, Walter Matthau is beaten up by Elvis Presley in this cinema classic. Can you name the film?
- **A.** *King Creole*
- **B.** *Speedway*
- **C.** *Jailhouse Rock*
- **D.** *It Happened at the World's Fair*

125. What Hollywood icon established Malpaso Productions?
- **A.** Jack Nicholson
- **B.** Clint Eastwood
- **C.** Warren Beatty
- **D.** Robert Duvall

126. Douglas Fairbanks made nearly fifty films. What was his final silent film?
- **A.** *The Iron Mask*
- **B.** *The Private Life of Don Juan*
- **C.** *The Taming of the Shrew*
- **D.** *The Mark of Zorro*

127. What, according to his daughter Nancy, were Frank Sinatra's last words before dying?
- **A.** "I doubt I have time for a martini now"
- **B.** "How about one for the road?"
- **C.** "I'm losing"
- **D.** "I did it my way"

128. Which of these is *not* a television series on which Sally Field appeared?

A. *Gidget*

B. *Homicide*

C. *E.R.*

D. *The Flying Nun*

129. With what film did legendary actor Henry Fonda make his debut?

A. *The Trail of the Lonesome Pine*

B. *Young Mr. Lincoln*

C. *The Farmer Takes a Wife*

D. *The Lady Eve*

130. In 1970, Jane Fonda was arrested and accused of attempting to smuggle pills onto an airplane. What kind of pills was she actually carrying?

A. Birth control pills

B. Vitamin pills

C. Painkillers

D. Energy pills

131. Jodie Foster's acting career began when she appeared in a television commercial at the age of three. What product was she endorsing in the commercial?

A. Ford automobiles

B. Coca-Cola brand soft drink

C. Blue Bunny ice cream

D. Coppertone lotion

132. In what film does Harrison Ford play a character named Bob Falfa?

A. *American Graffiti*

B. *What Lies Beneath*

C. *Force 10 from Navarone*

D. *Firewall*

133. What actor was Al Gore's roommate at Harvard?

A. Richard Dreyfuss

B. Tommy Lee Jones

C. Malcolm McDowell

D. Michael Caine

134. On what film did Jim Carrey receive his first (and so far only) screenwriting credit?

A. *The Mask*

B. *Ace Ventura: Pet Detective*

C. *Dumb & Dumber*

D. *The Cable Guy*

135. What branch of the armed forces did Morgan Freeman serve in?

A. Army

B. Navy

C. Marines

D. Air Force

141.

James Stewart's image will forever be intertwined with the honest, good-natured, "aw shucks" characters he played in films like *Mr. Smith Goes to Washington* and *It's a Wonderful Life*. While the perception that Stewart's work was comprised mainly of Capraesque, feel-good, life-affirming movies endures, it's a disservice to the masterful actor's body of work to remember him in so limited a scope. After all, the versatile Stewart also appeared in biopics like *The Stratton Story* and *The Spirit of St. Louis*, gritty westerns like *Winchester '73* and *The Shootist*, Hitchcock thrillers like *Vertigo* and *Rear Window*, and screwball comedies, romantic comedies, and dramas.

Because of his homegrown persona, many Americans affectionately referred to James Stewart as "Jimmy" Stewart. In how many films was he officially credited as Jimmy Stewart?

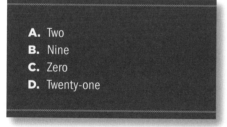

A. Two
B. Nine
C. Zero
D. Twenty-one

136. In what country was Paul Muni born?
A. Sicily
B. Bulgaria
C. The United States
D. Austria-Hungary

137. In which of his films does Gene Kelly dance with school children while singing "I Got Rhythm"?
A. *Singin' in the Rain*
B. *Summer Stock*
C. *An American in Paris*
D. *Anchors Aweigh*

138. Which of the following people was *not* portrayed in a movie by Henry Fonda?
A. General Douglas MacArthur
B. Thomas Edison
C. Clarence Darrow
D. Abraham Lincoln

139. Who played Clark Gable in the movie *Gable and Lombard*?
A. James Brolin
B. Jon Voight
C. Peter Jason
D. John Cassavetes

140. What was Burt Lancaster's last theatrically-released film?
A. *Rocket Gibraltar*
B. *Separate But Equal*
C. *Field of Dreams*
D. *Tough Guys*

141.

142. At what university was Burt Reynolds an all-star halfback?
A. Oklahoma State University
B. Oklahoma State
C. Florida State
D. The University of Arkansas

143. What Woody Allen-directed film features an uncredited appearance by Sylvester Stallone?
A. *Take the Money and Run*
B. *Bananas*
C. *Sleeper*
D. *Love and Death*

144. Who delivered the eulogy at Judy Garland's funeral?
A. Clark Gable
B. James Mason
C. Mickey Rooney
D. Liza Minnelli

145. Which actors were voted "Least Likely to Succeed" at the Pasadena Playhouse?

A. Al Pacino and Robert Duvall
C. Al Pacino and Dustin Hoffman
B. Gene Hackman and Dustin Hoffman
D. Robert Duvall and Gene Hackman

146. What is the title of Ava Gardner's posthumously released autobiography?

A. *Headstrong*
C. *On the Eighth Day...*
B. *Ava: My Story*
D. *Call Me Ava*

147. What was the last film in which Glenn Ford and Rita Hayworth appeared together?

A. *The Money Trap*
C. *Gilda*
B. *The Lady in Question*
D. *The Loves of Carmen*

148. Which of these Alfred Hitchcock films does *not* feature Grace Kelly?

A. *Dial M for Murder*
C. *To Catch a Thief*
B. *Topaz*
D. *Rear Window*

149. What was the name of the German shepherd that appeared with Roy Rogers in many of his films?

A. Trigger
C. Clyde
B. Bullet
D. Sparky

150. What is Nicole Kidman deathly afraid of?

A. Clowns
C. Heights
B. Butterflies
D. Marrying Scientologists

151. Which of William Holden's films sports the tagline "Once upon a time in Hollywood . . ."?

A. *S.O.B.*
C. *Born Yesterday*
B. *Sunset Boulevard*
D. *Executive Suite*

152. Who was known as the "Great Stone Face"?

A. Buster Keaton
C. Fatty Arbuckle
B. Harold Lloyd
D. Charles Chaplin

153. What was the first film Diane Keaton made with Woody Allen?

A. *Play It Again, Sam*
C. *Manhattan*
B. *Interiors*
D. *Annie Hall*

156.

Marlene Dietrich was already a star in her native Germany before relocating to Hollywood to appear in her mentor Josef von Sternberg's *Morocco*, for which she received her only Oscar nomination. She went on to enjoy a singing and acting career, appearing in such films as *The Scarlet Empress*, *A Foreign Affair*, and *Touch of Evil*. Despite the public's perception of Dietrich as an outsider—especially during World War II while the United States was at war with Germany—they were fascinated by her strong screen presence and assertive sexuality.

During Marlene Dietrich's Hollywood reign, one of her celebrity friends affectionately dubbed her "the Kraut." Who was this?

A. Orson Welles
B. Josef von Sternberg
C. Ernest Hemingway
D. James Stewart

154. Before finding success as an actress, Jessica Lange traveled to Paris to study a specific subject. What was it?
A. Literature
B. Mime
C. Juggling
D. Dancing

155. In what film does Sean Connery play Dustin Hoffman's father?
A. *American Buffalo*
B. *Hero*
C. *Family Business*
D. *Madigan's Million*

156.

157. William Holden delivered the shortest Oscar speech on record. What did he say?
A. "Thanks"
B. "Okay"
C. He just waved and said nothing
D. "Thank you"

158. What film was Grace Kelly making when she first met husband Prince Rainier Grimaldi III?
A. *The Bridges at Toko-Ri*
B. *Rear Window*
C. *To Catch a Thief*
D. *The Swan*

159. Whose memoir is titled *Living and Loving*?
A. Sophia Loren
B. Elizabeth Taylor
C. Mae West
D. Warren Beatty

160. What Hollywood icon was born Joseph Levitch?
A. Paul Newman
B. Errol Flynn
C. Jack Lemmon
D. Jerry Lewis

161. Elvis Presley died as the result of cardiac arrhythmia on August 16, 1977. In what city did he die?
A. Tupelo, Mississippi
B. Los Angeles, California
C. Memphis, Tennessee
D. Chicago, Illinois

162. Which of the following is *not* a film starring Bill Cosby and directed by Sidney Poitier?
A. *Ghost Dad*
B. *A Piece of the Action*
C. *Hickey & Boggs*
D. *Uptown Saturday Night*

163. On what television show did Humphrey Bogart make a posthumous appearance in 1995?

A. *Murder, She Wrote* **C.** *Days of Our Lives*

B. *Friends* **D.** *Tales from the Crypt*

164. Lauren Bacall appears in a Stephen King adaptation. What is this film?

A. *The Shawshank Redemption* **C.** *Stand By Me*

B. *The Stand* **D.** *Misery*

165. What icon did Tony Curtis liken to "kissing Adolf Hitler"?

A. Elizabeth Taylor **C.** Walter Matthau

B. Marilyn Monroe **D.** Robert Mitchum

166. What novel, according to biographer Joyce Milton, was inspired by events from the life of Charles Chaplin?

A. *The Little Tramps* **C.** *The Valley of the Dolls*

B. *Lolita* **D.** *East of Eden*

167. What actor was born Archibald Leach, but later became famous with his stage name?

A. Laurence Olivier **C.** Tony Randall

B. Cary Grant **D.** Tony Curtis

168. To what actor was Meryl Streep engaged but never married?

A. Robert De Niro **C.** John Heard

B. John Cazale **D.** Al Pacino

169. What legendary actors made their debuts in the 1930 film *Up the River*?

A. James Cagney and Humphrey Bogart **C.** Humphrey Bogart and Spencer Tracy

B. Walter Huston and Spencer Tracy **D.** James Cagney and Walter Huston

170. What actress did George Burns say he wanted to be his hundredth birthday present?

A. Brooke Shields **C.** Sharon Stone

B. Julia Roberts **D.** Sophia Loren

174.

Rita Hayworth, "The Love Goddess," is considered by many to be the archetypal Hollywood sex symbol. Between the years of 1926 and 1938, the former dancer with the famous legs appeared in more than twenty-five films. However, it wasn't until her turn in Howard Hawks's 1939 film *Only Angels Have Wings* that she truly gained the attention of critics and moviegoers. This breakthrough film ignited an impressive career that included such films as *Blood and Sand*, *Gilda*, and *You'll Never Get Rich*. The stunning redhead's sex symbol status was further solidified by a sultry layout in *Life* magazine, which single-handedly increased sales of the popular publication. During World War II, Hayworth became a popular pinup girl alongside Betty Grable and Lana Turner.

Hayworth was known for her trademark red hair. However, she appeared in one film as a blonde. What was this film?

A. *Gilda*
B. *Cover Girl*
C. *The Lady from Shanghai*
D. *Blood and Sand*

171. To whom was legendary actress Vivien Leigh married?
A. David O. Selznick
B. Laurence Olivier
C. Trevor Howard
D. Clark Gable

172. What legendary actor was born with the name John Charles Carter?
A. Charlton Heston
B. Groucho Marx
C. John Wayne
D. James Stewart

173. Which Rat Packer dated Dorothy Dandridge?
A. Frank Sinatra
B. Sammy Davis, Jr.
C. Peter Lawford
D. Dean Martin

174.

175. What is the title of the tell-all memoir penned by Bette Davis's daughter?
A. *Yes, Mother*
B. *Parenting the Bette Davis Way: A Cautionary Tale*
C. *My Mother's Keeper*
D. *Songs My Mother Taught Me*

176. What actress did Tom Cruise marry on May 9, 1987?
A. Nicole Kidman
B. Penelope Cruz
C. Mimi Rogers
D. Sharon Stone

177. Russell Crowe fronts a rock band. What is the name of this band?
A. Murder of Crowes
B. Death Cab for Cutie
C. 30 Odd Foot of Grunts
D. Hate Made Easy

178. What iconic actress was born Lucille LaSueur?
A. Bette Davis
B. Lucille Ball
C. Greta Garbo
D. Joan Crawford

179. In what film does Robert De Niro play a character named Gil Renard?
A. *This Boy's Life*
B. *Wag the Dog*
C. *The Fan*
D. *The Deer Hunter*

180. Following his death, James Dean's dialogue in the final scene of *Giant* had to be overdubbed by another actor. Who was this?
   A. Paul Newman
   B. Corey Allen
   C. Nick Adams
   D. Steve McQueen

181. What was the first film Clint Eastwood made with director Don Siegel?
   A. *Two Mules for Sister Sara*
   B. *Coogan's Bluff*
   C. *The Beguiled*
   D. *Dirty Harry*

182. What was Douglas Fairbanks's real last name?
   A. Wyczenski
   B. Thompson
   C. Ullman
   D. Edwards

183. Actor Issur Danielovitch Demsky goes by what better-known (and easier to pronounce) working name?
   A. Bela Lugosi
   B. Burt Reynolds
   C. Kirk Douglas
   D. Errol Flynn

184. To what actress was Steve McQueen married from 1973 to 1978?
   A. Faye Dunaway
   B. Natalie Wood
   C. Ali McGraw
   D. Susan Blakely

185. Who penned the memoir *Dean and Me (A Love Story)*?
   A. Jerry Lewis
   B. Frank Sinatra
   C. Sammy Davis, Jr.
   D. Joey Bishop

186. President Nixon received a Colt .45 handgun as a gift from which famous performer?
   A. Charlton Heston
   B. Elvis Presley
   C. Frank Sinatra
   D. Rock Hudson

187.

188. What is Jodie Foster's real first name?
   A. Caressa
   B. Frances
   C. Deborah
   D. Alicia

187.

George Clooney's first substantial role was on a short-lived 1984 comedy show titled *E/R*. (The show, which also featured Elliot Gould and Jason Alexander, is not to be mistaken for the similarly titled dramatic series that would later make Clooney a household name.) The actor then popped up in brief roles on television shows like *The Facts of Life*, *Roseanne*, and *The Golden Girls* before finding some minor film work and ultimately landing the role of Dr. Doug Ross on *ER* in 1994.

The series soon made him a star, and led to an Academy Award–winning career as a writer, director, producer, and actor. Although Clooney has frequently annoyed conservatives with criticism of George W. Bush's administration, there can be no doubt that Clooney is one of the most popular stars of his generation.

What was George Clooney's first film?

   A. *Return to Horror High*
   B. *Combat Academy*
   C. *Return of the Killer Tomatoes!*
   D. *Red Surf*

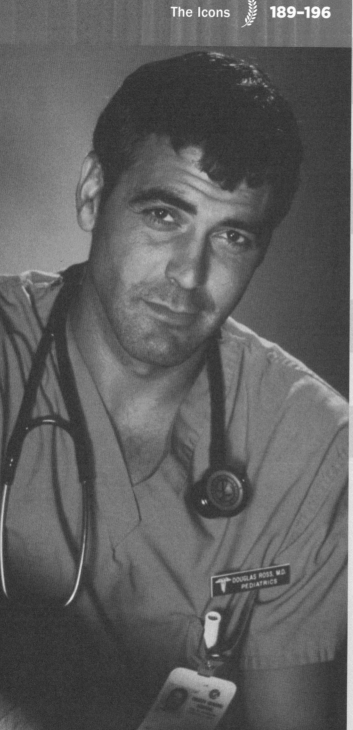

189. On what series did Harrison Ford make his television debut on February 1, 1967?

A. *Ironside*
B. *The Mod Squad*
C. *The Virginian*
D. *My Friend Tony*

190. Douglas Fairbanks uttered which of the following last words in the moments before his death?

A. "The end."
B. "I've never felt better."
C. "I would trade places with you, too."
D. "Death be not proud."

191. On what children's series did Morgan Freeman play a character named Easy Reader?

A. *Sesame Street*
B. *Electric Company*
C. *Mr. Roger's Neighborhood*
D. *Captain Kangaroo*

192. What Clint Eastwood vehicle features an early performance by Jim Carrey as a rock star?

A. *Pink Cadillac*
B. *Heartbreak Ridge*
C. *The Dead Pool*
D. *The Rookie*

193. How many Marx Brothers films feature Gummo Marx?

A. Three
B. Zero
C. Two
D. One

194. Name the actress who was never married to Richard Burton.

A. Elizabeth Taylor
B. Geraldine Fitzgerald
C. Sally Hay
D. Sybil Williams

195. How many roles did Alec Guinness play in *Kind Hearts and Coronets*?

A. Four
B. Two
C. Eight
D. Six

196. In what film does Groucho Marx play God?

A. *Will Success Spoil Rock Hunter?*
B. *The Story of Mankind*
C. *Skidoo*
D. *Double Dynamite*

197. In 1956, Montgomery Clift had a near-fatal automobile collision with a tree. Who discovered the wreckage?

A. Shelley Winters
B. Elizabeth Taylor
C. Rock Hudson
D. Richard Burton

198. Which noted actress was Joan Fontaine's older sister?

A. Joan Crawford
B. Jennifer Jones
C. Olivia de Havilland
D. Lillian Fontaine

199. Rock Hudson was given what comparatively staid birth name?

A. Ronald Hudson, Jr.
B. Roy Scherer, Jr.
C. Edward McMillan, Jr.
D. Jordan Benedict, Jr.

200. What was Anthony Quinn's final film?

A. *Oriundi*
B. *Avenging Angelo*
C. *Seven Servants*
D. *Gotti*

201. Which of the following is the title of an album recorded by Judy Garland?

A. *Judy Garland: Songs of My Youth*
B. *Judy Garland at Carnegie Hall*
C. *Judy Garland Sings for Lovers*
D. *Judy Garland: Songs from the Movies*

202. Why, according to Clark Gable, did fans pay to see him onscreen?

A. "Because I'm good looking and I get the girl."
B. "I know life is great, and they know I know it."
C. "I'm a good-looking man with talent."
D. "They want to see if I fail."

203. Ava Gardner was married to all of these men but one. Which one?

A. Artie Shaw
B. Mickey Rooney
C. Miguel Dominguin
D. Frank Sinatra

204.

205. How many times has Mickey Rooney been married?

A. Six
B. Eight
C. Seven
D. Nine

204.

On June 5, 1984, Hollywood icon Rock Hudson was diagnosed with AIDS. Hudson had been appearing as a regular on the television series *Dynasty*, but had begun to experience difficulty speaking and suffer from severe memory loss. His doctors and publicists attempted to conceal the illness, instead telling reporters he had cancer. However, the following year the effects of the disease were becoming apparent and a Hudson spokesperson finally revealed his condition. The sixty-year-old star's death on October 2, 1985 had a tremendous impact on the public's perception of the disease, as Hudson was the first big star it had claimed.

Rock Hudson was cremated after his death. What was done with his ashes?

A. They were scattered in the countryside
B. They were released from a plane
C. They were scattered at sea
D. They were kept by his lover

206. Which of these films does *not* feature Grace Kelly?

A. *On the Waterfront*　　C. *Rear Window*

B. *High Noon*　　D. *To Catch a Thief*

207. What affliction claimed the life of Vivien Leigh?

A. Tuberculosis　　C. Cancer

B. Emphysema　　D. Diabetes

208. Name Jack Lemmon's first project with filmmaker Billy Wilder.

A. *The Apartment*　　C. *The Fortune Cookie*

B. *Irma la Douce*　　D. *Some Like It Hot*

209. What actress did director Mitchel Leisen dub "the profane angel"?

A. Bette Davis　　C. Sophia Loren

B. Carole Lombard　　D. Joan Crawford

210. What was the last film Marilyn Monroe completed before her death?

A. *The Misfits*　　C. *Something's Got to Give*

B. *Let's Make Love*　　D. *Some Like It Hot*

211. Which of these is the title of an autobiography by Joan Crawford?

A. *My Name Is Joan*　　C. *Mommie Dearest*

B. *My Way of Life*　　D. *Joan: Her Story*

212. Tom Cruise is not only an actor, but also a producer. What was the first film he produced?

A. *Magnolia*　　C. *Mission: Impossible*

B. *Vanilla Sky*　　D. *Days of Thunder*

213. Who, according to Bette Davis, is getting old *not* for?

A. Her　　C. The young

B. The beautiful　　D. Sissies

214. How many of Dorothy Dandridge's films were directed by Otto Preminger?

A. One　　C. Three

B. Two　　D. Four

215. Douglas Fairbanks was married to which actress?

A. Marion Davies
B. Mary Pickford
C. Claudette Colbert
D. Myrna Loy

216. What was the title of Henry Fonda's autobiography?

A. *This Life of Mine*
B. *My Life*
C. *My Name Is Henry*
D. *Fonda*

217. What is Harrison Ford's middle name?

A. Joshua
B. He has no middle name
C. John
D. Joseph

218. In what film did Doris Day and Rock Hudson first appear together?

A. *Pillow Talk*
B. *Send Me No Flowers*
C. *Please Don't Eat the Daisies*
D. *Lover Come Back*

219. From what did Judy Garland die?

A. Overdose
B. Ovarian cancer
C. Blood alcohol poisoning
D. Pneumonia

220.

221. At what age did Shirley Temple begin acting?

A. Three
B. Two
C. One
D. Four

222. What was the title of Lillian Gish's autobiography?

A. *Born with the Movies*
B. *The Movies, Mr. Griffith, and Me*
C. *Scenes from the Life of an Actress*
D. *Birth of a Nation and Beyond*

223. In the 1996 version of *Hamlet*, Jack Lemmon filled the role of which character?

A. Polonius
B. Ghost
C. Marcellus
D. Claudius

224. In what sequel did icon Michelle Pfeiffer appear in her first major screen role?

A. *Lethal Weapon 2*
B. *Terminator 2: Judgment Day*
C. *Grease 2*
D. *Gremlins 2: The New Batch*

220.

Denzel Washington's first film role was in a 1977 made-for-television movie titled *Wilma*. However, his breakthrough came in 1982 as a regular on the popular television drama *St. Elsewhere*. Washington then embarked upon an impressive movie career that includes *Cry Freedom*, *Glory*, *Malcolm X*, *Philadelphia*, and *Training Day*. As one of the most gifted actors in the history of cinema, Washington has received five Oscar nominations and two wins—the most ever by an African-American performer. Besides his work as an actor, Washington is also an accomplished producer and director.

Denzel Washington has appeared in five Spike Lee movies. Which of the following movies starring Washington was *not* directed by Lee?

A. *Malcolm X*
B. *Glory*
C. *He Got Game*
D. *Mo' Better Blues*

225. Shirley MacLaine appeared in *These Old Broads* with three of the following actresses. With which one did she *not* appear?

A. Joan Collins   C. Lauren Bacall

B. Elizabeth Taylor   D. Debbie Reynolds

226. To which of these men was Ida Lupino *not* married?

A. Howard Duff   C. Louis Hayward

B. Collier Young   D. Vincent Sherman

227. What actor called Marilyn Monroe "a professional amateur"?

A. Tony Curtis   C. Clark Gable

B. Laurence Olivier   D. Dean Martin

228. How old was Mary Pickford when she made her screen debut in *Mrs. Jones Entertains*?

A. Sixteen   C. Fifteen

B. Fourteen   D. Thirteen

229. Whose autobiography was titled *The Measure of a Man*?

A. Ronald Reagan   C. Gregory Peck

B. Sidney Poitier   D. John Holmes

230. How many different characters' voices were dubbed by Peter Sellers in *Malaga*?

A. Nine   C. Fourteen

B. Twenty   D. Thirteen

231. What does the "C" in George C. Scott's name stand for?

A. Conrad   C. Carson

B. Campbell   D. Nothing—he had no middle name

232. To which of these actors was Ginger Rogers *not* married?

A. Ward Bond   C. Jack Briggs

B. Lew Ayres   D. Jacques Bergerac

233. Where is the James Stewart Museum located?

A. Iowa City, Iowa   C. Parsons, Kansas

B. Indiana, Pennsylvania   D. Des Moines, Iowa

234. In which film does Meryl Streep say a dingo ate her baby?
- **A.** *Julia*
- **B.** *Dingo Diner*
- **C.** *Still of the Night*
- **D.** *A Cry in the Dark*

235. In what film did Barbra Streisand make her screen debut?
- **A.** *What's Up Doc?*
- **B.** *Funny Girl*
- **C.** *Hello, Dolly!*
- **D.** *Barefoot in the Park*

236.

237. What actress was born Frances Ethel Gumm?
- **A.** Vivien Leigh
- **B.** Judy Garland
- **C.** Mary Pickford
- **D.** Shirley Temple

238. Only one of these Tennessee Williams adaptations does *not* star Elizabeth Taylor. Which one?
- **A.** *Cat on a Hot Tin Roof*
- **B.** *The Glass Menagerie*
- **C.** *Suddenly, Last Summer*
- **D.** *Boom*

239. In 1944, Barbara Stanwyck was ranked the highest paid woman in the United States. How much did she make?
- **A.** $250,000
- **B.** $750,000
- **C.** $400,000
- **D.** $800,000

240. What Kevin Spacey-sung tune is played over the credits for *Midnight in the Garden of Good and Evil*?
- **A.** "Someone to Watch Over Me"
- **B.** "That Old Black Magic"
- **C.** "Midnight in the Garden of Good and Evil"
- **D.** "Mack the Knife"

241. Sissy Spacek was born on a holiday. Which one?
- **A.** Thanksgiving
- **B.** Independence Day
- **C.** Christmas
- **D.** Flag Day

242. What statement is engraved on Frank Sinatra's tombstone?
- **A.** "The best is yet to come."
- **B.** "I did it my way."
- **C.** "I did the best I could."
- **D.** "It was a good run."

236.

In 1978, comedian Robin Williams landed a breakout role on the television sitcom *Mork and Mindy*. He then starred in films such as *Popeye* and *The World According to Garp*, and his standup comedy specials *An Evening with Robin Williams*, *Robin Williams: Live at the Met*, and *Robin Williams Live on Broadway* were met with great acclaim. In 1987, Williams gave a career-making performance in Barry Levinson's *Good Morning, Vietnam*, for which he received an Oscar nomination. With starring roles in such noted and diverse films as *Aladdin*, *Dead Poets Society*, *Awakenings*, *Mrs. Doubtfire*, and *Good Will Hunting*, the versatile actor has displayed an uncanny ability to shift back and forth between comedy and drama with the greatest of ease.

What publication called Robin Williams the "Funniest Man Alive" in 1997?

- **A.** *Rolling Stone*
- **B.** *GQ*
- **C.** *Entertainment Weekly*
- **D.** *Time Magazine*

243. What subject did James Stewart study at Princeton?

A. Architecture

B. Literature

C. Engineering

D. Journalism

244. Whose production company was called Batjac Productions?

A. Glenn Ford

B. James Stewart

C. Douglas Fairbanks

D. John Wayne

245. In what film does Shirley Temple sing "Animal Crackers in My Soup"?

A. *Little Miss Marker*

B. *Bright Eyes*

C. *Curly Top*

D. *Wee Willie Winkie*

246. Why were Spencer Tracy and Katharine Hepburn never married during their twenty-five-year relationship?

A. They didn't believe in marriage

B. Tracy was already married to someone else

C. Hepburn was already married to someone else

D. They did get married

247. What did self-proclaimed psychic Criswell predict that Mae West would do in 1965?

A. Become U.S. president

B. Travel to Mars

C. Die

D. Marry Elvis Presley

248. In which of these films does John Wayne appear with his son Ethan?

A. *Rio Lobo*

B. *The Searchers*

C. *Hondo*

D. *McLintock!*

249. Which of these actors did Natalie Wood *not* date?

A. Frank Sinatra

B. Elvis Presley

C. Dennis Hopper

D. Raymond Burr

250. Errol Flynn and Olivia de Havilland played the characters Robin Hood and Maid Marion in the classic film *The Adventures of Robin Hood*. What actor played Little John?

A. Claude Rains

B. Alan Hale

C. Basil Rathbone

D. Melville Cooper

CHAPTER TWO:
CLASSIC FILMS

251. What is Tom O'Brien's nickname (and the character he is credited as) in the 1925 silent classic *The Big Parade*?

A. Lefty
B. Mikey
C. Banjo
D. Bull

252. What is the name of the precocious five-year-old played by Margaret O'Brien in *Meet Me in St. Louis*?

A. Lolly
B. Tootie
C. Rosie
D. None of the above

253. When 1941's *Citizen Kane* debuted, what performer received top billing?

A. Dorothy Comingore
B. Orson Welles
C. Agnes Moorehead
D. Joseph Cotton

254. Who appears in a brief cameo in *Psycho* standing outside Marion's office and wearing a cowboy hat?

A. Alfred Hitchcock
B. Robert Bloch
C. Tippi Hedren
D. James Stewart

256. *North By Northwest*, Alfred Hitchcock's gripping 1959 thriller, stars Cary Grant as a character with what name?

A. Martin Q. Fassbinder
B. David O. Selznick
C. Roger O. Thornhill
D. Stephen J. Spignesi

255. Which *My Darling Clementine* character says "I ain't committin' suicide on myself"?

A. Wyatt Earp
B. Doc Holliday
C. James Earp
D. None of the above

257. What is Nurse Ratched's first name in *One Flew Over the Cuckoo's Nest*?

A. Roberta
B. Esther
C. Mildred
D. Frieda

OPPOSITE Julie Andrews in *The Sound of Music*, 1965

258. Which of these actresses plays the mother of two deaf children in *Nashville*?

A. Geraldine Chaplin
B. Lily Tomlin
C. Karen Black
D. Shelley Duvall

259. Hitchcock's *Notorious* was based on a serialized story that ran in a popular magazine. What was this magazine?

A. *Life*
B. *True Crime*
C. *Saturday Evening Post*
D. *The New Yorker*

260. Milos Forman's 1984 film *Amadeus* tells the story of a mediocre composer's bitter jealousy toward the great Wolfgang Amadeus Mozart. What actor plays Mozart in this film?

A. Jeffrey Jones
B. F. Murray Abraham
C. Simon Callow
D. Tom Hulce

261. The films *To Have and Have Not* and *For Whom the Bell Tolls* were both adapted from the same author's work. Who is it?

A. Ernest Hemingway
B. J.D. Salinger
C. Norman Mailer
D. John Steinbeck

262.

263. What city's burning is depicted in the 1939 classic *Gone with the Wind*?

A. Savannah
B. Charlotte
C. Atlanta
D. Richmond

264. What actor plays the title character in the "Pink Panther" film *Inspector Clouseau*?

A. Peter Sellers
B. Alan Arkin
C. Ryan O' Neal
D. Roberto Benigni

265. *Red River* was adapted from a novel written by Borden Chase. What is the title of this novel?

A. *The Lonesome Trail*
B. *Red River*
C. *The Chisholm Trail*
D. *Dunson's Law*

262.

Billy Wilder's 1944 thriller *Double Indemnity* is widely considered the definitive example of film noir. The screenplay was adapted from James M. Cain's novella *Three of a Kind* by Wilder and novelist Raymond Chandler. The film, which stars Fred MacMurray, Barbara Stanwyck, and Edward G. Robinson, tells the story of an insurance salesman persuaded by a beautiful client to assist in the murder of her unsuspecting husband. The story line of both the novella and the film were loosely based upon a 1927 murder that took place in Queens, New York. The film received seven Oscar nominations, but these nominations failed to yield a single statuette.

At the end of the film, the insurance salesman is shot by the wife. He then goes to his office and confesses before dying. The original ending, which director Billy Wilder opted to excise, found the salesman dying in a completely different manner. How?

A. He commits suicide
B. He is executed by poisonous gas
C. He is executed by lethal injection
D. He is executed by hanging

266. John Wayne plays retired boxer Sean Thornton in John Ford's 1952 film *The Quiet Man*. What was Sean's boxing nickname?

A. Thorny Thornton

B. Bruiser Thornton

C. Sugar Sean Thornton

D. Trooper Thornton

267. *Paths of Glory*, Stanley Kubrick's 1957 classic, was filmed in what country?

A. Italy

B. Germany

C. Australia

D. England

268. A brouhaha erupts in *One Flew Over the Cuckoo's Nest* when McMurphy attempts to watch a sporting event on television. Name the event.

A. The NBA playoffs

B. The World Series

C. The Super Bowl

D. Wrestlemania

269. King Vidor later made a sequel to his film *The Crowd*. What is the title of this film?

A. *Huddled Masses*

B. *Our Daily Bread*

C. *Fallen Apples*

D. *The Final Teardrop*

270. What actor appeared as Dr. Frankenstein in *The Bride of Frankenstein*?

A. Boris Karloff

B. None of these

C. Ernest Thesiger

D. Colin Clive

271. Sterling Hayden played the character Brigadier General Ripper in the film *Dr. Strangelove*. What is Ripper's full name?

A. Rex Ripper

B. Bodice Ripper

C. Jack D. Ripper

D. Rip Ripper

272. What game do Elliott and his friends play in *E.T. the Extra-Terrestrial*?

A. Pac-Man

B. Chutes and Ladders

C. Dungeons and Dragons

D. Frogger

273. Robert Altman's *M*A*S*H* marked the screen debut of an NFL star. Who is this?

A. Jim Brown

B. Fred Dryer

C. O.J. Simpson

D. Fred Williamson

274. What, according to the tagline for *Easy Rider*, did a man go searching for?

A. Freedom

B. A good time

C. The truth

D. America

275. Director Erich von Stroheim's 1924 masterpiece *Greed* takes place in what city?

A. New York City

B. San Francisco

C. Boston

D. Chicago

276. In what film does Greta Garbo say, "Gimme a visky with ginger ale on the side"?

A. *Anna Christie*

B. *Anna Karenina*

C. *Ninotchka*

D. *Grand Hotel*

277. *Snow White and the Seven Dwarfs* was the first feature-length Disney film. What was the second?

A. *Fantasia*

B. *Dumbo*

C. *Cinderella*

D. *Pinocchio*

278. What *Gunsmoke* regular appears in *The Searchers* as Charlie?

A. Ken Curtis

B. Milburn Stone

C. Dennis Weaver

D. James Arness

279. In *Bringing Up Baby*, the 1938 screwball comedy directed by Howard Hawks, how old is title character Baby?

A. One

B. Three

C. Two

D. Four

280. What is the name of Will's deceased wife in the 1992 western *Unforgiven*?

A. Claudia

B. Sally

C. Emily

D. Delilah

281. What is the name of Sidney Poitier's character in *Guess Who's Coming to Dinner*?

A. John Prentice

B. Joey Drayton

C. Matt Drayton

D. Virgil Tibbs

285.

The Frank Capra film *It's a Wonderful Life* was a critical and commercial failure when it was released in 1946.

The film, which stars James Stewart as George, a suicidal man who is given the chance to see what the world would have been like had he never been born, has since gained a tremendous following and is recognized as a bona fide classic. Today it appears on many "greatest films" lists, and has become a staple of holiday television programming.

What is the name of George's brother who was awarded the Congressional Medal of Honor?

A. Robert
B. Harry
C. Tony
D. Samuel

282. Which of these films was *not* written by screenwriters Julius J. Epstein and Philip G. Epstein?
A. *Casablanca*
B. *Arsenic and Old Lace*
C. *Meet Me in St. Louis*
D. *Mr. Skeffington*

283. Peter Sellers plays a gardener in *Being There*. What is this gardener's name?
A. Lucky
B. Fortune
C. Karma
D. Chance

284. What is Baby Jane's last name in *Whatever Happened to Baby Jane?*
A. Henson
B. Hellman
C. Hudson
D. Hinman

285.

286. In *It Happened One Night*, what is Peter Warne's occupation?
A. Stock broker
B. Journalist
C. Novelist
D. College professor

287. What actor did newspapers prematurely (and erroneously) report as having been cast as the star of *Lawrence of Arabia*?
A. William Holden
B. Marlon Brando
C. Anthony Quinn
D. Elvis Presley

288. In what film does Marilyn Monroe sing "That Old Black Magic" for an unappreciative audience?
A. *Bus Stop*
B. *Some Like It Hot*
C. *The Seven Year Itch*
D. *All About Eve*

289. Which of these films is based on the story "Farewell to the Master" by Harry Bates?
A. *The War of the Worlds*
B. *Forbidden Planet*
C. *Invasion of the Body Snatchers*
D. *The Day the Earth Stood Still*

290. What actor passed on a role in *The Godfather* before appearing as the Godfather himself in the sequel?

A. Paul Sorvino **C.** James Caan

B. Robert De Niro **D.** Al Pacino

291. What is the name of the gumshoe played by Humphrey Bogart in *The Big Sleep*?

A. Philip Marlowe **C.** Mike Danger

B. Sam Spade **D.** Mike Hammer

292. Which of these actors does *not* appear in both *Rebel Without a Cause* and *Giant*?

A. Sal Mineo **C.** Corey Allen

B. James Dean **D.** Dennis Hopper

293. To whom does *On the Waterfront's* Terry Malloy say he "coulda been a contender"?

A. His brother **C.** His love interest

B. His priest **D.** His cousin

294. In Harold Lloyd's *The Freshman*, what is Harold Lamb's nickname?

A. Lamb Chop **C.** Cookie

B. Speedy **D.** Doc

295.

296. Who appears as the radio DJ in *American Graffiti*?

A. Wolfman Jack **C.** Alan Freed

B. Casey Kasem **D.** Dick Clark

297. In what film does Charles Chaplin appear as a character named Adenoid Hynkel?

A. *City Lights* **C.** *The Kid*

B. *The Great Dictator* **D.** *Limelight*

295.

With his social commentary *Guess Who's Coming to Dinner*, director Stanley Kramer tackled the subject of interracial relationships, which was still quite controversial at the time. The film tells the story of mixed-race lovers, played by Sidney Poitier and Katharine Houghton, at odds with their fathers, neither of whom wants his child to marry outside his own race.

"Sometimes there were objections," explained Kramer. "Why did I have to make the black man so personable, so intelligent, so educated? Well, it was because I was trying to make the point that since Poitier's character had all those qualities, if there was an objection to him marrying a white woman, it could only be because he was black!"

In what year was this classic film released?

A. 1966
B. 1968
C. 1967
D. 1969

298. What does Cool Hand Luke say he can eat fifty of?
- **A.** Finger sandwiches
- **B.** Fried worms
- **C.** Habanero peppers
- **D.** Hardboiled eggs

299. Who is the only performer from the film *M*A*S*H* to appear as a regular on the television series?
- **A.** Gary Burghoff
- **B.** Harry Morgan
- **C.** Alan Alda
- **D.** Tom Skerritt

300. What was the first movie to star the Beatles?
- **A.** *Yellow Submarine*
- **B.** *Help!*
- **C.** *A Hard Day's Night*
- **D.** *Let It Be*

301. Steven Spielberg's 1975 blockbuster *Jaws* tells the story of an island that is being terrorized by a shark. What is the name of this island?
- **A.** Rock Island
- **B.** Amity Island
- **C.** Brody Island
- **D.** Shark Island

302. What actor played the Hunchback of Notre Dame?
- **A.** Charles Laughton
- **B.** Irving Thalberg
- **C.** Edmond O'Brien
- **D.** Thomas Mitchell

303. In what 1932 film does a character played by George Raft continually flip a coin in the air?
- **A.** *Some Like It Hot*
- **B.** *Ocean's Eleven*
- **C.** *Skidoo*
- **D.** *Scarface*

304. In *Bridge on the River Kwai*, what is referred to as the "oven"?
- **A.** The incinerator
- **B.** A corrugated metal box
- **C.** A firey pit
- **D.** A sauna

305. In *The African Queen*, what river is said to be "death a dozen times over"?
- **A.** The Nile
- **B.** The Joliba
- **C.** The Ulanga
- **D.** The Niger

306. What actor is credited on *All About Eve*, but does not appear in the film?

A. Eddie Fisher

B. Jose Ferrer

C. Leslie Howard

D. Ward Bond

307. In *Some Like It Hot*, what does Marilyn Monroe conclude causes millionaires to have weak eyes?

A. Reading bank statements

B. Counting their money

C. Reading *The Wall Street Journal*

D. Searching for ways to put one over on the poor

308. For how much is the racetrack heist in Stanley Kubrick's *The Killing*?

A. $500,000

B. $1 million

C. $2 million

D. $3 million

309. *The Lady from Shanghai* was adapted from a novel titled *If I Die Before I Wake*. Who wrote this novel?

A. Orson Welles

B. Sherwood King

C. Jim Thompson

D. Ward Greene

310. What filmmaker makes a brief cameo as an army corporal in *The Best Years of Our Lives*?

A. John Huston

B. Blake Edwards

C. William Wyler

D. Howard Hawks

311.

312. In *To Kill a Mockingbird*, what does Atticus forbid Scout to do?

A. Curse

B. Play with guns

C. Ostracize others

D. Fight

313. Which of these actors does *not* appear as one of the three treacherous sons in *The Lion in Winter*?

A. Anthony Hopkins

B. Nigel Terry

C. Timothy Dalton

D. John Castle

311.

With his 1950 film *Sunset Boulevard*, starring William Holden, Gloria Swanson, and Erich von Stroheim, writer/director Billy Wilder (with co-writers Charles Brackett and D.M. Marshman, Jr.) parodies Hollywood and its all-too-frequent practice of discarding its stars like yesterday's trash.

Sunset Boulevard was met with critical acclaim, garnering eleven Academy Award nominations and three wins. It's been praised for a screenplay that crackles with sharply written and endlessly quotable dialogue, and John F. Seitz's stunning black-and-white photography is as beautiful as anything ever filmed. Today *Sunset Boulevard* is recognized as one of the finest American films ever produced.

In the film's opening, what does Joe Gillis lament that he always wanted?

A. A pony

B. A million dollars

C. A swimming pool

D. A bullet in the back

314. Which of these epics was *not* written by screenwriter Robert Bolt?

A. *Lawrence of Arabia*

C. *Doctor Zhivago*

B. *The Man Who Would Be King*

D. *A Man for All Seasons*

315. In *Marty*, what is Marty Piletti's occupation?

A. Truck driver

C. Pawnbroker

B. Butcher

D. Custodian

316. How much do Walter and Phyllis plan to make from Mr. Dietrichson's life insurance policy in *Double Indemnity*?

A. $100,000

C. $300,000

B. $500,000

D. $250,000

317. Dustin Hoffman plays the character Ratso in *Midnight Cowboy*. What is Ratso's real name?

A. Rocco

C. Philly

B. Salvatore

D. Enrico

318. In what store does Santa Claus work in *Miracle on 34th Street*?

A. Gimbel's

C. Macy's

B. Kringle's

D. Saks Fifth Avenue

319. *It Happened One Night* was later remade as a musical. What was the title of this reincarnation?

A. *You Can't Run Away from It*

C. *Would I Lie to You?*

B. *The Spiral Road*

D. *It Happened One Night*

320. What film chronicles the production of a play titled *Springtime for Hitler*?

A. *To Be or Not to Be*

C. *The Great Dictator*

B. *The Producers*

D. *Singin' in the Rain*

321. Which of these comic actors made the movie *Sherlock, Jr.*?

A. Harold Lloyd

C. Buster Keaton

B. Charles Chaplin

D. Fatty Arbuckle

322. Which *The Best Years of Our Lives* performer wrote the memoir *The Best Years of My Life*?
- **A.** Harold Russell
- **B.** Myrna Loy
- **C.** Fredric March
- **D.** Dana Andrews

323. In 1973's *Sleeper*, how many years does Miles say it's been since he had sex "if you count my marriage"?
- **A.** 101
- **B.** 102
- **C.** 204
- **D.** 205

324. Rod Steiger plays the character Viktor Komarovsky in the 1965 David Lean film *Doctor Zhivago*. What is Komarovsky's occupation?
- **A.** Judge
- **B.** Doctor
- **C.** Lawyer
- **D.** Detective

325. What is the title character's full name in *Spartacus*?
- **A.** Spartacus
- **B.** Marcus Spartacus
- **C.** Thracian Spartacus
- **D.** Spartacus Lentulus

326. In whose apartment does Alfred Hitchcock appear briefly in *Rear Window*?
- **A.** Mr. Thorwald's
- **B.** Miss Torso's
- **C.** The songwriter's
- **D.** Miss Lonely Heart's

327. Who is Maria expected to marry in *West Side Story*?
- **A.** Riff
- **B.** Tony
- **C.** Chino
- **D.** Bernardo

328. In *North By Northwest*, what does Eve say she never discusses love on?
- **A.** Tuesday
- **B.** A train
- **C.** The first date
- **D.** An empty stomach

329. In *Butch Cassidy and the Sundance Kid*, Butch concludes that the outlaws have three things going for them. Which of these is *not* one of them?
- **A.** Experience
- **B.** Leadership
- **C.** Survival instinct
- **D.** Maturity

335.

When *Casablanca* went into production, there were no signs that the project would become a classic film. Warner Bros. script reader Stephen Karnott dismissed the initial story line (adapted from an unproduced play) as "sophisticated hokum." Paul Henreid, who plays Victor Laszlo, didn't want to appear in the movie and feared it might damage his career. And Ingrid Bergman reportedly expressed concerns throughout filming because the script wasn't yet completed, so no one knew whether or not Rick and Ilsa would walk happily into the sunset together at the end of the film.

Despite all of this, *Casablanca* has become one of the most respected films in the history of American cinema. Film critic Roger Ebert noted that *Casablanca* is "probably on more lists as the greatest film of all time than any other single title, including *Citizen Kane*."

In *Casablanca*, how many times does Humphrey Bogart's character Rick say, "Play it again, Sam"?

A. Two
B. One
C. Zero
D. Three

---

330. In *The Philadelphia Story*, Cary Grant and Katharine Hepburn play the characters Dexter and Tracy. What is Dexter's pet name for Tracy?
A. Dot
B. Lips
C. Red
D. Slim

331. What is the name of the cabbie played by Peter Boyle in *Taxi Driver*?
A. Sport
B. Wizard
C. Bunny
D. Hambone

332. Vivien Leigh plays the character Blanche in Elia Kazan's 1951 film, *A Streetcar Named Desire*. What is Blanche's last name?
A. Dubois
B. Walby
C. Cheshire
D. Kowalski

333. Who, according to screenwriter Carl Gottlieb, actually wrote the *Indianapolis* monologue in *Jaws*?
A. John Milius
B. Steven Spielberg
C. Robert Shaw
D. Peter Benchley

334. Who proclaims that all women are poison in Disney's *Snow White and the Seven Dwarfs*?
A. Grumpy
B. Sneezy
C. Dopey
D. Doc

335.

336. Which future *Sex and the City* star appears in *Amadeus*?
A. Sarah Jessica Parker
B. Cynthia Nixon
C. Kim Cattrall
D. Kristin Davis

337. What is the name of the memorably annoying theme music for *Doctor Zhivago*?
A. "Searching (Yuri's Theme)"
B. "Theme from *Doctor Zhivago*"
C. "Lara's Theme"
D. "Yearning"

338. Which of these is *not* the name of one of the Stoneman children in *The Birth of a Nation*?
A. Elsie
B. Phil
C. Tod
D. James

339. *Rear Window*, Alfred Hitchcock's 1954 film starring James Stewart, is based upon a short story by what author?

A. Cornell Woolrich

B. Raymond Chandler

C. Mickey Spillane

D. Dashiell Hammett

340. In the final line of the classic 1933 film *King Kong*, what is said to have killed Kong?

A. Love

B. Desire

C. Bullets

D. Beauty

341. What actor plays the marine biologist character Matt Hooper in *Jaws*?

A. Robert Shaw

B. Richard Dreyfuss

C. Roy Scheider

D. Murray Hamilton

342. Which character proposes marriage to Dallas in the classic 1939 western *Stagecoach*?

A. Curly

B. Ringo

C. Peacock

D. Chris

343. Karen Allen plays Indiana Jones's love interest Marion in the film *Raiders of the Lost Ark*. What is Marion's last name?

A. Rosenberg

B. Ravenwood

C. Davenport

D. Stonewood

344. What is the name of the soap opera on which Dorothy Michaels appears in *Tootsie*?

A. *Southwest General*

B. *Strangers in the Night*

C. *The Rich and the Beautiful*

D. *Friends and Lovers*

345. Which of these things is not something Elster says "spell San Francisco" in *Vertigo*?

A. Power

B. Color

C. Energy

D. Freedom

346. Jenny bares not only her soul, but also her backside during her gig as a singer in *Forrest Gump*. Under what stage name does she sing?

A. Bobbi Monroe

B. Bobbi Starr

C. Bobbi Dillon

D. Bobbi Taylor

353.

Francis Ford Coppola's 1972 film *The Godfather*, an adaptation of a novel by Mario Puzo, set the standard for gangster movies. The film, which stars Al Pacino, Marlon Brando, and James Caan, is also considered one of the greatest films ever produced. *The Godfather* is a nearly flawless film that excels in every aspect imaginable.

The sprawling epic has maintained its popularity in the years since its release, spawning two sequel films, a sequel novel (Mark Winegardner's *The Godfather Returns*), and even a video game.

Interestingly, violence in *The Godfather* is almost always preceded by the appearance of fruit. What kind?

A. Apples
B. Bananas
C. Oranges
D. Pears

347. What actor plays Liberty Valance in *The Man Who Shot Liberty Valance*?
A. John Wayne
B. Lee Marvin
C. Edmond O'Brien
D. James Stewart

348. What kind of disguise does Raymond wear on his assassination mission in *The Manchurian Candidate*?
A. Policeman
B. Priest
C. Telephone company repairman
D. Security guard

349. In *Ben-Hur*, who does Esther conclude will receive mercy?
A. The loving
B. The honorable
C. The merciful
D. The faithful

350. Laurence Olivier plays Heathcliff in the 1939 William Wyler film *Wuthering Heights*. How does Heathcliff die in the film?
A. He falls down the stairs
B. He freezes to death
C. He hangs himself
D. He does not die

351. Which of these films is *not* a part of director George Stevens's "American Trilogy"?
A. *Shane*
B. *A Place in the Sun*
C. *Giant*
D. *Penny Serenade*

352. How many female singing roles are there in *An American in Paris*?
A. Twelve
B. One
C. Zero
D. Thirty-three

353.

354. What actress plays boxer Rocky Balboa's love interest Adrian in the 1976 film *Rocky*?
A. Mia Farrow
B. Talia Shire
C. Brigitte Nielsen
D. Diane Keaton

355. Paul Muni plays the character Tony in the original 1932 Howard Hawks version of *Scarface*. What is Tony's last name?

A. Montana
C. Camonte
B. Cicero
D. Imperioli

356. In *Pulp Fiction*, what is the combination to the briefcase Jules and Vincent retrieve for Marcellus?

A. 123
C. 409
B. 007
D. 666

357. What is the first name of Robert De Niro's character in the 1977 Martin Scorsese classic *Taxi Driver*?

A. Darrell
C. Trevor
B. Travis
D. Gavin

358. HAL, the computer in *2001: A Space Odyssey*, is voiced by what actor?

A. Douglas Rain
C. Frank Miller
B. Martin Balsam
D. Gary Lockwood

359. What kind of fruit does Louis Dega have delivered to Papillon's cell in *Papillon*?

A. Banana
C. Papaya
B. Coconut
D. Kiwi

360. What actor plays Big Harold in the 1986 Vietnam War film *Platoon*?

A. Forest Whitaker
C. Willem Dafoe
B. Tom Berenger
D. Keith David

361. To what city does Charles Lindbergh fly in *The Spirit of St. Louis*?

A. New York City
C. Rome
B. Paris
D. Peking

362. In *Goodfellas*, what singer sends champagne to Henry and Karen's table?

A. Frank Sinatra
C. Bobby Vinton
B. Johnny Fontane
D. Tony Bennett

365.

When Stanley Kubrick's *2001: A Space Odyssey* was released in 1968, audiences were unsure what to make of it. The film was so completely different from anything that had preceded it that even critics were divided. Stanley Kauffman of *The New Republic* slammed the film, which he called "so dull, it even dulls our interest in the technical ingenuity for the sake of which Kubrick has allowed it to become dull." The great *New Yorker* critic Pauline Kael, never at a loss for words, called the film "a monumentally unimaginative movie." Other critics, however, were quick to hail *2001* as a timeless masterpiece, pointing to its beautiful imagery and masterful marriage of sight and sound.

Kubrick originally hired a composer to score the film, but later removed the commissioned score and replaced it with works of classical music. Who was the original composer?

A. Wendy Carlos
B. Nelson Riddle
C. Alex North
D. Gerald Fried

363. In *A Place in the Sun*, who jokes, "I always wanted to look like a bellhop"?
A. Bellows
B. George Eastman
C. Earl Eastman
D. Frank Marlowe

364. Who portrays Jesus Christ in *The Greatest Story Ever Told*?
A. Van Heflin
B. Max Von Sydow
C. Charlton Heston
D. Martin Landau

365.

366. What disease does Big Daddy suffer from in *Cat on a Hot Tin Roof*?
A. Cancer
B. Diabetes
C. Polio
D. Tuberculosis

367. *Charade*, the 1963 Stanley Donen thriller starring Cary Grant, takes place in what cosmopolitan city?
A. Palermo
B. Paris
C. Venice
D. Savoie

368. Although Quentin Tarantino generally receives all the credit for *Pulp Fiction*, in fact, he partnered with another scribe. Who was Tarantino's cowriter?
A. David Veloz
B. Roger Avary
C. Rand Vossler
D. Craig Hamann

369. What is Macreedy's first name in 1955's *Bad Day at Black Rock*?
A. Edwin
B. Edward
C. Larry
D. John

370. What legendary filmmaker first planned to bring the story of *A Place in the Sun* to the screen, but ultimately could not?
A. Sergei Eisenstein
B. Josef von Sternberg
C. George Eastman
D. Erich von Stroheim

371. In what film does John Wayne play a character known as the Ringo Kid?
- **A.** *The Searchers*
- **B.** *The Man Who Shot Liberty Valance*
- **C.** *Stagecoach*
- **D.** *Rio Lobo*

372. What song does Snow White sing at the well in *Snow White and the Seven Dwarfs*?
- **A.** "I'm Wishing"
- **B.** "One Song"
- **C.** "Music in Your Soup"
- **D.** "Superfreak"

373. In *The Caine Mutiny*, who is dubbed "Old Yellow Stains"?
- **A.** Lieutenant Greenwald
- **B.** Lieutenant Keefer
- **C.** Lieutenant Maryk
- **D.** Lieutenant Commander Queeg

374. Who performed the songs "Tootsie" and "It Might Be You" for the film *Tootsie*?
- **A.** Stephen Bishop
- **B.** Peter Cetera
- **C.** Michael McDonald
- **D.** Air Supply

375. *Breakfast at Tiffany's* is a 1961 film directed by Blake Edwards and starring Audrey Hepburn. Whose novel was this film adapted from?
- **A.** Norman Mailer
- **B.** Gore Vidal
- **C.** Truman Capote
- **D.** George Axelrod

376. What is Ding Bell's nickname in *It's a Mad, Mad, Mad, Mad World*?
- **A.** Dingbat
- **B.** Ding Dong
- **C.** Dingo
- **D.** Dingy

377.

378. What is the name of the title character in the 1955 Otto Preminger film *The Man with the Golden Arm*?
- **A.** Frankie
- **B.** Carlo
- **C.** Louie
- **D.** Sam

377.

Alfred Hitchcock's 1960 film *Psycho*, an adaptation of a novel by Robert Bloch, garnered a level of respect from mainstream critics that few horror films do. The film was considered controversial because of its infamous barely-nude shower scene and also because of its unorthodox shift in protagonists midway through the film.

Psycho left an indelible impression not only on viewers (who can honestly say they've never thought of the bathroom murder sequence while taking a shower?), but also on film history itself. The film, considered one of Hitchcock's finest, is analyzed in college courses, is listed on just about every "greatest films" list, and is judged by most a true masterpiece.

What is main character Norman Bates's middle name?

- **A.** Francis
- **B.** William
- **C.** Morgan
- **D.** Richard

379. At the start of *The Grapes of Wrath*, protagonist Tom has been away for several years. Where has he been?

- **A.** The Navy
- **B.** Job Corps
- **C.** Prison
- **D.** The French Foreign Legion

380. In *Psycho*, what does Norman conclude that a son is a poor substitute for?

- **A.** A lover
- **B.** A friend
- **C.** An employee
- **D.** An employer

381. Jack Nicholson plays lead character Jake in the Roman Polanski film *Chinatown*. What is Jake's last name?

- **A.** Gettys
- **B.** Gittes
- **C.** Ginty
- **D.** Gindy

382. Who plays Felix Ungar in the 1968 film *The Odd Couple*?

- **A.** Jack Lemmon
- **B.** Tony Randall
- **C.** Walter Matthau
- **D.** Jack Klugman

383. Who played Babe Ruth in the 1942 Sam Wood film *The Pride of the Yankees*?

- **A.** Dan Duryea
- **B.** Walter Brennan
- **C.** Babe Ruth
- **D.** Harry Harvey

384. *2001: A Space Odyssey* is divided into three sections. Which of these is *not* the title of one of the sections?

- **A.** "Jupiter Mission 18 Months Later"
- **B.** "Jupiter Mission Day One"
- **C.** "The Dawn of Man"
- **D.** "Jupiter and Beyond the Infinite"

385. Which of these classic films does *not* feature actor Walter Brennan?

- **A.** *Mr. Deeds Goes to Town*
- **B.** *To Have and Have Not*
- **C.** *Sergeant York*
- **D.** *My Darling Clementine*

386. What actor appears in *The Maltese Falcon* as the character Captain Jacobi?

- **A.** Elisha Cook, Jr.
- **B.** Walter Huston
- **C.** Tim Holt
- **D.** Sidney Greestreet

387. Whose novel was *One Flew Over the Cuckoo's Nest* adapted from?

A. Norman Mailer   C. Ken Kesey

B. Bo Goldman   D. Tom Wolfe

388. *Little Women*, George Cukor's 1933 film starring Katharine Hepburn, takes place in what Massachusetts city?

A. Concord   C. Medford

B. Salisbury   D. Amesbury

389. What type of man does *The Grapes of Wrath's* Tom Joad believe the government cares the most about?

A. A rich man   C. A dead man

B. A black man   D. A crazy man

390.

391. In *To Kill a Mockingbird*, who does Sheriff Tate suggest Atticus should allow to bury the dead?

A. Justice   C. The dead

B. Time   D. Righteousness

392. *The Wild One*, a 1953 Laszlo Benedek film starring Marlon Brando and Lee Marvin, is narrated by what actor?

A. Marlon Brando   C. Lee Marvin

B. Hugh Sanders   D. Jay C. Flippen

393. Jean Heather plays Mr. Dietrichson's meddlesome daughter in the film *Double Indemnity*. What is her name?

A. Phyllis   C. Rebecca

B. Lola   D. Brandy

394. Mr. Andrews offers a reward for Ellie in *It Happened One Night*. How much is the reward?

A. $10,000   C. $327.64

B. $500   D. $100,000

390.

Raging Bull, the 1980 film directed by Martin Scorsese, is the definitive boxing movie. Although Robert De Niro had already appeared in such classics as *The Godfather Part II*, *The Deer Hunter*, and *Taxi Driver*, he further secured his status as one of the most respected actors in history when he gained a reported sixty pounds for the role. Like many classics, *Raging Bull* was initially met with mixed reviews. It did, however, garner eight Oscar nominations, with a win for De Niro's bravura performance and another for Thelma Schoonmaker's dynamic editing.

What real-life boxer is portrayed by De Niro in *Raging Bull*?

A. Jake La Motta

B. Rocky Graziano

C. Max Baer

D. Rocky Marciano

395. What does Dill expect to find in the basement of the courthouse in *To Kill a Mockingbird*?

A. Instruments of torture

B. People being held captive

C. A machine gun

D. An alien spacecraft

396. Which of these is *not* a film directed by Alfred Hitchcock and starring James Stewart?

A. *Rope*

B. *Rear Window*

C. *The Wrong Man*

D. *The Man Who Knew Too Much*

397. In *West Side Story*, who's "got a rep that's bigger than the whole West Side"?

A. Bernardo

B. Tony

C. Riff

D. Chino

398. In *North By Northwest*, what does the "O" in Roger O. Thornhill's name stand for?

A. Oscar

B. Octavio

C. Nothing

D. Orville

399. Alone for a long time at a deserted Army fort, *Dances with Wolves'* John J. Dunbar must find friendship in his horse and a wild wolf. What is the name of Dunbar's horse?

A. Cisco

B. Dixie

C. Pie

D. Two Socks

400. In what film does Charles Chaplin famously eat a pair of leather boots?

A. *Modern Times*

B. *City Lights*

C. *The Gold Rush*

D. *The Kid*

401. *American Graffiti* is widely known for its soundtrack, which consists of many classic songs from the late 1950s and early 1960s. Which of these classic songs does *not* appear in the film?

A. "Heart and Soul"

B. "Peggy Sue"

C. "Party Doll"

D. "I Only Have Eyes for You"

402. Name the singer who makes a brief cameo as himself in *Fargo*.

A. Mel Tormé

B. Sergio Mendes

C. Jose Feliciano

D. Neil Sedaka

403. In *Platoon*, how many times does Elias shoot Barnes?
- **A.** Zero
- **B.** One
- **C.** Two
- **D.** Three

404. Rock Hudson plays the character Bick in the 1956 George Stevens classic *Giant*. What is Bick's last name?
- **A.** Bickerson
- **B.** Bogosian
- **C.** Bixby
- **D.** Benedict

405. In *Modern Times*, who is the inventor of the Billows Feeding Machine?
- **A.** Franklin Wadsworth Billows
- **B.** Chester H. Billows III
- **C.** J. Widdecombe Billows
- **D.** Reginald Danforth Billows III

406. For what film did Dustin Hoffman walk with a stone in his shoe to make his character's limp appear more realistic?
- **A.** *The Graduate*
- **B.** *Midnight Cowboy*
- **C.** *Rain Man*
- **D.** *All the President's Men*

407. What is the name of Robert Shaw's boat in *Jaws*?
- **A.** *Orca*
- **B.** *Alimento de Tiburon*
- **C.** *Blue Orchid*
- **D.** *Sea Mistress*

408.

409. What is the only film to feature both Charles Chaplin and Buster Keaton?
- **A.** *Double Trouble*
- **B.** *Limelight*
- **C.** *Monsieur Verdoux*
- **D.** *A Countess from Hong Kong*

410. What is the real name of the terrier who played Dorothy's hairy pal Toto in *The Wizard of Oz*?
- **A.** Tommy
- **B.** Teddy
- **C.** Telly
- **D.** Terry

408.

Raiders of the Lost Ark, the 1981 collaboration between cinema giants Steven Spielberg and George Lucas, was conceived by Lucas as a big-budget update of serials from the 1930s and 1940s (as was *Star Wars*), and introduced the world to the iconic adventurer Indiana Jones. A true work of genius, *Raiders* elevated Harrison Ford to leading-man status, spawned three sequels (to date), a television series, countless novels, comic books, video games, and toys, and remains one of Spielberg's most loved films.

Harrison Ford was not the original actor cast in the role of Indiana Jones. Who was unable to play the part due to scheduling conflicts?

- **A.** Nick Nolte
- **B.** Burt Reynolds
- **C.** Richard Chamberlain
- **D.** Tom Selleck

411. Who got his start with an uncredited appearance as a neighbor in *The Graduate*?
- **A.** Harrison Ford
- **B.** Richard Dreyfuss
- **C.** Robert De Niro
- **D.** Jeff Bridges

412. The word "mafia" does not appear once in the film *The Godfather*. How many times is this word used in the sequel, *The Godfather Part II*?
- **A.** Zero
- **B.** Twice
- **C.** Once
- **D.** Three times

413. What song plays during the opening credits of Frank Darabont's 1994 film *The Shawshank Redemption*?
- **A.** "Lovesick Blues"
- **B.** "Willie and the Hand Jive"
- **C.** "If I Didn't Care"
- **D.** "Put the Blame on Mame"

414. The title of *From Here to Eternity* comes from a line in a Rudyard Kipling poem. What is the name of the poem?
- **A.** "Gentlemen Rankers"
- **B.** "Soldier, Soldier"
- **C.** "Troopin'"
- **D.** "The Lost Legion"

415. Who was first hired to write the screenplay for *On the Waterfront* (and later fired)?
- **A.** Edward Albee
- **B.** Noel Coward
- **C.** Eugene O'Neill
- **D.** Arthur Miller

416. *All About Eve* is a classic 1950 film directed by Joseph L. Mankiewicz. Who plays the title character in this film?
- **A.** Bette Davis
- **B.** Anne Baxter
- **C.** Celeste Holm
- **D.** Marilyn Monroe

417. What subtitle for the original *Star Wars* was tacked on to later rereleases?
- **A.** *A New Hope*
- **B.** *Attack of the Clones*
- **C.** *Return of Stilted Dialogue*
- **D.** *The Legend Begins*

418. What, according to Steven Spielberg, was the name of the animatronic shark used in *Jaws*?
- **A.** Fred
- **B.** Lem
- **C.** Morty
- **D.** Bruce

419. Which of the following Alfred Hitchcock films was cowritten by his wife, Alma Reville?
- **A.** *Suspicion*
- **B.** *Psycho*
- **C.** *Rear Window*
- **D.** *North By Northwest*

420. Additional scenes for Orson Welles's *The Magnificent Ambersons* were directed by a different director. Who was this?

A. Norman Foster
C. Robert Wise
B. Stanley Cortez
D. Jack Moss

421. What does *Gone with the Wind* belle Scarlett O'Hara conclude that Rhett Butler is not?

A. A gentleman
C. Distinguished
B. Honorable
D. Affable

422. *Papillon* is a classic prison film starring Steve McQueen and Dustin Hoffman. Its title, *Papillon*, is a French word. What does it mean?

A. Coyote
C. Butterfly
B. Prisoner
D. Moonlight

423. What film features a scene in which screenwriter Buck Henry pitches a sequel to *The Graduate*?

A. *See This Movie*
C. *Swimming with Sharks*
B. *The Muse*
D. *The Player*

424. Who notes that the woods are filled with lions, tigers, and bears in *The Wizard of Oz*?

A. The Scarecrow
C. Dorothy
B. The Tin Man
D. The Lion

425. In *The Good, the Bad, and the Ugly*, what actor represents the "ugly"?

A. Clint Eastwood
C. Gian Maria Volonte
B. Eli Wallach
D. Lee Van Cleef

426.

427. What film is ranked at number two on the AFI's list of the one hundred greatest American films?

A. *The Godfather*
C. *Gone with the Wind*
B. *Casablanca*
D. *The Searchers*

426.

Franklin J. Schaffner's 1970 biopic *Patton* chronicles the World War II exploits of General George Patton, who commanded major units in Sicily, Africa, and the European Theater of Operations. Actor George C. Scott, who had appeared previously in *Anatomy of a Murder*, *The Hustler*, and *Dr. Strangelove*, delivers one of the most powerful performances ever captured on celluloid in his portrayal of the great general. After appearing in earlier standout films, Scott was already a well-regarded "A-list" actor, but *Patton* made him a true star. The film was also significant as it marked the first big success in the career of Francis Ford Coppola, who won an Oscar for co-writing the screenplay.

At the time of its release, *Patton* was a tough sell for some, as American soldiers were still fighting and dying in Vietnam. Today, however, the film is generally recognized as a masterpiece.

A made-for-television sequel to *Patton* was produced in 1989. What is the title of this film?

A. *The Last Days of Patton*
B. *Patton Pending*
C. *The Dying Wish of a General*
D. *Patton: A War's End*

428. Which *Star Wars* cast member worked as a carpenter before finding success as an actor?

A. Mark Hamill   C. Billy Dee Williams

B. James Earl Jones   D. Harrison Ford

429. Francis Ford Coppola rereleased what 1927 silent film in 1981?

A. *The Birth of a Nation*   C. *Broken Blossoms*

B. *Napoléon*   D. *Battleship Potemkin*

430. Which of these films was *not* altered or recut against its director's wishes?

A. *Greed*   C. *The Bride of Frankenstein*

B. *Major Dundee*   D. *The Magnificent Ambersons*

431. Dooley Wilson, who played *Casablanca*'s piano man Sam, was a real-life musician. What instrument did he play?

A. Guitar   C. Piano

B. Clarinet   D. Drums

432. Who purchased the Rosebud sled from *Citizen Kane* for $60,500 in 1982?

A. Orson Welles   C. Michael Jackson

B. Steven Spielberg   D. George Lucas

433. Who played the character Kaspar Gutman in the classic 1941 crime film *The Maltese Falcon*?

A. Humphrey Bogart   C. Peter Lorre

B. Sydney Greenstreet   D. Elisha Cook, Jr.

434. What unique credentials did producer Branko Lustig have that helped him make *Schindler's List*?

A. He was a prisoner at Auschwitz   C. He cowrote the book from which it was adapted

B. He fought in World War II   D. Oskar Schindler was his uncle

435. What is the name of the family whose party Benjamin crashes in *The Graduate*?

A. Kasson   C. Dequina

B. Singleman   D. Hoisington

436. In *Touch of Evil*, the 1958 film noir directed by Orson Welles, what actor plays the creepy hotel night manager?
- **A.** Dennis Weaver
- **B.** Ray Collins
- **C.** Anthony Perkins
- **D.** Billy House

437. In which of these films did Jason Robards portray legendary gunman Doc Holliday?
- **A.** *My Darling Clementine*
- **B.** *Gunfight at the O.K. Corral*
- **C.** *Hour of the Gun*
- **D.** *Frontier Marshal*

438. *His Girl Friday*, a 1940 film directed by Howard Hawks and starring Cary Grant and Rosalind Russell, initially used what working title?
- **A.** *The Bigger they Are*
- **B.** *Battle of the Sexes*
- **C.** *Him vs. Her*
- **D.** *Hildy and Walter*

439. Who played the Scarecrow in *The Wizard of Oz*?
- **A.** Frank Morgan
- **B.** Ray Bolger
- **C.** Buddy Ebsen
- **D.** Jack Haley

440. What confection does Norman eat while getting rid of Marion's car in *Psycho*?
- **A.** Jellybeans
- **B.** Candy corn
- **C.** Jawbreakers
- **D.** A candy bar

441.

442. In *Mr. Smith Goes to Washington*, what is Mr. Smith's first name?
- **A.** Longfellow
- **B.** Jefferson
- **C.** Stanley
- **D.** Emmitt

443. In *Treasure of the Sierra Madre*, Cody suggests three things Dobbs and company can do with him. Which of these is *not* one of his suggestions?
- **A.** Kill him
- **B.** Accept him as a partner
- **C.** Pay him to leave
- **D.** Run him off

441.

George Lucas's *American Graffiti* opened to less-than-stellar critical and commercial reception when it was released in 1973. The screenplay, written by Lucas, Gloria Katz, and Willard Huyck, follows a group of middle-class teenagers on the last night of their senior year in May 1962.

Set against a backdrop of classic rock-and-roll tunes, the film, which stars Ron Howard, Harrison Ford, and Richard Dreyfuss, successfully captures the essence of a bygone era. While there is significantly less hoopla surrounding *American Graffiti* than *Star Wars*, many consider the former to be Lucas's true masterpiece.

A sequel entitled *More American Graffiti* was produced in 1979. Which of the original characters makes a cameo in the sequel as a police officer?

- **A.** John Fields
- **B.** John Milner
- **C.** Bob Falfa
- **D.** Curt Henderson

444. What novel does *Annie Hall*'s Alvy Singer suggest *My Sexual Problem* could be a sequel to?

- **A.** *The Red Badge of Courage*
- **B.** *Emma*
- **C.** *The Turn of the Screw*
- **D.** *The Great Gatsby*

445. In *Raging Bull*, who does Jake say "ain't pretty no more"?

- **A.** Himself
- **B.** Sugar Ray Robinson
- **C.** His wife, Vickie
- **D.** Janiro

446. Whose novella, *Heart of Darkness*, is Francis Ford Coppola's 1979 war film *Apocalypse Now* based upon?

- **A.** Joseph Conrad
- **B.** John Milius
- **C.** Ambrose Bierce
- **D.** Stephen Crane

447. What does the friendly alien title character in *E.T.* do with a toy car?

- **A.** He throws it
- **B.** He tries to eat it
- **C.** He fashions a communicator out of it
- **D.** He hits himself in the head with it

448. According to *Bonnie and Clyde*, how many people did the Barrow gang murder?

- **A.** Seven
- **B.** Eighteen
- **C.** Twenty-three
- **D.** Twelve

449. Which of these is not a character played by Peter Sellers in *Dr. Strangelove*?

- **A.** Merkin Muffley
- **B.** Major T.J. Kong
- **C.** Group Captain Mandrake
- **D.** Dr. Strangelove

450. What filmmaker makes a cameo appearance as Senator #2 in *The Godfather Part II*?

- **A.** Don Siegel
- **B.** Roger Corman
- **C.** Samuel Fuller
- **D.** Jonathan Demme

451. In *The Philadelphia Story*, Macauley Connor says Kittridge respects only one thing—what?

- **A.** Money
- **B.** Himself
- **C.** A nice pair of legs
- **D.** None of the above

452. Whose novel served as the source material for *From Here to Eternity*?

A. James A. Michener

B. James Jones

C. Stephen J. Spignesi

D. James Clavell

453. What, according to a song sung in *M*A*S*H*, is painless?

A. Suicide

B. Insanity

C. Cynicism

D. Death

454. What is the name of the Von Trapp family butler in *The Sound of Music*?

A. Hans

B. Max

C. Franz

D. Frederic

455. F. Murray Abraham is best known for playing the character Salieri in *Amadeus*. What is Salieri's first name?

A. Antonio

B. Leopold

C. Joseph

D. Ferdinand

456. In *All Quiet on the Western Front*, what does Kemmerich wake up to find missing?

A. Both of his legs

B. One of his arms

C. One of his legs

D. Both of his arms

457. Which of these films does *not* feature both Orson Welles and Joseph Cotten?

A. *Journey Into Fear*

B. *The Stranger*

C. *F for Fake*

D. *Duel in the Sun*

458.

459. What is the name of Sal Mineo's character in *Rebel Without a Cause*?

A. Plato

B. Socrates

C. Aristotle

D. Homer

458.

In 1969, *The Wild Bunch* made a star out of its journeyman director, Sam Peckinpah, and today it's considered a watershed movie in the history of American cinema. The film is significant in how it raised the bar for cinematic violence, filling the screen with bloody sequences and a massive body count that rivaled that of the war raging in Vietnam at the time of its release. Where most previous westerns hadn't shown any blood when someone was shot, *The Wild Bunch* used gallons upon gallons. Adding to the impact of the graphically violent scenes was Peckinpah's revolutionary usage of slow motion during gunfights. By slowing down the action, Peckinpah successfully showed viewers the grisly consequences of violence in a way that had never been done before.

When *The Wild Bunch* was resubmitted to the MPAA in 1993, its rating was changed to NC-17. What had it been rated prior to this?

A. PG

B. R

C. X

D. It was unrated

460. James Stewart plays the character Scottie in the classic Alfred Hitchcock thriller *Vertigo*. What is Scottie's real name?

A. Alexander Spottiswood

B. Donald Westlake

C. John Ferguson

D. Chris Watson

461. What is the name of the medicine man played by Graham Greene in *Dances with Wolves*?

A. Wind in His Hair

B. Kicking Bird

C. Stands with a Fist

D. Uses Bad Comb-over to Conceal Receding Hairline

462. Franklin J. Schaffner's *Patton* was filmed in what country?

A. Spain

B. New Zealand

C. Germany

D. Italy

463. Robert De Niro plays the character known as Jimmy the Gent in *Goodfellas*. What is Jimmy's real name?

A. Jimmy Conway

B. Jimmy Petrello

C. Jimmy Doyle

D. Jimmy Cabrera

464. Who directed the 1962 cold war thriller *The Manchurian Candidate*?

A. Roman Polanski

B. Milos Forman

C. John Schlesinger

D. John Frankenheimer

465. What actor appears as the character George Hanson in *Easy Rider*?

A. Peter Fonda

B. Jack Nicholson

C. Phil Spector

D. Dennis Hopper

466. What fictitious brand of cigarettes did Quentin Tarantino create for *Pulp Fiction*?

A. Black Label

B. Red Apple

C. Smokestack

D. Black Stripe

467. Pulp novelist Jim Thompson co-wrote the screenplay for which classic film?

A. Paths of Glory

B. Bad Day at Black Rock

C. The Getaway

D. The Maltese Falcon

468. Tony Curtis plays the character Joe, a musician dressed as a woman, in the film *Some Like It Hot*. What instrument does Joe play?

A. Trumpet

B. Piano

C. Bass guitar

D. Saxophone

469. Clarence is the name of the angel played by Henry Travers in the classic film *It's a Wonderful Life*. What is Clarence's last name?

A. Oddbody

B. Angelman

C. O'Herlihy

D. Darrow

470.

471. A fictitious language that combines Russian and English is used in Stanley Kubrick's *A Clockwork Orange*. What is the name of this language?

A. Nadsat

B. Droog

C. Udweneki

D. Gibberish

472. What is the name of Butch and Sundance's gang in *Butch Cassidy and the Sundance Kid*?

A. The Wild Bunch

B. The Barrows Gang

C. The Six-Gun Gang

D. The Hole-In-The-Wall Gang

473. In *Dr. Strangelove*, General Ripper hatches a plan and calls it what?

A. Plan R

B. Plan 35

C. Plan ABC

D. Plan 9

474. What city is Mike Hammer driving to at the beginning of *Kiss Me Deadly*?

A. San Francisco

B. New York City

C. Los Angeles

D. Chicago

475. Who does Gene Hackman play in *The French Connection*?

A. Popeye Doyle

B. Ryan Hixon

C. Sam Timmerman

D. Samuel French

470.

A poor boy from the Memphis projects signed a record deal with RCA in 1955, and the name Elvis Presley quickly became legend. After his first two studio albums hit #1, he crossed over into movies, laying the foundation for the careers of countless future musician/actors, including Isaac Hayes, Harry Connick, Jr., Courtney Love, and Ice Cube.

A brief tour of duty in the Army didn't slow down Elvis's career at all—as soon as he was discharged, he headed back to Hollywood. Hits like *G.I. Blues*, *Blue Hawaii*, and *Viva Las Vegas* proved Elvis and company's ability to fine-tune the film/soundtrack marketing machine. His slew of Hawaiian films, along with spring-break vehicles like *Girl Happy* (set in Fort Lauderdale) and *Fun in Acapulco* (tropical Mexico), helped fuel the beach-movie craze of the 1960s. By the mid-'60s he was cranking out three movies a year, alongside of-the-moment bombshells like Ann-Margret, Tuesday Weld, and quintessential Bond girl Ursula Andress.

In what film did Elvis Presley make his acting debut?

A. *King Creole*

B. *Love Me Tender*

C. *Loving You*

D. *Jailhouse Rock*

476. What famous steed appeared in *Gone with the Wind* as Gerald O'Hara's horse?
- **A.** Trigger
- **B.** Seabiscuit
- **C.** Silver
- **D.** Mister Ed

477. In *Sunset Boulevard* what does Joe Gillis dub the washed-up actors who meet to play cards?
- **A.** The living dead
- **B.** The wax works
- **C.** The walking dead
- **D.** The not gone but already forgotten

478. Who was the narrator in the original 1940 version of *Fantasia*?
- **A.** Hugh Douglas
- **B.** Walt Disney
- **C.** Deems Taylor
- **D.** Bob Hope

479. Who was the first actor cast as Terry Malloy in *On the Waterfront*?
- **A.** Frank Sinatra
- **B.** Rock Hudson
- **C.** Karl Malden
- **D.** Marlon Brando

480. How many female speaking roles are there in *Lawrence of Arabia*?
- **A.** Three
- **B.** One
- **C.** Two
- **D.** Zero

481. What is the title of the Charles Chaplin film conceived by Orson Welles?
- **A.** *Limelight*
- **B.** *City Lights*
- **C.** *Monsieur Verdoux*
- **D.** *A Countess from Hong Kong*

482. Who appears in a cameo in *Jaws* as a reporter on the beach?
- **A.** Steven Spielberg
- **B.** Peter Benchley
- **C.** John Williams
- **D.** John Milius

483. In *Raiders of the Lost Ark*, what type of creature does Indy say he hates?
- **A.** Spiders
- **B.** Women
- **C.** Pirahnas
- **D.** Snakes

484. What is the "one word" Mr. McGuire offers Benjamin in *The Graduate*?

   A. Plastics

   B. Sex

   C. Education

   D. Adultery

485. In *The Godfather Part II*, whom does Michael say will not live to see the new year?

   A. Himself

   B. Fredo Corleone

   C. Hyman Roth

   D. Don Fanucci

486. Who sings "Climb Every Mountain" in *The Sound of Music*?

   A. The Reverend Mother

   B. Maria

   C. Elsa

   D. Captain Von Trapp

487. In *Amadeus*, what does the name Amadeus mean?

   A. Beloved of God

   B. Gift of God

   C. Divine Instrument

   D. We couldn't think of anything else to name you

488. In *All Quiet on the Western Front*, who tells a dead soldier "You're better off than me"?

   A. Katczinski

   B. Tjaden

   C. Paul

   D. Kimmerick

489. In *The Third Man*, what is Martins's first name?

   A. Holly

   B. Oswald

   C. Dane

   D. Harry

490. Which actor enjoys a pool table–top romp with Cybill Shepard in *The Last Picture Show*?

   A. Timothy Bottoms

   B. Jeff Bridges

   C. Ben Johnson

   D. Clu Gulager

491. What filmmaker appears in the role of Claude Lacombe in *Close Encounters of the Third Kind*?

   A. Claude Chabrol

   B. François Truffaut

   C. Jean-Luc Godard

   D. Eric Rohmer

492. Gary Sinise plays the legless character Lieutenant Dan in *Forrest Gump*. What is Lieutenant Dan's last name?

   A. Taylor

   B. Enright

   C. Butler

   D. Mercer

496.

Stanley Kubrick's 1971 film *A Clockwork Orange* was extremely controversial at the time of its release due to its sexual and violent content. The film, which Kubrick adapted from Anthony Burgess's novel of the same title, tells the story of a criminal named Alex DeLarge (played by Malcolm McDowell) who is given aversion therapy to help him become a proper member of society. When the film was initially released in the United States, it was slapped with an "X" rating. Two years later, Kubrick excised thirty seconds of the film and it was re-released with an "R" rating. In the United Kingdom, *A Clockwork Orange* allegedly inspired copycat acts of sexual violence, leading to its ultimately being withdrawn from release.

Music plays a key role in establishing the film's disturbing tone. During one particularly violent scene, Alex sings an Arthur Freed tune. What song is this?

A. "Good Morning"
B. "You Were Meant for Me"
C. "Singin' in the Rain"
D. "Make 'Em Laugh"

493. In *Goodfellas*, what is Henry's only complaint about the tomato sauce in prison?
A. Not enough onions
C. Too many peppers
B. Too many onions
D. Not enough peppers

494. At the beginning of *Rebel Without a Cause*, what kind of toy is Jim holding?
A. A yo-yo
C. A plastic bat
B. A monkey
D. A Slinky

495. Which director appears in a cameo as a meter reader in the 1956 version of *Invasion of the Body Snatchers*?
A. Samuel Fuller
C. Sam Peckinpah
B. Don Siegel
D. Roger Corman

496.

497. In *Deliverance*, which of the four adventurers is an insurance salesman?
A. Ed
C. Bobby
B. Lewis
D. Drew

498. What is the name of the man Andy's wife was having an affair with in *The Shawshank Redemption*?
A. Sean Westhoff
C. Ryan Robertson
B. Josh Barnett
D. Glenn Quentin

499. What is the occupation of Henry Fonda's juror in *12 Angry Men*?
A. Math teacher
C. Salesman
B. Architect
D. Slumlord

500. In the most famous exchange from *Pulp Fiction*, Jules quotes a passage from the Bible. What is this passage?
A. Ezekiel 35:12
C. Ezekiel 25:17
B. Ezekiel 7:17
D. Ezekiel 35:70

CHAPTER THREE:

QUOTES AND DIALOGUE

501. In *Bridge on the River Kwai*, Colonel Saito says, "This is war!" What does he say it is *not*?
A. A day in the park
B. A democracy
C. A game of cricket
D. Supposed to be fun

502. In *Giant*, what is Jett Rink's response when told that "money isn't everything"?
A. "No, it's more than that. It's more than everything."
B. "Not when you've got it."
C. "Grow up, little girl. Money makes the world go 'round."
D. "Go tell that to the chubby little man behind the desk down at the bank."

503. In what film does John Wayne say, "Fill your hands, you son of a bitch"?
A. *The Cowboys*
B. *The Shootist*
C. *True Grit*
D. *Rooster Cogburn*

504. To what director does Norma Desmond say she's ready for her close-up in *Sunset Boulevard*?
A. Cecil B. DeMille
B. D.W. Griffith
C. Billy Wilder
D. George Cukor

505. What actor says "Make him an offer he can't refuse" in *The Godfather*?
A. Marlon Brando
B. Robert Duvall
C. Al Pacino
D. Robert De Niro

506. What was the first film in which Clint Eastwood said the line, "Go ahead, make my day"?
A. *Dirty Harry*
B. *Sudden Impact*
C. *The Dead Pool*
D. *The Enforcer*

507. Of what does *Apocalypse Now's* Lieutenant Colonel Kilgore say he loves the smell?
A. Gunpowder
B. Fresh blood
C. Napalm
D. Fear

OPPOSITE Tom Cruise and Dustin Hoffman in *Rain Man*, 1988

508. In *Titanic*, what does Jack call the "one good thing about Paris"?

A. That he's no longer in it

B. That there are a lot of girls there who will take off their clothes

C. That the cost of a prostitute is cheaper than the cost of dinner

D. "The one good thing about Paris is that there is nothing good about Paris."

509.

510. Which of these things does Raymond say "sucks" in *Rain Man*?

A. Tom Cruise's acting

B. His brother

C. Kmart

D. Running out of clean socks

511. In *Charade*, what does Reggie Lampert say is "like drinking coffee through a veil"?

A. Smoking cigarettes

B. The taste of beer

C. Drinking cheap wine

D. Drinking coffee through a veil

512. What are the last spoken words in *I Am a Fugitive from a Chain Gang*?

A. "I steal."

B. "And so another life ends . . ."

C. "*Que sera, sera.*"

D. "Goodbye, Helen."

513. In what way does *Raiders of the Lost Ark's* Toht say Americans are "all the same"?

A. They are arrogant without reason to be

B. They are always overdressing for the wrong occasions

C. They wander blindly through life

D. They are stupidly careless with the lives of others

514. What does *Casablanca's* Rick tell Ilsa they'll "always have"?

A. Love

B. Memories

C. Paris

D. Each other

515. In *Crash*, what does Anthony say is just "black people demeaning other black people"?

A. Gangbanging

B. Black politicians

C. Hip-hop music

D. Jealousy

509.

The iconic 1953 film *Shane*, helmed by George Stevens, was adapted from the novel by Jack Schaefer, and is an undisputed classic western. *Shane* was the second entry in what has come to be known as Stevens's "American trilogy," which also includes *A Place in the Sun* and *Giant*. The film chronicles the story of a heroic gunfighter (Alan Ladd, in his most memorable role) who comes to the aid of homesteaders who are being threatened and terrorized by a ruthless cattle baron and his band of heavies.

The film was nominated for six Academy Awards, winning a single statuette for its cinematography. (Sadly, Ladd wasn't even nominated for his bravura performance.) The film, which is listed on nearly every "greatest films" list, remains one of the most powerful westerns ever produced. Many successors have copied elements of *Shane*, but few compare.

In one memorable scene, Ryker asks Shane, "What are you?" What is Shane's reply?

A. "None of your business."

B. "A friend of Joe Starrett's."

C. "Shut your mouth."

D. "Nothing."

516. When Loach asks Jake about his nose in *Chinatown*, whom does Jake say is responsible for his injury?

  A. A mugger
  B. Loach's wife
  C. Noah Cross
  D. A hooker

517. In *Crimson Tide*, Captain Ramsey says, "We're here to protect democracy." What does he say they are not there for?

  A. To practice it
  B. To worry about the enemy's safety
  C. To start World War III
  D. To argue about the best way to do it

518. In what film does Spock say "The needs of the many outweigh the needs of the few" before dying?

  A. *Star Trek: The Motion Picture*
  B. *Star Trek IV: The Voyage Home*
  C. *Star Trek III: The Search for Spock*
  D. *Star Trek: The Wrath of Khan*

519. In *Desperado*, the bartender informs Steve Buscemi that the only beer he has is "piss-warm chango." What is Buscemi's response?

  A. "That's my brand."
  B. "Uh . . . I think I'll pass."
  C. "Sounds terrific!"
  D. "That oughta hit the spot."

520. In *To Kill a Mockingbird*, what does Atticus say his father told him to remember?

  A. To never treat another human being badly
  B. That every human being is equal
  C. To always tell the truth
  D. That it's a sin to kill a mockingbird

521. Elliot says, "You're fat," when weighing his alien friend in *E.T. the Extra-Terrestrial*. How much does E.T. weigh?

  A. 25 pounds
  B. 30 pounds
  C. 40 pounds
  D. 35 pounds

522. In *The Hustler*, who tells Eddie that he's a "born loser"?

  A. Bert Gordon
  B. Minnesota Fats
  C. Sarah Packard
  D. Charlie Burns

523. What, according to a German loudspeaker in *Saving Private Ryan*, "is kaput"?

  A. The American government
  B. The White House
  C. The Statue of Liberty
  D. The allied forces

524. In *The Shining*, Dick Hallorann says buildings are like people. In what way?

  A. Some are good and some are bad
  B. Some shine and some don't
  C. Many of them are pretty on the outside, but ugly on the inside
  D. More poorly built than they appear

525. In *Midnight Cowboy*, who does Joe Buck argue "ain't no fag"?

A. Jesus

B. The president

C. John Wayne

D. Albert Einstein

526. What does *Annie Hall's* Alvy Singer say "is like a shark"?

A. A relationship

B. Annie's brother

C. A lobster

D. A New Yorker

527. What does Harry Potter say are more important than books and cleverness in *Harry Potter and the Sorcerer's Stone*?

A. Sequels and merchandising

B. Friendship and bravery

C. Bravery and trust

D. Trust and skill

528. What, according to *Arsenic and Old Lace's* Mortimer Brewster, is Brewster code for?

A. Russian spy

B. Very important person

C. Roosevelt

D. Friend

529. In *The Wizard of Oz*, why does Auntie Em say she cannot tell Almira Gulch what she really thinks about her?

A. Because saying such things would hurt her own ears

B. Because some things ought not to be said

C. Because Almira is rich and powerful

D. Because she's a Christian woman

530. What does *Caddyshack's* Al Czervik say someone should get when purchasing a hat like Judge Smails's?

A. Arrested

B. A free bowl of soup

C. An apology

D. Institutionalized

531. What does Dr. Dreyfuss tell C.C. Baxter to be in *The Apartment*?

A. A better person

B. Careful to drink plenty of fluids

C. A *mensch*

D. Aware of the feelings of others

532. In *The Shawshank Redemption*, Red says that prison life consists of two things. Routine and what else?

A. Lots of looking over one's shoulder

B. More routine

C. Boredom

D. Daydreaming about the real world

536.

Citizen Kane is widely considered the single greatest motion picture in the history of the cinema. The 1941 film directed by Orson Welles was loosely based upon the life of media mogul William Randolph Hearst. Welles's ambitious film is considered one of the most significant milestones in the history of the medium because it developed and/or enhanced techniques that were unconventional at the time, such as the creative use of deep focus photography, experimental lighting, low-angle shots, overlapping dialogue, long uninterrupted shots, nonlinear storytelling, expressionist photography, a subjective camera, and many other revolutionary techniques. Perhaps the single most impressive aspect of *Citizen Kane* is the fact that Welles, the creative force behind the film, was only twenty-five at the time he made it.

In the film, how long does Charles Foster Kane conclude it will take him to lose the newspaper if he continues losing a million dollars per year?

A. Sixty years
B. Forty years
C. Fifty years
D. Thirty years

533. In the movie *Unforgiven*, Ned tells Billy Munny that they "ain't bad men no more." What does he say they are?
A. A couple of men trying to forget the past
B. Lucky
C. Farmers
D. Domesticated old men

534. What does *Gone with the Wind*'s Mammy say "would be better" for Scarlett?
A. Savannah
B. A good husband
C. Stability
D. Rest

535. In *Field of Dreams*, Ray's wife Annie asks what she should do if "the voice" calls while he's away. What is Ray's response?
A. "Give it my phone number."
B. "Pretend like you don't hear it."
C. "Tell him I'll be gone until Tuesday."
D. "Take a message."

536.

537. Just before Han is about to be frozen in *The Empire Strikes Back*, Leia tells him she loves him. What is his response?
A. He says nothing.
B. "I know."
C. "Yeah."
D. "I love you, too."

538. In *The Deer Hunter*, who says "One shot is what it's all about"?
A. Stosh
B. Michael
C. Nick
D. Steven

539. In *American Beauty*, Jim Olmeyer asks Lester what he wants from a workout. What is Lester's response?
A. "I want to look good naked."
B. "I wanna look like I did when I was eighteen."
C. "I want to pick up girls."
D. "I want to look like a Greek god, only with more sex appeal."

540. In *Boyz N the Hood*, a woman asks Doughboy why he always has to refer to women as "bitch, ho, or hoochie." What is his response?
A. "Don't act like no ho, I won't call you no ho."
B. "Shut up, ho."
C. "Cause that's what you are."
D. "Ask your mama."

541. In *Jaws*, Hooper says he "will not argue with a man who's lining up to be" something. What is this?
A. A hot lunch
B. Hors d'oeuvres
C. Jackass of the Year
D. Replaced in the sequel

542. What does the leader of the street punks say *The Terminator* is?

A. A couple sandwiches short of a picnic

B. A couple cans short of a six-pack

C. A couple brain cells short of a California governor

D. A couple brain cells short of being an idiot

543. In *Sleepless in Seattle*, Becky tells Annie that her problem is that she doesn't want to be in love. What does she say Annie does want?

A. To be referred to as the crazy old woman with all the cats

B. To complain about not being in love

C. To be in love in a movie

D. A relationship without commitment or fear of falling in love

544.

545. What does Auda abu Tayi tell *Lawrence of Arabia* that he is to his people?

A. A river

B. A rock

C. A god

D. A lion

546. In *Taxi Driver*, what does Travis Bickle say someone should do with New York City?

A. Erase it and start over

B. Flush it down the toilet

C. Step on it and squash it like a bug

D. Throw it away

547. In *Three Kings*, what does Archie say is the "most important thing in life"?

A. To be able to look at yourself in the mirror

B. Respect

C. Necessity

D. Self-respect

548. A customer in *Clerks* compliments the cat sitting on the counter and asks what its name is. What is Randal's response?

A. "Shut up and get out."

B. "Annoying customer."

C. "I don't know, what's your wife's name?"

D. "Pussy."

549. Who does *Treasure of the Sierra Madre's* Fred C. Dobbs say has been better to him than any woman?

A. Lady Luck

B. Gold

C. The mountain

D. The mine

550. In *Good Will Hunting*, Will tells Sean that he read his novel the previous night. What is Sean's response?

A. "So you're the one."

B. "I'm sorry."

C. "You're the first."

D. "I'm sorry, but no refunds."

544.

Martin Scorsese's 1990 film *Goodfellas*, adapted from Nicholas Pileggi's nonfiction book *Wiseguy*, tells the story of real-life mobster-turned-informant Henry Hill, played by Ray Liotta. Although the film took some liberties with the truth, many crime experts have called it the most realistic film ever made about the Mafia. *Goodfellas* received six Academy Award nominations, winning a single Oscar for Joe Pesci's unforgettable performance as mobster Tommy DeVito. *Total Film*, a British film publication, has called it the greatest film ever made.

In the film, what does Henry conclude to be "better than Citibank"?

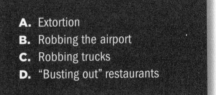

A. Extortion

B. Robbing the airport

C. Robbing trucks

D. "Busting out" restaurants

551. In *Schindler's List*, who says that Jews "put a spell on you, you know"?

A. Helen Hirsch

B. Amon Goeth

C. Oskar Schindler

D. Itzhak Stern

552. In *The Seven Year Itch*, what does The Girl suggest dunking in champagne?

A. Her

B. Doughnuts

C. Finger sandwiches

D. Potato chips

553. What does Oliver say means "never having to say you're sorry" in *Love Story*?

A. Marriage

B. Love

C. Being an adult

D. None of these

554. In *High Fidelity*, a movie starring John Cusack based on the eponymous Nick Hornby novel, what question does Rob begin the movie with?

A. "How do you know if you've made it into the all-time top five most memorable break up list?"

B. "What's the point? It never goes anywhere."

C. "What came first? The music or the misery?"

D. "Is it better to burn out than to fade away?"

555. In *The 40-Year-Old Virgin*, Andy says he respects women so much that he . . .

A. Stays away from them

B. Tries not to curse around them

C. Listens to what they have to say

D. Watches *Maid in Manhattan*

556. What does Radio Raheem say the "right hand and the left hand" represent in *Do the Right Thing*?

A. Good and evil

B. Love and hate

C. Black and white

D. The living and the dead

557. In *Reservoir Dogs*, who does Mr. Pink say is "dead as Dillinger"?

A. Mr. White

B. Mr. Orange

C. Nice Guy Eddie

D. Mr. Blue

558. In *Platoon*, Sergeant O'Neill tells Sergeant Barnes that he's afraid he's about to die. What is Barnes's response?

A. "Everybody gotta die sometime, Red."

B. "Tell it to Saint Peter, Red."

C. "Tell it to the gravediggers, Red."

D. "Can't say I'd miss you any, Red."

559. In *Airplane!*, what kind of movies does Captain Oveur ask young Joey if he likes?

A. Porno movies

B. Snuff films

C. Movies about gladiators

D. Musicals

560. In *The Sixth Sense*, who does Anna Crowe say Malcolm sounds like when he's been drinking?

A. Dr. Seuss
B. Bob Dylan
C. William Shatner
D. An old Korean man

561. The most memorable scene in the David Mamet adaptation *Glengarry Glen Ross* depicts motivational speaker Blake (Alec Baldwin) "motivating" the salesmen by saying: "Put that coffee down. Coffee is for . . ."

A. Real men
B. Salesmen
C. Closers
D. Winners

562. *For a Few Dollars More*'s Colonel Mortimer tells Wild, "I generally smoke just after I eat. Why don't you come back in about ten minutes?" What is Wild's response?

A. "Smoke this!"
B. "Ten minutes you'll be smoking in hell!"
C. "I've taken all the sass I'm gonna take from you, mister!"
D. "You're not gonna be alive that long!"

563. In *The Godfather Part II*, Michael explains, "I don't feel I have to wipe everybody out, Tom." Who does he say he does feel he has to wipe out?

A. His enemies
B. People who cross him
C. His brother, Fredo
D. Pat Geary

564.

565. In *Memento*, what does Leonard say makes memories "irrelevant"?

A. Truth
B. Facts
C. A reason to lie
D. A need for things to be different

566. Ash, the android in *Alien*, says, "I can't lie to you about your chances, but . . ." What does he then say?

A. "You have my sympathies."
B. "I will wish you luck, friend."
C. "If I were capable of doing so, I would."
D. "It was nice knowing you."

567. In *A Clockwork Orange*, what does Alex say "comes to thems that wait"?

A. Wisdom
B. Survival instinct
C. Initiative
D. A loss of morality

568. What is *The Shootist*'s John Bernard Books's response when told that he swears too much?

A. "Go %#$& yourself."
B. "The hell I do."
C. "Go to hell."
D. "Damned right I do."

564.

Basing a theme-park ride on a hit movie is nothing new—but basing a movie on a theme-park ride is another story. Disney's decision to make a $140 million movie out of its own thirty-year-old ride, Pirates of the Caribbean, sounded like great marketing, but would that really mean great filmmaking? Luckily for *Pirates of the Caribbean: The Curse of the Black Pearl*, anti-heartthrob Johnny Depp doesn't need a box-office guarantee to sign on to a movie (*Dead Man*, anyone?). His Keith Richards-esque performance as Captain Jack Sparrow truly made the film while cementing his star status. In *Pirates*, the sashaying Sparrow joins forces with Will Turner (Orlando Bloom) when Turner's almost-sweetheart Elizabeth Swann (Keira Knightley) is kidnapped by the pirate crew of the *Black Pearl*—but only because Sparrow wants the *Black Pearl* for himself.

When Will accuses the captain of cheating, what is Sparrow's response?

A. "Of course I cheated!"
B. "And?"
C. "Pirate!"
D. "Prove it!"

569. In *Rebecca*, Mrs. Danvers asks, "Did you ever see anything so delicate?" To what is she referring?

- **A.** A painting of herself when she was younger
- **B.** A rose
- **C.** A negligee
- **D.** A painting of Rebecca

570. In *Touch of Evil*, Schwartz says, "Hank was a great detective all right . . ." What is Tanya's response to this?

- **A.** "And a lousy cop."
- **B.** "Compared to what?"
- **C.** "He's a great detective just so long as he's dead."
- **D.** "Despite all evidence to the contrary."

571. What does *A Time to Kill*'s Lucien Wilbanks proclaim "ain't easy"?

- **A.** Righting wrongs
- **B.** Bringing justice to the unjust
- **C.** Saving the world
- **D.** Stomaching racism

572. In *Lethal Weapon*, Riggs tells a hooker, "I want you to come home and watch television with me." What does he say he wants her to watch with him?

- **A.** *The Dukes of Hazzard*
- **B.** *The Three Stooges*
- **C.** *Looney Toons*
- **D.** Pay-per-view wrestling

573. Of what does *Amadeus*'s Salieri say he "cannot remember a time"?

- **A.** When he didn't want to write music
- **B.** When Emperor Joseph II gave him the credit he deserved
- **C.** When he didn't hate Mozart
- **D.** When he didn't know Mozart's name

574. In *Kill Bill: Vol. 2*, The Bride asks Bill, "How did you find me?" What is his response?

- **A.** "It wasn't hard, kiddo."
- **B.** "I'm the man."
- **C.** "I have my ways."
- **D.** "It's what I do."

575. Lieutenant Dan asks Forrest Gump, "Have you found Jesus yet, Gump?" What is Forrest's response?

- **A.** "Not yet, but I'm gonna find him one of these days."
- **B.** "Why, do you know where he is?"
- **C.** "I didn't know I was supposed to be looking for him."
- **D.** "I found a man I thought was Jesus, but he wasn't Jesus. He was just a man riding a motorcycle."

576. In *Fargo*, who tells Marge, "So you married old Norm son-of-a-Gunderson"?

- **A.** Mike Yanagita
- **B.** Stan Grossman
- **C.** Carl Showalter
- **D.** Lou

577. Brian in *Life of Brian* asks his mother, "Have I got a big nose, Mum?" What is her response?

A. "I didn't have immaculate conception for this crap!"

B. "Stop thinking about sex!"

C. "Does a bear . . . um, you know . . . um, just go to sleep, okay?"

D. "Being able to smell the fish at the market wasn't hint enough?"

578. In *Toy Story*, what kind of meeting does Woody proclaim to have been "a big success"?

A. A meeting on bedroom cleanliness

B. A plastic corrosion meeting

C. A preventative maintenance meeting

D. A meeting on toy safety

579. Who, according to *Magnolia*'s Jimmy Gator, says, "We might be through with the past, but the past ain't through with us"?

A. Nostradamus

A. Life

C. Fredrich Nietzsche

D. The Book

580. In *All the President's Men*, Clark MacGregor warns, "If you print that, our relationship will be terminated." What is Woodward's response to this?

A. "We don't have a relationship."

B. "Consider it terminated then."

C. "Maybe we can talk about this after tonight's edition comes out, huh?"

D. "And I was just starting to like you."

581. What does *Almost Famous*'s Lester Bangs call the "booze they feed you"?

A. Scotch

B. Acceptance

C. Friendship

D. Sex and drugs

582. *Harold and Maude*'s Harold observes, "You sure have a way with people." What is Maude's response to this?

A. "Who cares about people?"

B. "Well, they're my species!"

C. "People shmeeple."

D. "It's better than having everyone hate you, you know."

583. Where does *Doctor Zhivago*'s Gromeko say "good marriages are born"?

A. In bed

B. In heaven

C. In the kitchen

D. In trust

584.

585. In *Walk the Line*, who does Luther Perkins say "sure talks a lot of poon"?

A. Johnny Cash

B. Elvis Presley

C. Waylon Jennings

D. Jerry Lee Lewis

584.

British secret agent James Bond, one of the screen's most compelling characters, was created by novelist Ian Fleming in 1952.

Two years later, Barry Nelson became the first actor to play the character Bond in a one-hour television adaptation of *Casino Royale*. The first feature film adaptation was 1962's *Dr. No*, which starred Sean Connery. In the years since, the Bond character has appeared in more than twenty films. Since Connery's departure from the series, agent 007 has been played by George Lazenby, Roger Moore, Timothy Dalton, Pierce Brosnan, Daniel Craig, and by six different actors (Peter Sellers, David Niven, Ursula Andress, Woody Allen, Daliah Lavi, and Terence Cooper) in the "unofficial" 1967 Bond film *Casino Royale*.

One of the most famous lines in film history is "Bond, James Bond." In what film did this line first appear?

A. *Thunderball*

B. *On Her Majesty's Secret Service*

C. *Never Say Never Again*

D. *Dr. No*

586. "[A man's word] ain't what counts," explains *The Wild Bunch*'s Dutch Engstrom. What does he believe does count?

A. If a man does his best to keep his word, even if he falls short

B. None of these

C. Whether or not he had any choice but to agree to such a thing

D. To whom he gives his word

587. In *The Conversation*, Harry Caul says, "I'm not afraid of death." What does he say he *is* afraid of?

A. Women

B. Murder

C. Tight spaces

D. Suspicious-looking men wearing sunglasses and black coats

588. What does *Anchorman* Ron Burgundy believe means "whale's vagina"?

A. San Diego

B. *Carpe diem*

C. *Titanic*

D. *Donde esta*

589. In *Harvey*, what does Elwood P. Dowd say he's "wrestled with . . . for thirty-five years"?

A. Whether or not he should tell anyone about Harvey

B. The knowledge that he was the only one who could see Harvey

C. Reality

D. Psychotic behavior

590. Who, in *Duck Soup*, says, "I got a good mind to join a club and beat you over the head with it"?

A. Rufus T. Firefly

B. Wolf J. Flywheel

C. Captain Spaulding

D. J. Cheever Loophole

591. In *Fight Club*, what does the narrator say "people are always asking"?

A. If he knows Tyler Durden

B. What his secret is

C. Why he has a chip on his shoulder

D. How to join Fight Club

592. In *It's a Wonderful Life*, who does Zuzu say told her that "every time a bell rings, an angel gets his wings"?

A. The minister

B. Her teacher

C. Her mother

D. A man named Clarence

593. What does the coroner in *Vertigo* say the law "has little to say" about?

A. NFL running backs accused of murdering their wives

B. Good intentions

C. Suspicious-looking accidents

D. Things left undone

594. What character in *Dr. Strangelove* asserts, "Your Commie has no regard for human life"?

A. General Turgidson
B. General Ripper
C. Group Captain Mandrake
D. President Merkin Muffley

595. "You do some time, they never let you go," complains one of *The Usual Suspects*. "You know, they treat you like a criminal." Who says this?

A. Keaton
B. Verbal
C. Hockney
D. Fenster

596. Who says "I feel sorry for you . . . what it must feel like to *want* to throw the switch" in *12 Angry Men*?

A. Juror #3 (Lee J. Cobb)
B. Juror #1 (Martin Balsam)
C. Juror #7 (Jack Warden)
D. Juror #8 (Henry Fonda)

597. In *Rear Window*, what does Stella say has caused the human race more trouble than anything else?

A. Intelligence
B. Greed
C. Curiosity
D. Jealousy

598. "You know me," says *Eternal Sunshine of the Spotless Mind*'s Clementine. "I'm impulsive." What is Joel's response to this?

A. "Yes, and?"
B. "Yes, it's written there on your forehead: impulsiveness."
C. "That's what I love about you."
D. "I don't see what harm a little impulsiveness could do . . ."

599. In *On the Waterfront*, what does Terry say his "life won't be worth" if he rats?

A. The $20 he got for his last fight
B. A nickel
C. The paper they'll print his death certificate on
D. The dirt he'll be buried beneath

600.

601. In the film *Swingers*, the group debates how long a man should wait to call a woman he's just met. Who remarks, "Two days is like industry standard"?

A. Sue
B. Trent
C. Mike
D. Rob

602. In *The Green Mile*, John Coffey says, "He mean. He stepped on Del's mouse." To whom is he referring?

A. Warden Moores
B. "Wild Bill" Wharton
C. Percy Wetmore
D. "Brutal" Howell

600.

The 1946 film noir *The Big Sleep* was adapted from Raymond Chandler's first novel and directed by Howard Hawks. It starred two of the era's hottest actors: the moody Humphrey Bogart and screen siren Lauren Bacall. The release of the film came in the middle of what was called the "Bogie and Bacall" phenomenon, just after their marriage and co-starring roles in the box-office hit *To Have and Have Not*.

The screenplay, written by William Faulkner, Leigh Brackett, and Jules Furthman, tells the thrilling tale of private detective Phillip Marlowe (Bogart) as he encounters the bizarre and deadly events surrounding the Sternwood family. As the plot progresses, Marlowe falls in love with one member of the family: Bacall's character Vivian Sternwood Rutledge.

Helmed by Howard Hawks, Oscar-nominated director of the popular 1941 war movie *Sergeant York*, *The Big Sleep* has been included in Roger Ebert's "100 Great Movies" list, and holds a place in the National Film Registry.

Partway through the film, General Sternwood asks Marlowe, "How do you like your brandy, sir?" What is Marlowe's reply?

A. "In a glass"
B. "From a bottle"
C. "Wet"
D. "Handed to me by a blonde, preferably undressed"

603. In *Butch Cassidy and the Sundance Kid*, a fellow card player realizes his mistake in accusing Sundance of cheating: "If I draw on you, you'll kill me." What is Sundance's reply?

- **A.** "Then you'll be dead and a lousy card player."
- **B.** "There's that possibility."
- **C.** "So am I cheating or not?"
- **D.** "Then they'll have to stop our game to clean up the blood."

604. What does *Patton* say "no bastard ever won a war" by doing?

- **A.** Acting like he's bulletproof
- **B.** Dying for his country
- **C.** Being selfish
- **D.** Trying to be heroic

605. In *Stand By Me*, what does Gordie proclaim to be "a stupid waste of time"?

- **A.** Searching for a dead body
- **B.** Writing
- **C.** Listening to his friends
- **D.** Homework

606. In *The Player*, a delivery boy mistakes Alan Rudolph for Martin Scorsese. Alan says he's not Scorsese, but that he knows someone. Who?

- **A.** Harvey Keitel
- **B.** Martin Scorsese
- **C.** Nicolas Pileggi
- **D.** Robert De Niro

607. In what film does Al Pacino deliver his famous "you're out of order" monologue?

- **A.** *Bobby Deerfield*
- **B.** *Author! Author!*
- **C.** *. . . And Justice for All*
- **D.** *Dog Day Afternoon*

608. In *The Philadelphia Story*, Macaulay Connor asks Tracy if love would be inconvenient. What is her reply?

- **A.** "I should think so."
- **B.** "Terribly."
- **C.** "I've never been in love, so I can't really say."
- **D.** "Isn't it always?"

609. Who does Jim *"Cinderella Man"* Braddock say he would fight for $250?

- **A.** President Roosevelt
- **B.** Joe Gould's wife
- **C.** His mother-in-law
- **D.** God

610. What is the name of the "stuntman, champion bodybuilder" Bo Catlett introduces in *Get Shorty* as the guy who "throws out things I don't want"?

- **A.** Ronnie Wingate
- **B.** Yayo Portillo
- **C.** Elliot Wilhelm
- **D.** Bear

611. *A Christmas Story's* Mr. Parker asks, "What is the name of the Lone Ranger's nephew's horse?" What does Mother answer, saying "everybody knows that"?

- **A.** Victor
- **B.** Domino
- **C.** Cartwright
- **D.** Jason

612. What does *Spartacus* say "as long as we live, we must" do?

A. "Continue fighting until there's no one left to fight."

B. "Live life to the fullest."

C. "Remain true to ourselves."

D. "Remember the sacrifices of those before us."

613. Out of "a hundred million terrorists in the world," *Die Hard*'s John McClane laments that he has to kill one with feet smaller than:

A. An infant

B. His sister

C. His grandmother

D. The Keebler elves

614.

615. In *The Great Escape*, Sedgwick says, "*Liubliu?* . . . What's it mean?" What is Danny's response to this?

A. "Peace be unto you."

B. "I love you."

C. "Which way to the grocery store?"

D. "My hat is too small."

616. In *The Silence of the Lambs*, Lecter recognizes "that accent you've tried so desperately to shed." From where does Lecter conclude that Starling hails?

A. West Virginia

B. South Carolina

C. Georgia

D. Arkansas

617. Who, in *Paths of Glory*, does Corporal Paris say will be alive after he is dead?

A. Colonel Dax

B. A cockroach

C. The buzzards picking at the dead

D. General Broulard

618. Complete this sentence: In *Hotel Rwanda*, George Rutaganda explains, "When people ask me, good listeners, why do I hate all the Tutsi, I say . . ."

A. "Read our history."

B. "They are an affront to mankind."

C. "It is for the same reason the sun shines brightly."

D. "They are heathens and murderers."

619. "He shot my father six times," explains *L.A. Confidential*'s Ed Exley, "and got away clean. No one even knew who he was. I just made the name up to give him some personality." What is this name?

A. Keyser Soze

B. Captain Dudley Smith

C. Rollo Tomasi

D. Django Rivera

620. In *Sin City*, Marv says, "I love hitmen." Why does he say he loves them?

A. "They give you what you need if you can get the drop on 'em."

B. "They're trash, but the people they kill? Well, they're trash, too."

C. "Hitmen murder for profit—capitalism at its finest."

D. "No matter what you do to them, you don't feel bad."

614.

Audiences had never seen anything quite like Quentin Tarantino's tour-de-force *Pulp Fiction* prior to its release in 1994, despite the fact that the film relies on old story lines and, in some cases, liberal borrowing of plot devices, situations, and dialogue. *Pulp Fiction* managed to meld these elements into something new and refreshing. The film's incessantly quotable dialogue, nonlinear story line, and sheer quirkiness made it an instant cult classic. The film reestablished John Travolta as an "A-list" Hollywood star, revived Bruce Willis's career, propelled Samuel L. Jackson to new heights, and immediately spawned a legion of copycats. It's often cited as the launching pad for an independent film movement. *Pulp Fiction* was nominated for seven Oscars, winning one for its screenplay. It received many other nominations and awards, including the prestigious Golden Palm Award at Cannes.

In the film, what food does Jules call "the cornerstone of any nutritious breakfast"?

A. Hot dogs

B. Hamburgers

C. Pizza

D. Egg rolls

621. *Million Dollar Baby's* Frankie Dunn says, "*Mo cuishle,*" before ending Maggie's story. What does he say *mo cuishle* means?

A. "Goodnight, my dear"

B. "Seek peace"

C. "My darling, my blood"

D. "In this life or the next"

622. In *Batman Begins*, Bruce Wayne tells a fellow prisoner, "You're not the devil." What does he then say the man is?

A. Dead meat

B. Practice

C. Unconscious

D. Pitiful

623. Who, in *Donnie Darko*, says, "I can do anything I want. And so can you"?

A. Frank

B. Samantha Darko

C. Professor Kenneth Monnitoff

D. Donnie Darko

624. In *The Adventures of Robin Hood*, what does Robin say he speaks "fluently"?

A. Truth

B. Treason

C. His mind

D. None of these

625. Who does *True Romance's* Vincenzo Coccotti say are "great liars," "the best in the world"?

A. Jews

B. Blacks

C. Police officers

D. Sicilians

626. In *Before Sunrise*, what does Jesse say he sometimes dreams about?

A. "Being an old man with a nice little wife to live with me . . . to die with me"

B. "Being an angel and seeing all the little things people do when they think no one sees them"

C. "Being a good father and a good husband"

D. "Falling in love"

627. "There is a major network interested in me," Phil informs his coworkers in *Groundhog Day*. What network does Larry joke that it is?

A. The Fishing Channel

B. Black Entertainment Television

C. The Home Shopping Network

D. The Home Improvement Channel

628. In *The Searchers*, Ethan says he will find the Indians "just as sure as" what?

A. The turning of the earth

B. The sky is blue

C. He's breathing

D. Water is wet

629. What does Martha say George cannot afford to do on his salary in *Who's Afraid of Virginia Woolf*?

A. Develop a conscience

B. Anything worth doing

C. Fall in love with a younger woman

D. Waste good alcohol

630.

631. In *Brokeback Mountain*, to whom does Jack say, "Fast or slow, I like the direction you're going"?

A. Ennis

B. Cassie

C. Monroe

D. Lureen

632. In *Citizen Kane*, Charles Foster Kane says if something had been different, he might "have been a really great man." What was this?

A. If he hadn't been rich

B. If he'd never fallen in love with Susan Alexander

C. If he hadn't craved power

D. If his parents had loved him

633. In *Goodfellas*, who says, "Go home and get your [expletive] shine box"?

A. Tommy DeVito

B. Henry Hill

C. Billy Batts

D. Jimmy Conway

634. In *Seven*, Somerset quotes someone as saying, "The world is a fine place and worth fighting for." Who wrote this?

A. Jack Kerouac

B. Ernest Hemingway

C. John Steinbeck

D. Norman Mailer

635. In *The Manchurian Candidate*, who does Marco say is "impossible to like"?

A. Raymond Shaw

B. Mrs. Iselin

C. Senator Jordan

D. Senator Iselin

636. What does *Some Like It Hot's* Sugar say "must be worth their weight in gold"?

A. Gold coins

B. Gold bars

C. Diamonds

D. German barabonds

637. In *Strangers on a Train*, Bruno says, "Don't worry, I'm not going to shoot you, Mr. Haines." Why does he say he's not going to shoot him?

A. It would be a waste of a bullet

B. He'd rather have lunch before killing a man

C. The sound hurts his ears

D. It might disturb Mother

630.

Blake Edwards's 1961 film *Breakfast at Tiffany's*, an adaptation of a novella by Truman Capote, is one of the most popular romantic comedies of all time. The film stars the late great Audrey Hepburn as Holly Golightly, a high-priced call girl in search of a sugar daddy to finance the jet set lifestyle she envisions for herself. When she meets Paul Varjak (George Peppard), a struggling writer who is being kept by an older woman, she must reassess her goals. While some aspects of the film don't hold up today (such as Mickey Rooney's offensive racial caricature, Yunioshi), *Breakfast at Tiffany's* is still a classic by any definition of the word. And even if George Axelrod's screenplay is substantially different from the novella—one of the most frequent complaints about the film—it is smart, funny, and well written.

Complete Holly's statement from the film: "I've got to do something about the way I look. I mean, a girl just can't go to Sing Sing with . . ."

A. Curlers in her hair

B. A green face

C. A pimple on her nose

D. Turquoise high heels

638. *Forrest Gump* tells the President, "I gotta pee." Which president does he say this to?

A. Richard Nixon

B. John Kennedy

C. Jimmy Carter

D. Lyndon B. Johnson

639. When does *The Apartment*'s Fran Kubelik say a woman should not wear mascara?

A. On a rainy day

B. When she's in love

C. When she's in love with a married man

D. To church

640. What are Will Kane's first words in *High Noon*?

A. "I do."

B. "Outlaws!"

C. "Ever thought of working as a deputy?"

D. "I always knew one day this tin star would get me into trouble."

641. In *Notorious*, Alicia states, "There's nothing like a love song to . . ."

A. "Remind you what you don't have."

B. "Make a girl cry."

C. "Give you a good laugh."

D. "Put your life into perspective."

642. In *Once Upon a Time in America*, Fat Moe asks, "What have you been doing all these years?" What is Noodles's response?

A. "Killing people."

B. "Going to bed early."

C. "Watching a lot of television, I guess."

D. "Reading."

643. In the film *Chasing Amy*, who delivers the line "You're chasing Amy"?

A. Silent Bob

B. Holden

C. Banky

D. Hooper

644. In *Quiz Show*, what does Congressman Derounian say he cannot commend Charles Van Doren for doing?

A. Lying

B. Cheating

C. Telling the truth

D. Defrauding the American public

645. In the 1987 comedy *The Princess Bride*, what does Westley say when Fezzick asks him why he's wearing a mask?

A. "They're terribly comfortable."

B. "I was burned by acid; thanks for asking."

C. "I love the color."

D. "Everyone who's anyone will be wearing them in the future."

646. In *The Killing*, what does Johnny Clay say Sherry has "where most women have a heart"?

A. A black hole

B. A question mark

C. Barbed wire

D. A dollar sign

647. What, according to *The African Queen's* Rose Sayer, is "what we are put in this world to rise above"?

A. Nature

B. Evil

C. Primal urges

D. Sin

648. What does *Gladiator's* Maximus say "smiles at us all"?

A. Mortality

B. Luck

C. The gods

D. Death

649. In *V for Vendetta*, what does Evey say "works better than a Guy Fawkes mask"?

A. A quick sword

B. Beauty

C. A fake I.D.

D. A properly told lie

650.

651. In *Brief Encounter*, when does Margaret Jesson say "there aren't any pantomimes"?

A. June

B. August

C. July

D. September

652. "You're an ambitious man, Mr. *Gandhi*," observes Vince Walker. What is Gandhi's response?

A. "I think not."

B. "I hope not."

C. "The desire to do what is right is sometimes mistaken for ambition."

D. "My ambition serves a greater purpose."

653. What does *Boogie Nights's* Floyd Gondolli say "tells the truth"?

A. Money

B. The camera

C. Videotape

D. The heart

654. In what movie does Al Pacino scream "Attica! Attica!"?

A. *Scarecrow*

B. *Dog Day Afternoon*

C. *The Panic in Needle Park*

D. *Author! Author!*

650.

The Graduate, a 1967 film directed by Mike Nichols and adapted from Charles Webb's novel, tells the story of a wandering college graduate named Benjamin Braddock (Dustin Hoffman in his first starring role). He is seduced by the wife (Anne Bancroft) of his father's business partner, and then falls in love with her daughter. Aside from its masterful performances and witty screenplay, *The Graduate* is also remembered for its soundtrack performed by Simon and Garfunkel. Songs like "Mrs. Robinson" and lines of dialogue such as "Are you trying to seduce me, Mrs. Robinson?" have become a part of the public consciousness. The film, which has also been adapted into a Broadway play, was ranked seventh on the American Film Institute's list of the greatest American films and also its list of the all-time funniest films (ranked ninth).

In the film Benjamin's father asks, "Would you mind telling me then what those four years of college were for? What was the point of all that hard work?" What is Benjamin's response to this?

A. "I don't know."

B. "You got me."

C. "It was something to do, I guess."

D. "You're the one who wanted me to go."

655. What does *Before Sunset's* Jesse say he is "designed" to do?
- **A.** Be dissatisfied
- **B.** Be lonely
- **C.** Be unhappy
- **D.** Be unrealistic

656. To whom does *Mystic River's* Jimmy Markum say, "I know in my soul I contributed to your death"?
- **A.** Katie
- **B.** Celeste
- **C.** Annabeth
- **D.** Dave

657. What language, according to *Big Fish's* Ed Bloom, do "African parrots in their native home of the Congo" speak?
- **A.** Pig Latin
- **B.** French
- **C.** Chinese
- **D.** Kenyan

658. In *The Lady Vanishes*, who does Gilbert say is "about as popular as a dose of strychnine"?
- **A.** Iris
- **B.** Dr. Hartz
- **C.** Himself
- **D.** Miss Froy

659. In what film does Woody Allen say, "It's a travesty of a mockery of a sham of a mockery of a travesty of two mockeries of a sham"?
- **A.** *Bananas*
- **B.** *Crimes and Misdemeanors*
- **C.** *Zelig*
- **D.** *Interiors*

660. In *Ghostbusters*, what does Winston advise Ray to say if anyone ever asks him if he's a god?
- **A.** "That depends. Which god are you referring to?"
- **B.** "Hell yes I'm a god."
- **C.** "That depends, do you want me to be a god?"
- **D.** "Yes."

661. In *American Graffiti*, Bob Falfa asks, "You know a guy around here with a piss-yellow deuce coupe, supposed to be hot stuff?" Who is that "guy"?
- **A.** Curt Henderson
- **B.** John Milner
- **C.** Steve Bolander
- **D.** Himself

662. In *Blue Velvet*, Frank Booth asks, "What kind of beer do you like to drink, neighbor?" What is Jeffrey Beaumont's response?
- **A.** "I don't really drink beer."
- **B.** "Budweiser."
- **C.** "Root beer."
- **D.** "Heineken."

663. What does *Dracula* (1931 version) say "must be glorious"?
- **A.** Always being right
- **B.** Being dead
- **C.** Having morals
- **D.** Being alive

664. In *The Last Picture Show*, Jacy says, "Thank God, I'm glad I weren't on fire—I would've burned to death. All you've got is one button undone." To whom is she speaking?

A. Duane Jackson

B. Sonny Crawford

C. Lester Marlow

D. Billy

665. In what film does Edward G. Robinson ask "Is this the end of Rico?"

A. *Little Caesar*

B. *White Heat*

C. *The Public Enemy*

D. *Tribute to a Bad Man*

666. In *Manhattan*, what does Isaac Davis say corned beef should not be?

A. Alive

B. Blue

C. Breathing

D. Hairy

667. In *My Fair Lady*, Henry Higgins says, "[They] don't care what they do actually, as long as they pronounce it properly." Who is he referring to?

A. Socialites

B. The French

C. Politicians

D. Educated men

668. In *Swingers*, Rob laments, "They went with someone who had more theme park experience." What part had he tried out for?

A. Goofy

B. Pluto

C. Mickey Mouse

D. Donald Duck

669. *Bull Durham's* Crash Davis remarks, "I was in the show." How long was he in the major leagues?

A. Eleven days

B. Forty-one days

C. Thirty-one days

D. Twenty-one days

670. In *Deliverance*, one of the mountain men says, "I'm gonna make you squeal like a pig." What is the name of the character he's speaking to?

A. Ed Gentry

B. Bobby Trippe

C. Drew Ballinger

D. Lewis Medlock

671. Jessica Rabbit of *Who Framed Roger Rabbit* says, "I'm not bad." What does she say she is?

A. "Real, real bad"

B. "Just a little naughty"

C. "Just too much for some fellas"

D. "Just drawn that way"

672. In *This Is Spinal Tap*, David explains, "He was the patron saint of quality footwear." What is the name of the saint to whom he is referring?

A. Saint Auggie

B. Saint Hubbins

C. Saint Elmer

D. Saint Nike

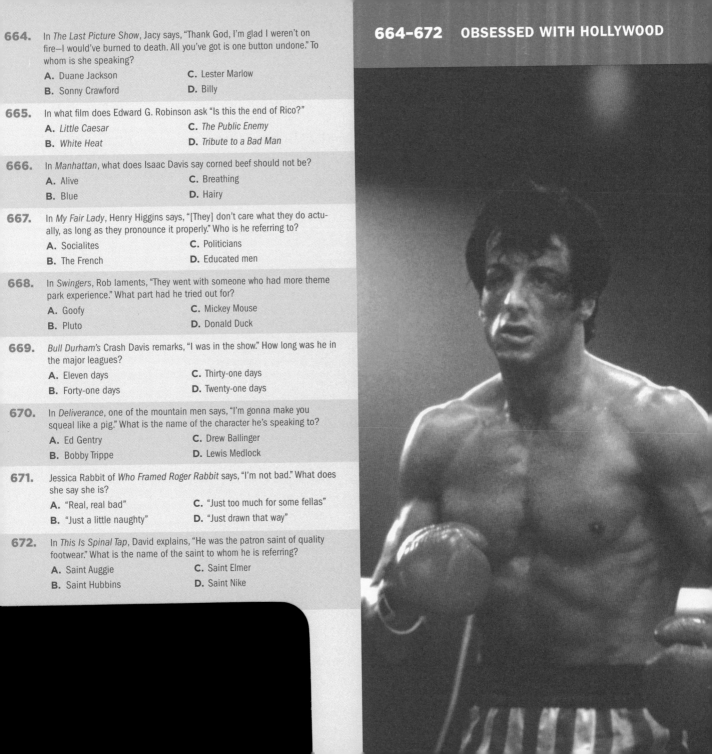

680.

The story behind the film *Rocky* was very much like the underdog story it depicts. The 1976 John G. Avildsen–directed film was shot in only 28 days on a budget of less than $1 million. However, the film was an instant success and earned more than $100 million at the box office. Written and produced by its star Sylvester Stallone, *Rocky* chronicles the rise of a working-class palooka named Rocky Balboa. The film, which Stallone claims to have written in a mere three days, was inspired by the true story of New Jersey boxer Chuck Wepner, who boxed Muhammad Ali and knocked him down. In 1977, *Rocky* earned 10 Academy Award nominations, winning three statues. Interestingly, Stallone was nominated for Best Actor and Best Original Screenplay, making him only the third person to be nominated in both categories in the same year. (The two actors who preceded him were Orson Welles for *Citizen Kane* and Charles Chaplin for *The Great Dictator*.)

Finish Mickey's sentence from *Rocky*: "You're gonna eat lightin' and . . ."

673. Complete Norman Bates's sentence from *Psycho*: "I think I must have one of those faces you can't help . . ."
A. "But be frightened of."
B. "Trusting."
C. "Believing."
D. "But be a little uneasy with."

674. What type of vehicle does *The Graduate*'s Benjamin say "old Elaine Robinson got started in"?
A. Jeep
B. Edsel
C. Chevy
D. Ford

675. *Halloween*'s Sheriff Brackett says of a half-eaten dog, "A man wouldn't do that." What is Loomis's response to this?
A. "Michael would."
B. "I assure you you're wrong."
C. "This isn't a man."
D. "He's only a man in the broadest sense of the word."

676. Which character in *Casablanca* is said to be "just like any other man, only more so"?
A. Rick Blaine
B. Victor Laszlo
C. Captain Renault
D. Major Strasser

677. In *An American In Paris*, what does Adam call a "pretentious way of saying I'm unemployed at the moment"?
A. Concert pianist
B. Expatriate
C. Man of leisure
D. Kept man

678. What made-up creature does *Napoleon Dynamite* say is "pretty much my favorite animal"?
A. Manticore
B. Ring-tailed lemur
C. Gryphon
D. Liger

679. What film features the line "give me librium or give me meth"?
A. *This Is Spinal Tap*
B. *The Boys in the Band*
C. *The Doors*
D. *Easy Rider*

680.

A. "Crap thunder"
B. "Then eat some more"
C. "Move the earth"
D. "Knock this guy into next week"

681. Complete Winston Wolf's line from *Pulp Fiction*: "That's thirty minutes away. I'll be there in . . ."
- **A.** "Five."
- **B.** "Ten."
- **C.** "Fifteen."
- **D.** "Twenty."

682. "One morning I shot an elephant in my pajamas," explains Groucho Marx. "How he got in my pajamas I dunno." What movie is this from?
- **A.** *Animal Crackers*
- **B.** *Cocoanuts*
- **C.** *Duck Soup*
- **D.** *Horse Feathers*

683. Complete Jimmy Foster's line from *Ocean's Eleven* (1960 version): "I made a cardinal rule never to answer the phone in . . ."
- **A.** The nude
- **B.** December
- **C.** A phone booth
- **D.** A bad mood

684. In *Scream*, which character says, "Please don't kill me, Mr. Ghostface, I wanna be in the sequel"?
- **A.** Sidney
- **B.** Randy
- **C.** Stu
- **D.** Tatum

685. In *Carrie*, Margaret White says, "These are godless times, Mrs. Snell." What is Mrs. Snell's response?
- **A.** "Hell yes they are."
- **B.** "There is no God."
- **C.** "Go to hell."
- **D.** "I'll drink to that."

686. Complete Paul's line from *All Quiet on the Western Front*: "When it comes to dying for country, it's better . . ."
- **A.** "Left to the professionals."
- **B.** "To do so on a full stomach."
- **C.** "Not to die at all."
- **D.** "To do it in the summer."

687. In *Papillon*, Clusiot asks Louis, "How come you ended up in a place like this?" What is his response?
- **A.** "Favoritism."
- **B.** "Just lucky, I guess."
- **C.** "God didn't hear my prayer."
- **D.** "Tough judge."

688.

689. What does *Hud* say is the only question he ever asks a woman?
- **A.** "Can you cook?"
- **B.** None of these
- **C.** "Would you make me breakfast before you go?"
- **D.** "What time is your husband coming home?"

688.

The 1994 Robert Zemeckis film *Forrest Gump*, adapted from the novel by Winston Groom, follows the picaresque travels of a simple man with an IQ of 75.

Tom Hanks's multi-layered performance as the title character garnered him recognition and accolades, including the Oscar for Best Actor. *Gump*, which also stars Gary Sinise and Robin Wright Penn, was a box-office phenomenon, raking in a reported $677 million worldwide. (Sadly, novelist Groom has stated that Paramount declared the film a commercial failure and, based on these claims, did not pay him his share of the box-office take.) The film received thirteen Academy Award nominations and ultimately took home six statuettes, including Best Picture and Best Director.

What, according to Forrest, did his Mama say was a part of life?

- **A.** Dying
- **B.** Trouble
- **C.** Sorrow
- **D.** Pain

690. *Philadelphia's* Joe Miller asks Andrew Beckett, "What's wrong with your face?" What is Beckett's response?

- **A.** "Would you believe chicken pox?"
- **B.** "That's why I'm here."
- **C.** "I have AIDS."
- **D.** "Ever hear of AIDS, Mr. Miller?"

691. What does *Casino's* Ace Rothstein say is the cardinal rule?

- **A.** "Provide them with the illusion that they can win."
- **B.** "Keep them coming back."
- **C.** "Entertain them while you take their money."
- **D.** "Keep them sitting at the table."

692. In *Guys and Dolls*, what Bible verse does Sky describe as being "the bit about the other cheek"?

- **A.** Luke 10:13
- **B.** Matthew 5:39
- **C.** Ezekiel 25:17
- **D.** John 3:16

693. To whom does *The Da Vinci Code's* Robert Langdon say, "You are the secret"?

- **A.** Silas
- **B.** The Mona Lisa
- **C.** Sophie Neveu
- **D.** A portrait of Leonardo Da Vinci

694. In *Beverly Hills Cop* Axel says, "This thing is nicer than my apartment." To what is he referring?

- **A.** His jail cell
- **B.** Taggart's office
- **C.** An expensive painting
- **D.** A police car

695. *Young Frankenstein's* Dr. Frederick Frankenstein suggests to Igor that he could take care of his hump. What is Igor's response?

- **A.** "Oh, this old thing?"
- **B.** "What hump?"
- **C.** "I was thinking of having it enlarged."
- **D.** "Maybe I can help you with your hump, too."

696. "Plant yourself," George Clooney demands. "Plants don't talk." What movie is this from?

- **A.** *From Dusk Till Dawn*
- **B.** *Three Kings*
- **C.** *Ocean's Eleven*
- **D.** *Ocean's Twelve*

697. In *National Lampoon's Vacation*, Clark asks Roy Wally, "If you were me, wouldn't you do the same thing for your children?" What is Roy's response?

- **A.** "Maybe . . . but without the gun."
- **B.** "Yes."
- **C.** "No."
- **D.** "I don't even like being around my family."

698. In *Lolita*, what does Humbert Humbert say "all the best people" do twice a day?

A. Shave

B. Apologize

C. Pray

D. Brush their teeth

699. What does *Grumpy Old Men*'s John Gustafson say he had not done since October 4, 1978?

A. Smile

B. Have sex

C. Kiss a woman

D. Kill someone

700. In *Return of the Jedi*, to whom is Princess Leia speaking when she says, "You are a jittery little thing, aren't you?"

A. Wicket

B. C3PO

C. R2D2

D. Yoda

701. In *Grease*, what does Danny tell Sandy "you can't just walk out of"?

A. Their relationship

B. A drive-in

C. A restaurant before the meal arrives

D. A commitment

702. At the end of *The Sting*, Henry Gondorff asks, "You're not gonna stick around for your share?" What is Johnny Hooker's response?

A. "Nah, I'd only blow it."

B. "Nah, getting it's the fun part."

C. "Nah, I'm gonna try going straight."

D. "Nah, money complicates things."

703. According to Max in *Midnight Express*, "midnight express" is a prison term for:

A. Execution

B. Survival

C. Escape

D. Payback

704. In *High Noon*, Helen says, "If Kane was my man, I'd never leave him like this." What does she say she would do?

A. Find a way to make him leave

B. Grab a gun and fight

C. Die beside him

D. Set a trap for the villains

705. "Incredible," remarks the title character from *Ferris Bueller's Day Off*. "One of the worst performances of my career and they never doubted it for a second." To whom is he referring?

A. The high school office

B. Sloane's parents

C. None of these

D. His parents

706. In *Terms of Endearment*, Aurora asks Garrett, "Would you like to come in?" What is his response?

A. "I'd rather roll naked over tacks."

B. "I'd rather stick needles in my eyes."

C. "I'd rather shoot myself."

D. "I'd rather run a cheese grater across my penis."

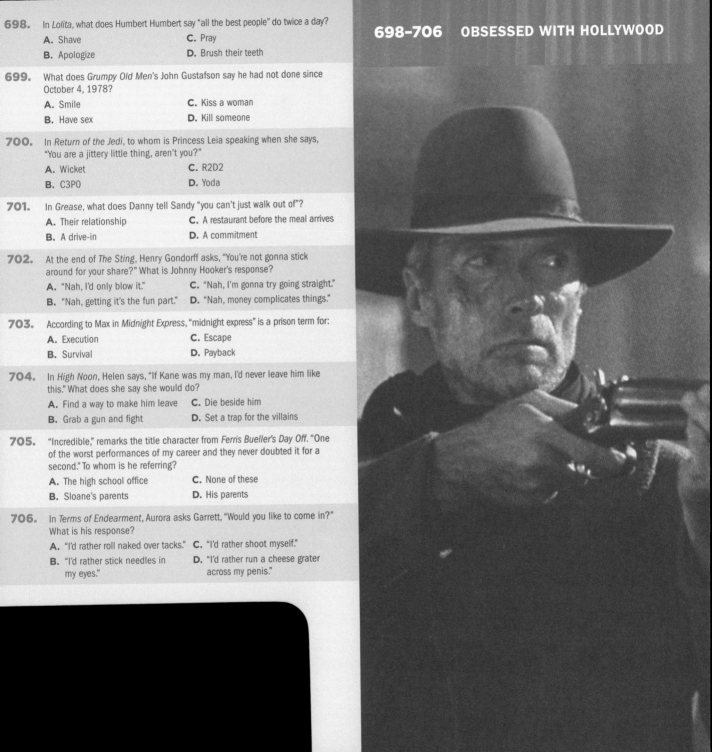

708.

Clint Eastwood's 1992 revisionist western *Unforgiven*, penned by screenwriter David Webb Peoples, stars Eastwood, Morgan Freeman, and Gene Hackman, and chronicles the story of a broken-down aging gunfighter who agrees to take on one last job. The film, which Eastwood dedicated to long-departed mentors Don Siegel and Sergio Leone, is notable because it cast the gunfighter in a much different light than the traditional westerns that had preceded it. Here, the gunslinger wasn't heroic with nerves of steel, but rather a cold, cowardly man who found his strength in the bottom of a whiskey bottle, creating an examination of the relationship between alcohol and violence. *Unforgiven* received nine Academy Award nominations, taking home four statuettes including Best Picture and Best Director.

In the film, Eastwood's character Will Munny says, "That's right. I've killed women and children. I've killed everything that walks or crawls at one time or another, and I'm here to kill you." To whom is he speaking?

A. Quick Mike
B. Little Bill
C. English Bob
D. Skinny Dubois

---

707. *The Caine Mutiny*'s Lieutenant Tom Keefer observes, "He's a Freudian delight; he crawls with clues." Who is he referring to?

A. Lieutenant Commander Queeg   **C.** Lieutenant Maryk
B. Captain Bligh   **D.** Lieutenant Greenwald

708.

709. Complete C.D. Bales's line from *Roxanne*: "I wanna look like..."

A. James Brown   **C.** Diana Ross
B. Phyllis Diller   **D.** Ed McMahon

710. In what movie does Woody Allen say, "I had a great evening; it was like the Nuremberg trials"?

A. *Hannah and Her Sisters*   **C.** *Crimes and Misdemeanors*
B. *Annie Hall*   **D.** *Manhattan*

711. Who does *Fear and Loathing in Las Vegas*'s Raoul Duke conclude a druggie can learn to handle seeing crawling up their leg with a knife in their teeth?

A. President Nixon   **C.** A crazed wolf on acid
B. Their dead grandmother   **D.** A quadruple amputee with rage in his eyes

712. In *The Breakfast Club*, Bender says, "You know what I got for Christmas last year?" What does he say he received?

A. Nothing   **C.** A six-pack of beer
B. A carton of cigarettes   **D.** A gun

713. In *Spider-Man*, what does Peter conclude that "not everyone is meant to" do?

A. "Make a difference"   **C.** "Fight crime"
B. "Be a superhero"   **D.** "Be something great"

714. *Dr. Strangelove*'s Gen. Ripper says, "I do not avoid women, Mandrake." What does he then say he denies women?

A. The truth   **C.** His mind
B. His essence   **D.** The opportunity to fight like a man

715. In *Top Gun*, Carole says, "God, he loved flying with you, Maverick. But he would have done it anyway . . . without you." To whom is she referring?

A. Viper   **C.** Iceman
B. Maverick's father   **D.** Goose

716. What movie does *You've Got Mail*'s Joe Fox believe "answer[s] all of life's questions"?

A. *The Godfather* **C.** *Casablanca*
B. *Annie Hall* **D.** *The Meaning of Life*

717. In *Bruce Almighty*, God says, "You want to see a miracle?" What does he then say people should do?

A. Be the miracle **C.** Try a little harder
B. Make their own miracles **D.** Stop praying and start doing

718.

719. In *Good Morning, Vietnam*, what does Garlick believe a man does not do when things are all right?

A. Listen to polka albums at high speed **C.** Refer to Pat Boone as a beautiful genius
B. Refer to Lieutenant Hauk as a laugh riot **D.** Make friends with the Viet Cong

720. In *For Love of the Game*, Jane asks, "What if my face was all scraped off and I was totally disfigured and had no arms and legs and I was completely paralyzed. Would you still love me?" What is Billy's response?

A. "Can I get back to you on that one?" **C.** "No, but I'll love you until that day comes."
B. "Yeah, but sex would be out of the question." **D.** "No, but we could still be friends."

721. In *X-Men*, Rogue asks Wolverine about his claws. "When they come out . . . does it hurt?" What is Wolverine's response?

A. "Some times more than others." **C.** "Not as much as they hurt the other guy."
B. "Every time." **D.** "You know that feeling when you get salt in a fresh cut?"

722. Complete this sentence from *Nacho Libre*: "I was wondering if you might want to join me in my quarters this night . . ."

A. "For a turkey pot pie." **C.** "For a bout of lovemaking."
B. "For some disco dancing." **D.** "For some toast."

723. How does *The Fast and the Furious*'s Dom say he lives his life?

A. A second at a time **C.** A quarter mile at a time
B. At the speed of adrenaline **D.** As dangerously as possible

718.

The 1939 film *Gone with the Wind*, adapted from the best-selling novel by Margaret Mitchell, is reportedly the highest-grossing motion picture in history (when adjusted for inflation). The two years the film spent in production are now legendary; producer David O. Selznick tested *hundreds* of starlets (including Katharine Hepburn and Carole Lombard) for the role of heroine Scarlett O'Hara. Selznick did not settle on an actress (Vivien Leigh, then virtually unknown in the United States, won the role) until after filming was already underway. Selznick also displayed a similar indecisiveness with his behind-the-scenes crew, playing musical directors and replacing his cinematographer midway through shooting.

Gone with the Wind premiered on December 15, 1939, and was met with great acclaim. The film received a staggering fifteen Academy Award nominations, winning ten, including Best Picture, Best Director, and Best Adapted Screenplay. Today, nearly seventy years after the film's production, it is still recognized as one of the finest and most enjoyable films ever made.

Finish this statement made by Mammy in the film: "You can't show your bosom 'fore . . ."

A. "One o'clock"
B. "Four o'clock"
C. "Two o'clock"
D. "Three o'clock"

724. In what film does W. C. Fields say, "I'm very fond of children . . . girl children, around eighteen and twenty"?

A. *Never Give a Sucker an Even Break* **C.** *You Can't Cheat an Honest Man*
B. *My Little Chickadee* **D.** *The Bank Dick*

725. What does Jesus say before dying in *The Passion of the Christ*?

A. "It is finished." **C.** "It is accomplished."
B. "It is completed." **D.** "All things considered, I'd rather be in Philadelphia."

726. In *The Player*, June tells Griffin she doesn't go to the movies. Why?

A. "Most of them suck" **C.** "The prices are too high"
B. "Life is too short" **D.** "I only like black-and-white movies"

727. In *Mother*, John Henderson's mother concludes he's not a famous enough writer to do something. What is it?

A. Go nuts **C.** Kill himself
B. Be pretentious **D.** Be so strange

728. What is the name of the annoying waiter in *Office Space* who says, "Sounds like a case of the Mondays"?

A. Michael **C.** Brian
B. Peter **D.** Mike

729. What does *Thank You for Smoking's* Nick Naylor say his job requires?

A. An ability to find truth in lies **C.** A moral flexibility
B. A tolerance for the intolerable **D.** An ambiguous code of ethics

730. In *Dogma*, who does Jay blame for bringing him and Silent Bob to Illinois?

A. Steven Spielberg **C.** John Hughes
B. Frank Capra **D.** Kevin Smith

731. In *Signs*, Officer Caroline asks, "How's work at the gas station?" What is Merrill's response?

A. "Bad enough" **C.** "It makes me want to kill myself"
B. "Stimulating" **D.** "All I dreamed it would be"

732. What does *Finding Nemo's* Dory say one must do when life gets them down?

A. "Just keep swimming" **C.** "Put on a smile"
B. "Make lemonade, but only if you got lemons . . . and sugar" **D.** None of these

733. In *White Men Can't Jump*, what are the "four words" Sidney has for Billy?

A. "Stop playing basketball."

B. "Listen to the woman."

C. "In your face."

D. "You can't hear Jimi."

734. In *The Way We Were*, Hubbell suggests, "People are more important than their principles." What is Katie's response?

A. "Nothing is more important than principles."

B. "You can say that only because you have no principles."

C. "People are their principles."

D. "Sometime, invite me to the idealistic planet you're from."

735.

736. Complete Navin R. Johnson's question from *The Jerk*: "You mean I'm not . . ."

A. "A genius?"

B. "Black?"

C. "Really your son?"

D. "A woman?"

737. In *Pretty Woman*, what does Vivian say is her "favorite name in the whole world"?

A. John

B. Vivian

C. Edward

D. Dick

738. What does *Armageddon's* Chick Chapple confide that he's never told anyone before?

A. That he's gay

B. That he's scared to die

C. That he hates flying

D. That he always wanted to be a dancer

739. In *There's Something About Mary*, Pat Healy asks, "What the hell is Brett Favre doing here?" Favre replies that he's in town to play the local team. What team is this?

A. Dallas Cowboys

B. Miami Dolphins

C. New York Giants

D. Los Angeles Rams

740. How does *Sergeant York* say he learned to fire a rifle?

A. None of these

B. He read a book about marksmanship

C. From shooting bottles off fence posts

D. His uncle Chester taught him

741. What, according to *Mary Poppins*, is there "an element of" in everything?

A. Ritual

B. Boredom

C. Fun

D. Music

735.

Director Mike Nichols' 1966 classic black comedy *Who's Afraid of Virginia Woolf* was adapted from Edward Albee's play of the same title. The film features only four credited performers—Elizabeth Taylor, Richard Burton, George Segal, and Sandy Dennis—and depicts the interactions between two couples sharing dinner. Significant because it raised the bar for cinematic sexual implication and profanity, it was the first American film to use words and phrases like "bugger," "goddamn," and "hump the hostess." This film helped to usher in a more relaxed attitude toward screen sexuality and the use of profanity, and is often cited as a catalyst to the Motion Picture Association of America's film-rating system established in 1968.

Who's Afraid of Virginia Woolf received thirteen Academy Award nominations, resulting in five wins.

In the film, Martha exclaims, "What a dump!" This famous line is a Bette Davis quote from another film. What is this film?

A. *What Ever Happened to Baby Jane?*

B. *All About Eve*

C. *Storm Center*

D. *Beyond the Forest*

742. In *Austin Powers: International Man of Mystery*, what does Dr. Evil say happens when Mr. Bigglesworth gets upset?

A. "You don't even wanna know what happens then."

B. "Bad things happen."

C. "People die."

D. "He gets indigestion."

743. Which *Blazing Saddles* character says, "I must have killed more men than Cecil B. DeMille"?

A. Bart

B. Jim

C. Mongo

D. Taggart

744. In *The French Connection* Popeye Doyle says, "Now I'm gonna bust your ass for those three bags and I'm gonna nail you for picking your feet in . . ."

A. Poughkeepsie

B. Schenectedy

C. Brownsville

D. Louisville

745. In a famous line from *Wall Street*, who does Bud say "loves Anacot Steel"?

A. Yellow Horse Shoe

B. Blue Horse Shoe

C. Green Horse Shoe

D. Black Horse Shoe

746. In *Marathon Man*, what three-word question does Christian Szell repeatedly ask Thomas Leavy?

A. "Are you alone?"

B. "Where is it?"

C. "Is it safe?"

D. "Who else knows?"

747. What does Joker say is the only thing the dead know in *Full Metal Jacket*?

A. How to lie perfectly still

B. That it is better to be alive

C. That they should have kept their heads down

D. Just how long forever really is

748. In *Braveheart*, what does William Wallace's father say "makes us men"?

A. "Our bravery"

B. "Our beliefs"

C. "Our wits"

D. "Our courage"

749. What does Jake LaMotta say Sugar Ray Robinson never did in the Martin Scorsese classic *Raging Bull*?

A. Win

B. Knock him down

C. Hit him hard

D. Gain his respect

750. In what film does a character played by Jack Nicholson say, "I would like to drink a toast to Batman . . . Superman . . . and the Human Torch!"?

A. *Carnal Knowledge*

B. *The Last Detail*

C. *The Border*

D. *Batman*

CHAPTER FOUR:
THE ACADEMY AWARDS

751. Who became the oldest male performer to win an Oscar in 1974?
A. Groucho Marx
C. Orson Welles
B. Charles Chaplin
D. Buster Keaton

752. For what 1943 film did the song "You'll Never Know" win an Oscar?
A. *Star Spangled Rhythm*
C. *Cabin in the Sky*
B. *The Sky's the Limit*
D. *Hello, Frisco, Hello*

753. How many of the top ten films on the American Film Institute's list of the hundred greatest American films were nominated for Best Picture?
A. One
C. Three
B. Six
D. Nine

754. What was the first color film to win the Oscar for Best Picture?
A. *The Wizard of Oz*
C. *Manhattan Parade*
B. *Gone With the Wind*
D. *Song of the West*

755. Which of these performances won John Wayne an Oscar?
A. *True Grit*
C. *Stagecoach*
B. *The Searchers*
D. *The Shootist*

756. Which of these actors was not nominated posthumously for Best Actor?
A. Steve McQueen
C. Spencer Tracy
B. Peter Finch
D. Massimo Troisi

757. Who were the first performers to be nominated for an Oscar for playing the same character in the same film?
A. Kate Winslet and Gloria Stuart
C. Gregory Peck and Robert De Niro
B. Marlon Brando and Robert De Niro
D. Bette Davis and Olivia DeHavilland

OPPOSITE Hilary Swank and Kevin Spacey holding their Oscars at the 72nd Annual Academy Awards in 2000

758. Who is the only person named Oscar ever to win an Oscar?

A. Oscar Micheaux

B. Oscar "Budd" Boetticher

C. Oscar Hammerstein II

D. Oscar Levant

759.

760. Which of these performers has not won Oscars in consecutive years?

A. Clark Gable

B. Spencer Tracy

C. Katharine Hepburn

D. Luise Rainer

761. What was the only X-rated film to win the Oscar for Best Picture?

A. *Last Tango in Paris*

B. *Greetings*

C. *Midnight Cowboy*

D. *One Night in Paris*

762. To whom did John Wayne present an Oscar in 1979, mispronouncing his name as he did so?

A. Michael Cimino

B. Paul Mazursky

C. Louis Garfinkle

D. Vilmos Zsigmond

763. What movie depicts movie tough guy Steven Seagal being nominated for an Oscar for the fictitious film *Snowball in Hell*?

A. *In & Out*

B. *Naked Gun 33 1/3: The Final Insult*

C. *The Player*

D. *The Muse*

764. What is the shortest performance to win an acting Oscar?

A. Anthony Hopkins, *Silence of the Lambs*

B. Orson Welles, *The Third Man*

C. Sylvia Miles, *Midnight Cowboy*

D. Judi Dench, *Shakespeare in Love*

765. Screenwriter Robert Towne won an Oscar for *Greystoke*, on which he had used the pseudonym P. H. Vazak. Who was P. H. Vazak?

A. Towne's physician

B. Towne's butler

C. Towne's dog

D. A character from an unpublished novel by Towne

759.

Today, three decades after his death, Charles Chaplin remains one of the screen's most enduring icons. While he is generally remembered by the masses as a skilled comedic actor, the multitalented Chaplin was also a superb director. (In addition, the Renaissance man also wrote, produced, and scored his films.) Chaplin began his film career appearing in Keystone Studios silent shorts under the tutelage of Mack Sennett. There, Chaplin learned the ins and outs of filmmaking, and soon directed his own films. His early standouts include *The Kid*, *The Gold Rush*, and *The Circus*. Chaplin then crafted his greatest directorial achievement, 1931's *City Lights*, which remained largely silent despite the fact that everyone else in Hollywood was already making "talkies" by this time. Subsequent Chaplin gems include *Modern Times* (which, in 1936, also utilized sound effects and music, but contained no spoken dialogue), *The Great Dictator*, *Monsieur Verdoux*, and *Limelight*.

Chaplin was awarded an Oscar for *Limelight*'s score, but not until the film had already been released for some time. How many years after its initial release did Chaplin win the Oscar?

A. Three

B. Twenty

C. Eleven

D. Twenty-nine

766. Who has been nominated for more screenwriting Oscars than anyone in history?

A. Billy Wilder

B. Woody Allen

C. Francis Ford Coppola

D. Paddy Chayefsky

767. Which of these distinguished filmmakers has not received three or more Oscar nominations for Best Director?

A. John Ford

B. William Wyler

C. Frank Capra

D. John Huston

768. For what film has Sean Connery won his only Oscar to date?

A. *The Untouchables*

B. *The Molly Maguires*

C. *The Hill*

D. *The Man Who Would Be King*

769. For which of these performances did Faye Dunaway win an Oscar?

A. *Network*

B. *Three Days of the Condor*

C. *Bonnie and Clyde*

D. *Chinatown*

770. Who was the first Best Actor winner to have directed his own performance?

A. Orson Welles

B. John Huston

C. Laurence Olivier

D. Roberto Benigni

771. Which of these actresses reportedly used her Oscar as a bathroom doorstop?

A. Vivian Leigh

B. Joan Crawford

C. Bette Davis

D. Olivia DeHavilland

772. Which of these films won for Best Picture, but won no other Oscars?

A. *Chariots of Fire*

B. *The Broadway Melody*

C. *The Greatest Show on Earth*

D. *Around the World in 80 Days*

773. What was the first film to be released on video and/or DVD before winning Best Picture?

A. *Crash*

B. *Silence of the Lambs*

C. *Schindler's List*

D. *Forrest Gump*

774. Who was the oldest performer ever to win a competitive Oscar?

A. Don Ameche, *Cocoon*

B. Gloria Stuart, *Titanic*

C. George Burns, *The Sunshine Boys*

D. Jessica Tandy, *Driving Miss Daisy*

775. What documentary became the first film ever to have its Oscar revoked in 1969?

A. *Journey Into Self*

B. *Young Americans*

C. *Other Voices*

D. *Legendary Champions*

776. Who was standing onstage during the 1974 Oscars when a naked man streaked through the ceremony?

A. Charlton Heston

B. David Niven

C. Bob Hope

D. Jack Lemmon

777. Who was the first person to win an Oscar posthumously?

A. James Dean, *Giant*

B. Sidney Howard, *Gone with the Wind*

C. James Dean, *East of Eden*

D. Spencer Tracy, *Guess Who's Coming to Dinner*

778. Who is the only actor in history to be awarded two Oscars for the same performance?

A. Fredric March, *Dr. Jekyll and Mr. Hyde*

B. James Dean, *Giant*

C. Clark Gable, *It Happened One Night*

D. Harold Russell, *The Best Years of Our Lives*

779. Can you name the only white actor to win an Oscar for a performance in which he played a black character?

A. Orson Welles, *Othello*

B. Ronald Colman, *A Double Life*

C. Albert Finney, *The Dresser*

D. Laurence Olivier, *Othello*

780. What film became the first sequel to win the Oscar for Best Picture?

A. *The Lord of the Rings: Return of the King*

B. *The Godfather Part II*

C. *French Connection II*

D. *The Empire Strikes Back*

781. What novelist proved to be a poor sport by publicly criticizing *Crash*'s Best Picture win?

A. Larry McMurtry

B. Annie Proulx

C. Gore Vidal

D. Diana Ossana

787.

Meryl Streep is widely considered one of the most gifted performers of her era. Streep studied acting at Dartmouth, Vassar, and Yale before breaking into the film industry with a minor role (in a flashback scene) in Fred Zinnemann's 1977 film *Julia*. The versatile Streep has continued working ever since, delivering one masterful performance after another in film, television, and on Broadway. Her impressive list of film credits includes *A Cry in the Dark*, The *Deer Hunter*, *Manhattan*, *Kramer vs. Kramer*, *Out of Africa*, *The French Lieutenant's Woman*, *Silkwood*, *Ironweed*, and *The Bridges of Madison County*, just to name a few. For her work Streep has received (to date) twenty-one Golden Globe nominations, fourteen Oscar nominations, three Emmy nominations, and countless other nominations and awards.

For what film did Streep win her first Oscar?

A. *The Deer Hunter*
B. *Silkwood*
C. *Kramer vs. Kramer*
D. *Julia*

782. Which of the following performers appeared *only* in films nominated for Best Picture?
A. James Dean **C.** John Cazale
B. Howard Russell **D.** Gloria Stuart

783. What is the largest number of films ever nominated by the Academy in a single category?
A. Eleven **C.** Eighteen
B. Twenty-two **D.** Fourteen

784. Do you know which of these well-known filmmakers has *never* won a competitive Oscar?
A. Steven Spielberg **C.** John Carpenter
B. Alfred Hitchcock **D.** Francis Ford Coppola

785. Which of these films won Best Picture in 1955?
A. *The Caine Mutiny* **C.** *On the Waterfront*
B. *The Country Girl* **D.** *Seven Brides for Seven Brothers*

786. Which of these performers did not win an Oscar for their film debut?
A. Timothy Hutton **C.** Geoffrey Rush
B. Ben Kingsley **D.** Kate Winslet

787.

788. Which of these performers won an Oscar for a performance in which they said only one word?
A. Jane Wyman, *Johnny Belinda* **C.** John Mills, *Ryan's Daughter*
B. Patty Duke, *The Miracle Worker* **D.** Holly Hunter, *The Piano*

789. What two actresses were nominated in 1999 for playing the same role in different films?
A. Gwyneth Paltrow and Cate Blanchett **C.** Emily Watson and Gwyneth Paltrow
B. Emily Watson and Meryl Streep **D.** Cate Blanchett and Judi Dench

790. Who is the only actor to be nominated posthumously in two different years?

A. James Dean
B. Massimo Troisi
C. John Cazale
D. Natalie Wood

791. Who holds the distinctions of being the first Oscar winner and also the first winner to not attend the ceremony?

A. Richard Barthelmess
B. Emil Jannings
C. Gloria Swanson
D. Janet Gaynor

792. Do you know which of these celebrities has hosted the Academy Awards a record eighteen times?

A. Billy Crystal
B. Jack Benny
C. Bob Hope
D. Johnny Carson

793. What is the official name of the Oscar statuette?

A. Academy Award of Distinction
B. Academy Award of Excellence
C. Academy Award of Quality in Motion Pictures
D. Academy Award of Merit

794. For which film did cinematographer Hal Mohr become the first and only person to win an Oscar (via write-in) without being nominated?

A. *A Midsummer Night's Dream*
B. *Phantom of the Opera*
C. *The Four Poster*
D. *The Jazz Singer*

795.

796. What was the first foreign language film nominated for Best Picture?

A. *La Grande Illusion*
B. *Cries and Whispers*
C. *Il Postino*
D. *Z*

797. 1969 saw the first tie for Best Actress. Who were the two actresses who tied?

A. Katharine Hepburn and Vanessa Redgrave
B. Barbra Streisand and Katharine Hepburn
C. Patricia Neal and Ruth Gordon
D. Joanne Woodward and Vanessa Redgrave

795.

Tom Hanks came to national prominence as the star of the sitcom *Bosom Buddies*, which ran for two seasons. The show's producer Ian Praiser would later recall, "The first day I saw him on the set I thought, 'Too bad he won't be in television for long.' I knew he'd be a movie star in two years." Hanks's breakthrough came in 1984 with the hit film *Splash!* Four years later, Hanks scored his second hit with *Big*. However, it wasn't until his turn in the 1992 film *A League of Their Own* that Hanks became the unstoppable box-office force that he is today. His impressive film credits include *Sleepless in Seattle*, *Philadelphia*, *Forrest Gump*, *Apollo 13*, *Toy Story*, *Cast Away*, *Saving Private Ryan*, and *The Polar Express*, just to name a few. Hanks has become one of the biggest stars on the planet, and his films have grossed more than $3.1 billion. He has received five Oscar nominations, winning statuettes in two consecutive years.

Whose record did Hanks tie in 1995 when he won his second consecutive Best Actor Oscar?

A. Spencer Tracy
B. Laurence Olivier
C. James Stewart
D. Marlon Brando

798. What actor beat his acting teacher (Lee Strasberg) out of an Oscar in 1975?

A. Marlon Brando

C. Dustin Hoffman

B. Robert De Niro

D. Al Pacino

799. Which of these people has been nominated thirty-five times and received eight Oscars?

A. Max Factor

C. Walt Disney

B. Edith Head

D. David O. Selznick

800. What 1965 Shakespeare adaptation saw all four of its leads nominated for Oscars?

A. *Twelfth Night*

C. *Macbeth*

B. *Hamlet*

D. *Othello*

801. Who is the only person to receive Best Actor and Best Supporting Actor nominations for the same performance?

A. Clifton Webb, *Laura*

C. Claude Rains, *Mr. Skeffington*

B. Barry Fitzgerald, *Going My Way*

D. Charles Boyer, *Gaslight*

802. How many acting Oscars has Barbra Streisand won?

A. One

C. Three

B. Zero

D. Two

803. Who were Richard Burton, Robert Shaw, and Charles Laughton all nominated for portraying?

A. Henry V

C. Henry VIII

B. Henry VI

D. Henry VII

804. What was the first year in which three black performers were nominated for Best Actor or Best Actress?

A. 1967

C. 1973

B. 1970

D. 1976

805. Which of Marsha Mason's four Oscar nominations came for a film not written by her (now former) husband Neil Simon?

A. *The Goodbye Girl*

C. *Chapter Two*

B. *Only When I Laugh*

D. *Cinderella Liberty*

806. Who was the first Oscar winner to be buried in Arlington National Cemetery?

A. John Ford

B. Audie Murphy

C. Lee Marvin

D. James Stewart

807. For which of these classic films did George Cukor win an Oscar for Best Director?

A. *My Fair Lady*

B. *The Philadelphia Story*

C. *A Double Life*

D. *Little Women*

808. Who received the first Oscar ever awarded to a non-Hollywood film?

A. Leslie Howard, *Berkeley Square*

B. Charles Laughton, *The Private Life of Henry VIII*

C. Marcello Mastroianni, *La Dolce Vita*

D. Toshiro Mifune, *Rashomon*

809. Which of the following actors has not won an Oscar for playing someone with a disability?

A. Tom Hanks

B. Geoffrey Rush

C. Sean Penn

D. Dustin Hoffman

810. For what film did Paul Newman receive his only Oscar to date?

A. *The Color of Money*

B. *Cool Hand Luke*

C. *The Hustler*

D. *Cat on a Hot Tin Roof*

811. Only one of these filmmakers has won an Oscar for Best Director. Which one was it?

A. Orson Welles

B. Akira Kurosawa

C. Frank Borzage

D. Alfred Hitchcock

812. Who was the oldest person (thus far) to receive a nomination for Best Actor?

A. Henry Fonda, *On Golden Pond*

B. Clint Eastwood, *Million Dollar Baby*

C. Richard Farnsworth, *The Straight Story*

D. Laurence Olivier, *The Boys from Brazil*

813. Which of these performances landed William Hurt an Oscar?

A. *A History of Violence*

B. *Children of a Lesser God*

C. *Broadcast News*

D. *Kiss of the Spider Woman*

819.

The 1952 film *High Noon*, directed by Fred Zinnemann, is one of the finest westerns ever produced. Written by soon-to-be blacklisted screenwriter Carl Foreman, *High Noon* is the story of a lawman (Gary Cooper) forced to battle a band of baddies on his own when no one else will come to his aid. The fact that *High Noon* was an allegory for Hollywood blacklisting in the McCarthy era was not lost on many in the film industry. This probably aided *High Noon* at Oscar time, when the always-liberal Academy nominated the film for seven Oscars. (It won four, including Best Actor honors for Cooper.) The film's politics angered Hollywood conservatives like John Ford, Ward Bond, and John Wayne, who publicly supported blacklisting. (Ford and Wayne later crafted *Rio Bravo* as a right-wing response to *High Noon*.) Politics aside, *High Noon* is a brilliant film and is considered by many to be the definitive western.

Who sings the Oscar-winning song "High Noon (Do Not Foresake Me, Oh My Darlin')" in *High Noon*?

A. Dimitri Tiomkin
B. Lorne Green
C. Tex Ritter
D. Roy Rogers

814. Which actor did *not* win an Oscar for reprising a role he had originated on stage?
A. Marlon Brando, *A Streetcar Named Desire*
B. Yul Brynner, *The King and I*
C. Jose Ferrer, *Cyrano de Bergerac*
D. Rex Harrison, *My Fair Lady*

815. Who was the first performer to win an Oscar for a role in which they did not speak a single word?
A. Holly Hunter, *The Piano*
B. Jane Wyman, *Johnny Belinda*
C. Marlee Matlin, *Children of a Lesser God*
D. John Mills, *Ryan's Daughter*

816. Which of these foreign films received a record ten Oscar nominations?
A. *Fanny and Alexander*
B. *Das Boot*
C. *Life Is Beautiful*
D. *Crouching Tiger, Hidden Dragon*

817. Which of these talented filmmakers received nominations for acting, directing, writing, and producing the same film?
A. Orson Welles, *Citizen Kane*
B. Warren Beatty, *Reds*
C. Woody Allen, *Annie Hall*
D. Roberto Benigni, *Life Is Beautiful*

818. The film that did not win Oscars for Best Picture, Best Director, Best Actor, Best Actress, and Best Screenplay was:
A. *It Happened One Night*
B. *Gone With the Wind*
C. *One Flew Over the Cuckoo's Nest*
D. *Silence of the Lambs*

819.

820. What was the only TV movie to be adapted into a Best Picture-winning film?
A. *M*A*S*H*
B. *Schindler's List*
C. *Marty*
D. *Titanic*

821. What is the longest film ever to win Best Picture?
A. *The Lord of the Rings: Return of the King*
B. *Gone with the Wind*
C. *Dances with Wolves*
D. *Lawrence of Arabia*

822. What is the only animated film to be nominated for Best Picture?

A. *Bambi*

B. *Beauty and the Beast*

C. *Snow White and the Seven Dwarfs*

D. *Fantasia*

823. Which of these films holds the record for most Oscar nominations (eleven) without a single loss?

A. *West Side Story*

B. *Gone with the Wind*

C. *Titanic*

D. *The Lord of the Rings: Return of the King*

824. Three of these musicals won Best Picture. Which one did *not* win?

A. *An American in Paris*

B. *Oliver!*

C. *Singin' in the Rain*

D. *Chicago*

825. What director received his record twelfth Best Director Oscar nod in 1966?

A. George Cukor

B. William Wyler

C. William Wellman

D. John Ford

826. How many of the four performers with speaking roles in *Who's Afraid of Virginia Woolf?* received Oscar nominations?

A. One

B. Two

C. Three

D. Four

827. Who was the first rap artist or group to win an Oscar?

A. Will Smith

B. Eminem

C. "Marky" Mark Wahlberg

D. Three-Six Mafia

828. Who was the first African-American to win an Oscar?

A. Paul Robeson

B. Dorothy Dandridge

C. Oscar Micheaux

D. Hattie McDaniel

829. Can you name the person who became the first posthumous Oscar nominee in 1930?

A. Jeanne Eagels

B. Bessie Love

C. Ruth Chatterton

D. Betty Compson

835.

John Huston, the son of actor Walter Huston, is recognized as one of the most talented filmmakers in the history of cinema. Huston began his career working as a screenwriter and was at least partly responsible for writing films such as *High Sierra*, *The Stranger*, and *Dr. Ehrlich's Magic Bullet*. In 1941, Huston made his directorial debut with the classic thriller *The Maltese Falcon*. He then embarked upon a stellar career as a director, crafting such noted films as *The Treasure of the Sierra Madre*, *Key Largo*, *The Asphalt Jungle*, *The African Queen*, *Moby Dick*, *The Misfits*, *The Night of the Iguana*, and many others. Huston later proved to be a triple threat when he began acting in starring roles, beginning with 1963's *The Cardinal*. His acting credits include *The Kremlin Letter*, *Chinatown*, *The Wind and the Lion*, and Orson Welles's unfinished film *The Other Side of the Wind*.

Huston ultimately received fifteen Oscar nominations. In which of these categories did Huston *not* receive an Oscar nomination?

A. Best Picture
B. Best Actor
C. Best Director
D. Best Adapted Screenplay

830. For whom did a woman wearing Indian garb and calling herself Sacheen Littlefeather accept an Oscar?
A. John Wayne
C. Dustin Hoffman
B. Marlon Brando
D. Robert Redford

831. Who are the only two actors to win an Oscar for playing the same character?
A. Robert Mitchum and Gregory Peck
C. Robert Mitchum and Humphrey Bogart
B. Marlon Brando and Robert De Niro
D. Sean Connery and Steve McQueen

832. Can you name the first actor to win three Oscars?
A. Walter Brennan
C. James Stewart
B. Spencer Tracy
D. Tom Hanks

833. Prior to *Schindler's List*, what had been the last black-and-white film to win Best Picture?
A. *12 Angry Men*
C. *The Defiant Ones*
B. *Anatomy of a Murder*
D. *The Apartment*

834. Who was the first woman nominated for Best Director?
A. Lina Wertmuller
C. Penny Marshall
B. Sophia Coppola
D. Jane Campion

835.

836. Which of these films received 14 Oscar nominations?
A. *The Lord of the Rings: Return of the King*
C. *Titanic*
B. *West Side Story*
D. *Ben-Hur*

837. Which of these films won Best Picture at the 75th Academy Awards in 2002?
A. *Chicago*
C. *The Hours*
B. *Gangs of New York*
D. *The Pianist*

838. One of these films won Best Picture but was not nominated for Best Director. Which one?
A. *Dances with Wolves*
C. *Cimarron*
B. *Driving Miss Daisy*
D. *The Broadway Melody*

839. What was the only silent film to win Best Picture?

A. *The Big Parade*　　C. *Wings*

B. *City Lights*　　D. *Sunrise*

840. What was the first foreign language film to be nominated for both Best Picture and Best Foreign Language Film?

A. *Il Postino*　　C. *Life Is Beautiful*

B. *Satyricon*　　D. *Z*

841. Just after handless dynamite victim Harold Russell won his Oscar in 1947, what actor joked, "Where can I get a stick of dynamite?"

A. Bob Hope　　C. Cary Grant

B. Humphrey Bogart　　D. Frank Sinatra

842. For which of these films was Claude Rains not nominated for an Oscar?

A. *Mr. Skeffington*　　C. *Mr. Smith Goes to Washington*

B. *Casablanca*　　D. *Phantom of the Opera*

843. Do you know what film the song "Take My Breath Away" won an Oscar for?

A. *Cocktail*　　C. *Stand By Me*

B. *Top Gun*　　D. *The Princess Bride*

844.

845. What occurred for the first time at the 1944 Oscars?

A. Supporting performance winners received statuettes

B. The ceremony was cohosted by three people

C. An award was presented for Best Documentary

D. One performer received multiple nominations

846. What award is "given to a creative producer who has been responsible for a consistently high quality of motion picture production"?

A. The Award of Commendation

B. The Irving G. Thalberg Memorial Award

C. The Special Achievement Award

D. The Honorary Award

844.

Woody Allen's 1977 romantic comedy *Annie Hall* chronicles the relationship of a neurotic comedian named Alvy Singer and the flighty title character Annie. Woody Allen and Marshall Brickman wrote the screenplay for the film, which stars Allen, Diane Keaton, and Tony Roberts. The film is generally considered Allen's finest, and is memorable for its then-unorthodox scenes in which Allen would break from the film's action to speak directly to the camera. The film was nominated for five Oscars, winning four. In 2000, *Annie Hall* was voted the forty-second best comedy of all time in a poll conducted by *Total Film* magazine. In addition, *Annie Hall* appears on five of the American Film Institute's "all-time best" lists, including their lists of the greatest American films (#31) and greatest comedies (#4).

Woody Allen wasn't present the night he won three Oscars for *Annie Hall*. Where was he?

A. Getting drunk in a bar

B. In the hospital having his tonsils removed

C. Playing clarinet with his band in a pub

D. Shooting on location in Canada

847. What site has been the home of more Academy Award ceremonies than any other?

A. The Pantages Theatre

B. The Los Angeles Shrine Auditorium

C. The Biltmore Hotel

D. The Dorothy Chandler Pavilion

848. Where, in front of members of the press, did Joan Crawford accept her Oscar for *Mildred Pierce*?

A. In her bedroom

B. Outside Grauman's Chinese Theatre

C. On the beach

D. At a press conference in London

849. How many Oscar nominations did *Johnny Belinda* receive?

A. Ten

B. Eleven

C. Thirteen

D. Twelve

850. What filmmaker has directed more Oscar-winning performances than anyone else?

A. Howard Hawks

B. William Wyler

C. Otto Preminger

D. Elia Kazan

851. Who, on July 28, 1934, became the first performer to die after winning an Oscar?

A. Joanne Eagels

B. Warner Baxter

C. Marie Dressler

D. Mary Pickford

852. Whose Oscar was the first to be auctioned off?

A. Myrna Loy

B. Mary Pickford

C. Clark Gable

D. Harold Russell

853. Which of the following Claudette Colbert films was not nominated for Best Picture of 1934?

A. *Four Frightened People*

B. *It Happened One Night*

C. *Cleopatra*

D. *Imitation of Life*

854. What year were the Academy Awards televised for the first time?

A. 1955

B. 1954

C. 1953

D. 1956

855. How many Oscar nominations had actor/director Erich von Stroheim received prior to his nomination for *Sunset Boulevard*?

A. Zero

B. One

C. Two

D. Three

856. Which Oscar-nominated short subject cartoon was withdrawn from competition by its producers in 1950?

A. *For Scent-imental Reasons*

B. *Canary Row*

C. *Magic Fluke*

D. *Toy Tinkers*

857. Which of these actors was not nominated for Best Actor in 1947?

A. Harold Russell, *The Best Years of Our Lives*

B. Gregory Peck, *The Yearling*

C. Fredric March, *The Best Years of Our Lives*

D. James Stewart, *It's a Wonderful Life*

858. Only one of these performers has won two competitive Oscars. Which one?

A. James Stewart

B. Shelley Winters

C. John Wayne

D. Karen Black

859. Richard Burton won no Oscars. How many times was he nominated?

A. Zero

B. Nine

C. Five

D. Seven

860. Which of these songs from *Calamity Jane* won Best Original Song in 1954?

A. "Hive Full of Honey"

B. "The Deadwood Stage (Whip-Crack-Away)"

C. "Secret Love"

D. "Keep It Under Your Hat"

861. Three actors from *On the Waterfront* were nominated for Best Supporting Actor. Which of them won?

A. Rod Steiger

B. None of them won

C. Lee J. Cobb

D. Karl Malden

862. Who became the first person to win back-to-back Oscars for Best Supporting Actor in 1978?

A. Al Pacino

B. Dustin Hoffman

C. Peter Finch

D. Jason Robards

865.

John Wayne's acting career began in silent films in 1926, and continued until he became too sick with cancer to work after 1976's *The Shootist*. While this amazing fifty-year career produced many great films, Wayne was often considered more of a movie "star" than a talented actor. Today, however, Wayne is recognized as one of the all-time greats. A 2006 *Premiere* magazine industry poll ranked Wayne's performance in *The Searchers* as the eighty-seventh greatest performance in motion picture history. (In addition, noted filmmaker Steven Spielberg has called it the single greatest performance ever filmed.) Wayne would ultimately receive three Academy Award nominations: two Best Actor nominations and a third as producer of *The Alamo*. These nominations yielded a single statuette, awarded for acting.

For what film did Wayne win his sole Oscar?

A. *The Searchers*
B. *True Grit*
C. *Stagecoach*
D. *The Shootist*

863. Under what pseudonym did blacklisted screenwriter Dalton Trumbo win an Oscar for *The Brave One*?
A. Robert Rich
B. Donald O'Brien
C. Chris Watson
D. Joshua Barnett

864. What is the name of the producer who posthumously won an Oscar for *Ben-Hur*?
A. John Woolf
B. Sam Zimbalist
C. George Stevens
D. Otto Preminger

865.

866. One of these screenwriters has not won three writing Oscars. Which one?
A. John Huston
B. Paddy Chayefsky
C. Billy Wilder
D. Francis Ford Coppola

867. What is the only Best Picture winner adapted from a magazine article?
A. *Marty*
B. *You Can't Take It with You*
C. *On the Waterfront*
D. *Crash*

868. There has only been one film for which its screenwriters won multiple writing Oscars. What is this film?
A. *Treasure of the Sierra Madre*
B. *Going My Way*
C. *The Story of Louis Pasteur*
D. *Miracle on 34th Street*

869. For what film did novelist/screenwriter Larry McMurtry win an Oscar?
A. *Hud*
B. *Brokeback Mountain*
C. *The Last Picture Show*
D. *Terms of Endearment*

870. Who holds the record for most screenwriting nominations for a foreign film?
A. Jean-Luc Godard
B. Ingmar Bergman
C. Federico Fellini
D. François Truffaut

871. For which of these performances did Ingrid Bergman not win an Oscar?

A. *Anastasia*

B. *Murder on the Orient Express*

C. *Gaslight*

D. *Casablanca*

872. A fan jumped onstage at the 1962 Academy Awards and handed something to Bob Hope. What was it?

A. A single red rose

B. A photograph of himself

C. A homemade Oscar

D. A letter containing a death threat

873. What was significant regarding the 1965 Academy Awards?

A. This was the first year in which the host was African-American

B. An award for makeup was presented for the first time

C. The ceremony was delayed three days

D. A presenter suffered a heart attack during the ceremony

874. Who was the first actress to receive more than one Oscar for work in a single director's films?

A. Diane Keaton

B. Diane Wiest

C. Meryl Streep

D. Elizabeth Taylor

875. Which of these tunes from *Mary Poppins* won an Oscar for Best Original Song?

A. "A Spoonful of Sugar"

B. "The Perfect Nanny"

C. "Chim Chim Cher-ee"

D. "Supercalifragilisticexpialidocious"

876. One of these actresses has received Oscar nominations in five consecutive years. Which one?

A. Meryl Streep

B. Elizabeth Taylor

C. Bette Davis

D. Thelma Ritter

877.

878. Which of Melvyn Douglas's *Hud* collaborators accepted his Oscar in his absence?

A. Brandon De Wilde

B. Paul Newman

C. Martin Ritt

D. Patricia Neal

877.

When Jack Lemmon was born inside a Massachusetts elevator in 1925, no one could have guessed that one day he would be one of the most respected actors of all time. Before working in film, Lemmon studied acting at Harvard, enlisted in the Navy, and acted on television, radio, and Broadway. His film career began with an uncredited bit part in Michael Curtiz's 1949 comedy *The Lady Takes a Sailor*. Five years later he landed a breakout role in George Cukor's *It Should Happen to You*, which also starred Peter Lawford and Judy Holliday. After that, there was no stopping him. Lemmon appeared in many great films including *Some Like It Hot*, *The Apartment*, *Days of Wine and Roses*, *The Odd Couple*, *Save the Tiger*, *The China Syndrome*, and *Missing*. For his work Lemmon received many accolades including twenty-three Golden Globe nominations (resulting in six wins) and eight Oscar nominations (resulting in two wins).

For which film did Lemmon receive his sole Best Actor Oscar?

A. *Some Like It Hot*

B. *Save the Tiger*

C. *Tribute*

D. *Days of Wine and Roses*

879. Who, in 1975, became the first person ever to apologize for winning an Oscar?

- **A.** Ingrid Bergman
- **B.** Faye Dunaway
- **C.** William Holden
- **D.** Mario Puzo

880. Which of these films did not receive Oscar nominations in all four acting categories?

- **A.** *My Man Godfrey*
- **B.** *Reds*
- **C.** *The Godfather*
- **D.** *Network*

881. Who became the oldest female performer ever to receive an honorary Oscar in 1991?

- **A.** Myrna Loy
- **B.** Katharine Hepburn
- **C.** Mae West
- **D.** Lillian Gish

882. Only one of these films was nominated for Best Picture. Which one?

- **A.** *City Lights*
- **B.** *Snow White and the Seven Dwarfs*
- **C.** *The Third Man*
- **D.** *Decision Before Dawn*

883. What was the Best Picture category originally known as?

- **A.** Best Film
- **B.** Best Production
- **C.** Production of Superior Distinction
- **D.** Film of the Year

884. Who was the first actor to win Oscars in both the lead and supporting categories?

- **A.** Jack Lemmon
- **B.** Jack Nicholson
- **C.** Gene Hackman
- **D.** Robert Duvall

885. Which of these actors has not won an Oscar for Best Supporting Actor?

- **A.** Sidney Poitier
- **B.** Cuba Gooding, Jr.
- **C.** Louis Gossett, Jr.
- **D.** Morgan Freeman

886. Jason Robards has received an Oscar nomination for portraying all of these individuals except one. Who is this?

- **A.** Dashiell Hammett
- **B.** Andrei Sakharov
- **C.** Ben Bradlee
- **D.** Howard Hughes

887. Who was the first performer to be nominated for their film debut?
- **A.** Myrna Loy
- **B.** Sarah Bernhardt
- **C.** Lawrence Tibbett
- **D.** Barry Fitzgerald

888.

889. Who was the first African-American actor to win two Oscars?
- **A.** Samuel L. Jackson
- **B.** Denzel Washington
- **C.** Morgan Freeman
- **D.** Sidney Poitier

890. Who was the first (and, to date, only) dwarf ever nominated for an acting Oscar?
- **A.** Peter Dinklage
- **B.** Michael Dunn
- **C.** Eric Flaton
- **D.** Michael Dequina

891. How many performers have won two performing Oscars in the same year?
- **A.** Three
- **B.** One
- **C.** Two
- **D.** Zero

892. Who was the first actor to be nominated for a Best Supporting Oscar after already winning as a lead?
- **A.** Victor McLaglen
- **B.** Walter Brennan
- **C.** Melvyn Douglas
- **D.** Jack Lemmon

893. Who is the only actor to receive an Oscar nomination for playing an alien?
- **A.** Jeff Bridges, *Starman*
- **B.** Leonard Nimoy, *Star Trek the Motion Picture*
- **C.** Kevin Spacey, *K-Pax*
- **D.** Michael Jackson, *The Michael Jackson Story*

894. For what performance did Dorothy Dandridge receive her only Oscar nomination?
- **A.** *Porgy and Bess*
- **B.** *Carmen Jones*
- **C.** *Island in the Sun*
- **D.** *Tamango*

888.

Italian filmmaker Federico Fellini is considered one of the greatest directors in the history of film, achieving a level of acclaim in the United States that has only been afforded to a select few foreign filmmakers. Fellini's film career began in the late 1930s as a screenwriter. He would ultimately amass an impressive list of writing credits, which include the first two installments of Roberto Rossellini's "war trilogy" (*Rome, Open City*, which is considered the first true Neorealist film, and *Paisan*). Fellini didn't make his directorial debut until 1950's *Lights of Variety*, which he co-directed with veteran director Alberto Lattuada. Two years later he directed his first solo feature, *The White Sheik*. Despite his new-found success as a filmmaker, Fellini continued working as a scribe for other directors. His impressive directorial resume includes the films *La Strada*, *La Dolce Vita*, *8 1/2*, *Fellini-Satyricon*, and *Amarcord*.

For which of these films did Fellini *not* receive a nomination for Best Director?

- **A.** *Amarcord*
- **B.** *8 1/2*
- **C.** *La Strada*
- **D.** *La Dolce Vita*

895. The shortest Academy Awards ceremony of all time took place in 1929. How long did it last?

A. Thirty-four minutes and twenty-two seconds

B. Fourteen minutes and twenty-two seconds

C. Twenty-four minutes and twenty-two seconds

D. Four minutes and twenty-two seconds

896. What is the only film for which every single member of its cast was nominated?

A. *Who's Afraid of Viriginia Woolf?*

B. *Sleuth*

C. *Give 'Em Hell, Harry!*

D. *Tape*

897. What was unique regarding the ten performers nominated for Best Actor and Actress in 1985?

A. All of them were born in the United States

B. All of them were born outside the United States

C. All of them were born in 1960

D. All of them were born in 1959

898. Who is the youngest performer to win an Oscar?

A. Tatum O'Neal

B. Shirley Temple

C. Justin Henry

D. Anna Paquin

899. Who was awarded the first Oscar for a foreign language performance?

A. Robert De Niro, *The Godfather Part II*

B. Benicio Del Toro, *Traffic*

C. Sophia Loren, *Two Women*

D. Roberto Benigni, *Life Is Beautiful*

900. Who is the only person to win an Oscar for playing someone of the opposite gender?

A. Jaye Davidson, *The Crying Game*

B. Dustin Hoffman, *Tootsie*

C. Linda Hunt, *The Year of Living Dangerously*

D. Hilary Swank, *Boys Don't Cry*

901. How many competitive Oscars did Walt Disney win?

A. Eighteen

B. Twenty-two

C. Twenty

D. Twenty-four

902. Who has won the most Oscars for Best Director?

A. Steven Spielberg

B. John Ford

C. Frank Capra

D. William Wyler

903. Who was the first person to win an Oscar for their debut performance?

A. Gale Sondegaard, *Anthony Adverse*

B. Mercedes McCambridge, *All the King's Men*

C. Miyoski Umecki, *Sayonara*

D. Harold Russell, *The Best Years of Our Lives*

904. How many Oscar nominations has Peter O'Toole received?

A. Zero

B. Seven

C. Eight

D. Nine

905. For which of these films did Katharine Hepburn *not* win an Oscar?

A. *Morning Glory*

B. *Guess Who's Coming to Dinner*

C. *The African Queen*

D. *On Golden Pond*

906. Who was the first filmmaker to win an Oscar for his directorial debut?

A. Robert Redford, *Ordinary People*

B. Delbert Mann, *Marty*

C. James L. Brooks, *Terms of Endearment*

D. Jerome Robbins, *West Side STory*

907.

908. Composer Alex North was nominated fifteen times. How many Oscars did he win?

A. Seven

B. Zero

C. Fifteen

D. Sixteen

909. For what film did Charles Chaplin win his first Oscar?

A. *City Lights*

B. *Limelight*

C. *The Circus*

D. *The Gold Rush*

910. Composer Harold Arlen was nominated for three songs in 1944. Which of these songs was he *not* nominated for?

A. "One for My Baby"

B. "That Old Black Magic"

C. "Happiness Is a Thing Called Joe"

D. "My Shining Hour"

911. All but one of these films won Oscars for both Best Picture and Best Original Song—which one did not?

A. *Titanic*

B. *West Side Story*

C. *The Lord of the Rings: Return of the King*

D. *Going My Way*

907.

Katharine Hepburn is often cited as the greatest American film actress in history. After studying acting at Bryn Mawr College, Hepburn's Broadway performances eventually led her to Hollywood. After a number of screen tests, Hepburn was cast in the lead (alongside John Barrymore) in 1932's *A Bill of Divorcement*. The film was a box-office success and Hepburn received positive reviews for her performance. She then embarked upon a string of pictures for RKO, including the hit films *Morning Glory* and *Little Women*. From 1934 to 1940, Hepburn was labeled "Box-Office Poison" and acted in considerably more flops than hits. All of this changed, however, with the 1940 film *The Philadelphia Story*. After Hepburn's triumphant return to her winning ways, she appeared in one memorable role after another up until 1994's *Love Affair*, in which she made her final film appearance.

Hepburn holds the record for the most Best Actress nominations with twelve. Which of these performances did *not* earn Hepburn an Oscar nomination?

A. *Bringing Up Baby*

B. *Alice Adams*

C. *Morning Glory*

D. *Summertime*

912. Which of these films has the shortest running time of any Best Picture Oscar winner?

A. *It Happened One Night*　　C. *My Fair Lady*
B. *Marty*　　D. *The French Connection*

913. Who was the first performer ever to win back-to-back Oscars?

A. Spencer Tracy　　C. Jason Robards
B. Katharine Hepburn　　D. Luise Rainer

914. Who was the first actor to be nominated in four consecutive years?

A. Marlon Brando　　C. James Stewart
B. Peter O'Toole　　D. Jack Nicholson

915. In what year were the Academy Awards broadcast in color for the first time?

A. 1963　　C. 1966
B. 1964　　D. 1965

916. Who is the only performer to win three Best Supporting Actor Oscars?

A. Anthony Quinn　　C. Peter Ustinov
B. Walter Brennan　　D. Jason Robards

917. Who was the first actor to be nominated for Best Actor and Best Supporting Actor in the same year for different roles?

A. Al Pacino　　C. Barry Fitzgerald
B. Jamie Foxx　　D. Jack Lemmon

918. All but one of these father-and-daughter pairs has received Oscar nominations—which pair has not?

A. Jon Voight and Angelina Jolie　　C. Ryan O'Neal and Tatum O'Neal
B. John D. Barrymore and Drew Barrymore　　D. John Huston and Angelica Huston

919. Which of these actors has *not* been nominated for Best Supporting Actor four times?

A. Walter Brennan　　C. Al Pacino
B. Arthur Kennedy　　D. Jack Nicholson

920. Who won the 1958 Oscar for Best Actor?

A. Marlon Brando, *Sayonara*

B. Alec Guinness, *Bridge on the River Kwai*

C. Charles Laughton, *Witness for the Prosecution*

D. Anthony Quinn, *Wild Is the Wind*

921. Which of the two Oscar-nominated leads from *The Defiant Ones* took home a statuette?

A. Neither Poitier nor Curtis

B. Tony Curtis

C. Both Poitier and Curtis

D. Sidney Poitier

922. Who was the first Asian actress to win an Oscar?

A. Machiko Kyo, *Rashomon*

B. Ziyi Zhang, *Memoirs of a Geisha*

C. Miyoshi Umeki, *Sayonara*

D. Isuzu Yamada, *Throne of Blood*

923. Paul Muni received an Oscar nomination for his final film. What was this film?

A. *Stranger on the Prowl*

B. *The Good Earth*

C. *Angel on My Shoulder*

D. *The Last Angry Man*

924.

925. How many screenwriting Oscars has Federico Fellini won?

A. One

B. Zero

C. Two

D. Three

926. For which of these films did director Leo McCarey *not* receive an Oscar nomination for Best Director?

A. *My Son John*

B. *Love Affair*

C. *An Affair to Remember*

D. *My Favorite Wife*

927. What film did Al Pacino win his first Oscar for?

A. *Scent of a Woman*

B. *Serpico*

C. *The Godfather*

D. *Dog Day Afternoon*

924.

The late Spencer Tracy is considered one of the foremost thespians ever to be captured on celluloid. With a career spanning thirty-seven years, the prolific actor appeared in seventy-four films. Tracy's interest in acting took root when he was cast in a play while attending Ripon College in Wisconsin. His quest to become a professional actor took him to the American Academy of Dramatic Arts in New York, then to Broadway, and finally to Hollywood. Tracy made his acting debut as the lead in John Ford's 1930 comedy *Up the River*. Tracy then relocated to Hollywood and began churning out pictures; he appeared in twenty-five films in his first five years. The legendary actor's filmography includes such films as *Captains Courageous*, *Father of the Bride*, *Bad Day at Black Rock*, *Inherit the Wind*, *Judgment at Nuremberg*, and *Guess Who's Coming to Dinner*.

Tracy won back-to-back Oscars in 1938 and 1939. For what films did he win?

A. *Captains Courageous* and *Boys Town*

B. *San Francisco* and *Captains Courageous*

C. *Boys Town* and *Father of the Bride*

D. *San Francisco* and *Father of the Bride*

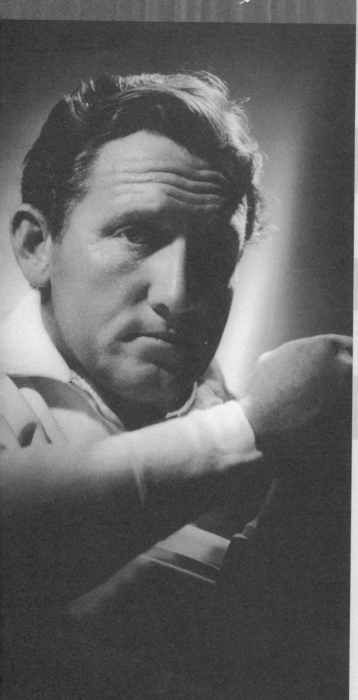

928. Which of these filmmakers has *not* won Oscars for producing, writing, and directing the same film?

A. George Stevens

B. David Lean

C. Fred Zinnemann

D. Michael Curtiz

929. What noted film expert authored the book *75 Years of the Oscar: The Official History of the Academy Awards*?

A. Richard Schickel

B. Robert Osborne

C. Roger Ebert

D. Jonathan Rosenbaum

930. All but one of these actors has won an Oscar for playing an alcoholic character—who is the odd man out?

A. Lionel Barrymore

B. Jack Lemmon

C. Ray Milland

D. Nicholas Cage

931. Which of these filmmakers has not received five or more Oscar nominations for Best Director?

A. Fred Zinnemann

B. David Lean

C. Michael Curtiz

D. George Stevens

932. For what film was John Gielgud awarded his only Oscar?

A. *Richard III*

B. *Arthur*

C. *Becket*

D. *Julius Caesar*

933. Which of these performances landed John Wayne his first acting Oscar nomination?

A. *Sands of Iwo Jima*

B. *True Grit*

C. *Stagecoach*

D. *The Searchers*

934. Only one of these distinguished filmmakers has never received an Oscar nomination for his acting. Who is this?

A. John Huston

B. Woody Allen

C. Richard Attenborough

D. Eric von Stroheim

935. Which of these films did *not* earn Clint Eastwood a nomination for Best Director?

A. *Unforgiven*

B. *Mystic River*

C. *Million Dollar Baby*

D. *The Bridges of Madison County*

936. What actor received back-to-back Oscar nominations for portraying Louis Pasteur and Emile Zola?

A. Charles Boyer

B. Robert Montgomery

C. Paul Muni

D. Fredric March

937. Who came forward and accepted Alice Brady's Best Supporting Actress Oscar?

A. An Alice Brady imposter

B. A drunken line producer

C. Her father

D. Alice Brady

938. One noted writer proclaimed of his Oscar, "It's an insult for them to offer me any honor as if they'd never heard of me—and it's very likely they never have." Who was this?

A. Jean-Paul Sartre

B. John Steinbeck

C. George Bernard Shaw

D. Tennessee Williams

939. For what film did Rod Steiger win an Oscar?

A. *On the Waterfront*

B. *The Pawnbroker*

C. *Doctor Zhivago*

D. *In the Heat of the Night*

940. In 1944 it was decided that Oscar statuettes should be made from something different due to the war. What were the statuettes then made of?

A. Papier-mâché

B. Plaster

C. Plastic

D. Stone

941. Why was the 1942 Oscar ceremony almost canceled?

A. Host Willie Winkie suffered a stroke

B. Because many actors and directors had gone to war

C. Because of the Pearl Harbor attack

D. Because William Randolph Hearst ordered it

942. For which of these films did Laurence Olivier receive his only acting Oscar?

A. *Hamlet*

B. *Marathon Man*

C. *Rebecca*

D. *The Boys from Brazil*

943. From 1937 through 1944, Best Supporting Actor and Actress winners did not receive the standard statuette. What did they receive?

A. A smaller copper statuette

B. Verbal accolades

C. A smaller plastic statuette

D. A smaller plaque

947.

Sidney Poitier, one of the screen's brightest stars, is similar to baseballer Jackie Robinson, another pioneering African-American, in that he will be remembered for more than just being one of the best at what he did. More than a respected actor, Poitier was an inspiring role model who paved the way for many other African-American performers who would follow. Poitier's breakthrough role came in Richard Brooks's 1955 film *Blackboard Jungle*. (The twenty-seven-year-old actor played a high school student!) Poitier's filmography as an actor includes such noted titles as *The Defiant Ones*, *Porgy and Bess*, *A Raisin in the Sun*, *Lilies of the Field*, *A Patch of Blue*, *To Sir, with Love*, *In the Heat of the Night*, and *Guess Who's Coming to Dinner*. Poitier then embarked upon a second career as a director, helming such films as *Uptown Saturday Night* and *Stir Crazy*. He became the first African-American actor to win a competitive Oscar (as opposed to an honorary award), and was knighted by Queen Elizabeth II in 1974.

For what film did Sidney Poitier win an Oscar?

A. *In the Heat of the Night*
B. *Lilies of the Field*
C. *The Defiant Ones*
D. *Guess Who's Coming to Dinner*

944. Who was the first sitting President of the United States to participate in the Academy Awards?
A. Ronald Reagan
B. Franklin Roosevelt
C. John F. Kennedy
D. Dwight Eisenhower

945. For what film did Russell Crowe win his first Oscar?
A. *Gladiator*
B. *The Insider*
C. *A Beautiful Mind*
D. *Cinderella Man*

946. Which of these performances landed Gary Cooper an Oscar?
A. *Mr. Deeds Goes to Town*
B. *Sergeant York*
C. *The Pride of the Yankees*
D. *For Whom the Bell Tolls*

947.

948. Why was the 1938 Academy Award ceremony postponed for a week?
A. Because of death threats
B. A massive fire
C. Heavy rainfall
D. A Screen Actors Guild strike

949. In 1942, the song "Pig Foot Pete" was erroneously nominated as being in the film *Hellzapoppin*. What film was this song actually in?
A. *The Mayor of 44th Street*
B. *Keep 'Em Flying*
C. *Flying with Music*
D. *Babes on Broadway*

950. James Stewart won only one competitive Oscar. What performance landed him the statuette?
A. *The Philadelphia Story*
B. *Rear Window*
C. *Mr. Smith Goes to Washington*
D. *Anatomy of a Murder*

951. Who was the first leading lady to win an Oscar for performing opposite Jack Nicholson?
A. Louise Fletcher
B. Karen Black
C. Shirley MacLaine
D. Helen Hunt

952. One actress quipped of her Oscar, "If I had an infinite amount of respect for the people who think I gave the greatest performance, then it would matter to me." Who said this?

A. Joanne Woodward

B. Bette Davis

C. Elizabeth Taylor

D. Olivia DeHavilland

953. Stephen Sondheim won the Best Song Oscar for *Dick Tracy's* "Sooner or Later." This was the second Disney film to feature a song with that title. What was the first?

A. *Song of the South*

B. *Treasure Island*

C. *Cinderella*

D. *Old Yeller*

954. For which of these performances did Paul Muni win an Oscar?

A. *The Story of Louis Pasteur*

B. *Scarface*

C. *I Am a Fugitive from a Chain Gang*

D. *Muni never won an Oscar*

955. In what category did Charles Chaplin's *Limelight* win?

A. Best Picture

B. Best Original Score

C. Best Director

D. Best Set Design

956. For four straight years (1979–82) an actress with the initials M.S. won the Best Supporting Actress Oscar. Which of these four actresses started that streak in 1979?

A. Maggie Smith

B. Meryl Streep

C. Mary Steenburgen

D. Maureen Stapleton

957. Who has the dubious distinction of being the first actress to lose for both Best Actress and Best Supporting Actress in the same year?

A. Emma Thompson

B. Sigourney Weaver

C. Fay Bainter

D. Jessica Lange

958. What filmmaker won the Oscar for Best Director for the first and only film he would ever direct?

A. Michael Cimino

B. Delbert Mann

C. Jerome Robbins

D. Joshua Logan

959. How many times had Paul Newman been nominated prior to winning his first Oscar?

A. Seven

B. Three

C. Zero

D. Five

965.

Many Hollywood insiders predicted that James Cameron's 1997 film *Titanic* would be a bigger disaster than the infamous 1912 sinking it depicts. They could not have been more wrong. The film, which made movie stars out of lead players Leonardo DiCaprio and Kate Winslet, shattered box-office records and raked in a staggering $1.8 billion worldwide. This set a new record, making *Titanic* the biggest box-office moneymaker in history (without adjusting for inflation). It was the first picture ever to earn more than $1 billion worldwide. *Titanic* became more than a simple film; it was an event. Even its soundtrack sold an astounding twenty million copies.

The following year, *Titanic* became the second film in history to receive fourteen Academy Award nominations. What film had previously accomplished this feat?

A. *Gone with the Wind*
B. *It Happened One Night*
C. *Network*
D. *All About Eve*

960. Why was the Academy Awards ceremony postponed a day in 1981?

A. Because of a fire in the ballroom where the ceremony was to be held
C. Because the Pope had been shot
B. Because of a massive earthquake
D. Because President Reagan had been shot

961. Who purchased Clark Gable's *It Happened One Night* Oscar in 1996?

A. Steven Spielberg
C. Frank Capra, Jr.
B. The Academy of Motion Picture Arts and Sciences
D. The Planet Hollywood theme restaurant chain

962. For what performance did Henry Fonda receive his only Oscar?

A. *12 Angry Men*
C. *The Grapes of Wrath*
B. *The Ox-Bow Incident*
D. *On Golden Pond*

963. Who was the first director whose film won Best Picture without his receiving a Best Director nomination?

A. Hugh Hudson, *Chariots of Fire*
C. William A. Wellman, *Wings*
B. Bruce Beresford, *Driving Miss Daisy*
D. Edmund Goulding, *Grand Hotel*

964. What film critic was honored at the 1999 Academy Awards ceremony?

A. Andrew Sarris
C. Gene Siskel
B. Leonard Maltin
D. Pauline Kael

965.

966. Who was the first filmmaker to win three Oscars for Best Director?

A. John Ford
C. William Wyler
B. Frank Capra
D. John Huston

967. What category was deemed obsolete after the first Academy Awards ceremony?

A. Silent Performance
C. Best Silent Film
B. Title Writing
D. Musical Accompaniment

968. Which of these animated films was *not* nominated for an Oscar?

A. *Shrek*

B. *Aladdin*

C. *Fantasia*

D. *Jimmy Neutron: Boy Genius*

969. The first Academy Award winners were notified in advance. How much notice did they receive?

A. Three months

B. Two months

C. One month

D. Four months

970. What is the only fantasy film to win Best Picture?

A. *The Lord of the Rings: The Return of the King*

B. *The Lord of the Rings: The Fellowship of the Ring*

C. *The Chronicles of Narnia: The Lion, the Witch and the Wardrobe*

D. *The Lord of the Rings: The Two Towers*

971. Which of these westerns did *not* win Best Picture?

A. *Unforgiven*

B. *Cimarron*

C. *Dances with Wolves*

D. *The Searchers*

972.

973. All but one of these actors have won Oscars for playing multiple roles in a film. Which one of them has *not*?

A. Peter Sellers, *Dr. Strangelove*

B. Fredric March, *Dr. Jekyll and Mr. Hyde*

C. Lee Marvin, *Cat Ballou*

D. Laurence Olivier, *Hamlet*

974. Which of these actors has not been nominated twice for playing the same character in different films?

A. Bing Crosby as Father O'Malley

B. Paul Newman as "Fast" Eddie Felson

C. Peter O'Toole for Henry II

D. Robert Duvall for Tom Hagen

975. Who was awarded the Best Screenplay Oscar in 1957 for *Bridge on the River Kwai*?

A. Carl Foreman

B. David Lean

C. Michael Wilson

D. Pierre Boulle

972.

Steve McQueen was one of the most popular actors ever to grace the silver screen. Like James Dean, McQueen has achieved an almost mythic status as the personification of "cool." (In fact, McQueen's nickname was the "King of Cool.") McQueen's penchant for fast cars (he was also a race car driver) and beautiful women (he stole Ali McGraw from her husband, producer Robert Evans) served to justify this status. Behind the scenes, the iconic actor had a reputation for being difficult to work with. He also refused to work unless he was paid exorbitant amounts of money. (At one time he was the highest-paid actor in Hollywood.) His list of credits includes such gems as *The Magnificent Seven*, *The Great Escape*, *The Sand Pebbles*, *The Thomas Crown Affair*, *Bullitt*, *The Getaway*, *Papillon*, and *The Towering Inferno*.

Steve McQueen received only one Oscar nomination. For what performance did he receive it?

A. *The Sand Pebbles*

B. *Papillon*

C. *The Cincinnati Kid*

D. *The Towering Inferno*

976. What was the first film to receive five acting nominations?

A. *All About Eve*
B. *Mrs. Miniver*
C. *Network*
D. *From Here to Eternity*

977. All of the following actresses except one have won an Oscar for playing a prostitute. Which one hasn't?

A. Mira Sorvino
B. Donna Reed
C. Greta Garbo
D. Jane Fonda

978. Who is the only performer to appear in three consecutive Best Picture winners?

A. Ward Bond
B. John Cazale
C. Harry Davenport
D. Talia Shire

979. Which of these films was awarded Best Picture at the 50th Academy Awards in 1977?

A. *The Goodbye Girl*
B. *Annie Hall*
C. *Julia*
D. *Star Wars*

980. Which of the following films won Best Picture but was not nominated for Best Screenplay?

A. *Schindler's List*
B. *Driving Miss Daisy*
C. *Titanic*
D. *Cimarron*

981. How many Best Actor nominations did the swashbuckling 1935 film *Mutiny on the Bounty* receive?

A. One
B. Three
C. Two
D. Four

982. Whose five-and-a-half minute Oscar speech is the longest ever?

A. Greer Garson
B. Sally Field
C. Halle Berry
D. Henry Fonda

983. For how many performances did Janet Gaynor win Best Actress in 1929?

A. One
B. Three
C. Two
D. Four

984. Who is the youngest filmmaker ever nominated for Best Director?

A. John Singleton

B. Steven Spielberg

C. Orson Welles

D. George Lucas

985. Bette Davis and Katharine Hepburn both received Best Actress nominations for playing characters with the same name. What is this name?

A. Margo Channing

B. Tracy Lord

C. Jane Hudson

D. Rose Sayer

986. *The Turning Point* received eleven nominations in 1978. How many Oscars did it win?

A. Zero

B. One

C. Seven

D. Eleven

987. Spencer Tracy's Oscar for *Captains Courageous* was engraved with the wrong name. What was the name?

A. Dick Tracy

B. Tracy Spencer

C. J.D. Spencer

D. Spencer Tressey

988. Who was the first composer to win three Oscars for Best Original Score?

A. Dimitri Tiomkin

B. John Barry

C. Max Steiner

D. John Williams

989. Where was the first Academy Awards ceremony held?

A. The Biltmore Hotel

B. The Hollywood Roosevelt Hotel

C. Grauman's Chinese Theatre

D. The Ambassador Hotel

990. What was unique regarding the 1930 Academy Awards?

A. There was no actual ceremony

B. There were no officially announced nominees

C. The Screen Actors Guild boycotted the awards

D. Write-in votes were accepted

991. From 1935 through 1938 Oscars for Best Score were not awarded to the composers. To whom were they awarded?

A. The film's director

B. The head of the music department

C. The musical producer

D. The film's producers

997.

Marlon Brando is widely considered one of the finest—if not *the* finest—actors ever to work in film. Brando studied acting at a number of different schools, but blossomed under the tutelage of famed acting coach Stella Adler at the New School's Dramatic Workshop. Brando then found work in theatre, eventually making a splash on Broadway. In 1950, he made his cinematic debut in Fred Zinnemann's *The Men*. The following year Brando became a bona fide star when he played the tormented Stanley Kowalski in Elia Kazan's *A Streetcar Named Desire*. (He had originated this role on Broadway four years earlier.)

Brando's incredible body of work also includes such noted films as *Viva Zapata!*, *The Wild One*, *On the Waterfront*, *Guys and Dolls*, *Mutiny on the Bounty*, *Reflections in a Golden Eye*, *The Godfather*, *Last Tango in Paris*, and *Apocalypse Now*.

For which of these films did Marlon Brando *not* receive an Oscar nomination?

A. *Viva Zapata!*
B. *Julius Caesar*
C. *A Dry White Season*
D. *Apocalypse Now*

992. Only one of these films won an Oscar for Best Picture. Which one?
   A. *Citizen Kane*   **C.** *Treasure of the Sierra Madre*
   B. *Ben-Hur*   **D.** *Doctor Zhivago*

993. Which of these films won Best Picture in 1959?
   A. *Cat on a Hot Tin Roof*   **C.** *The Defiant Ones*
   B. *Separate Tables*   **D.** *Gigi*

994. In the film *Talladega Nights*, Ricky Bobby proclaims that *Highlander* won an Academy Award. For what does he say it won?
   A. For being the most impressive entry in Sean Connery's filmography
   C. For being the greatest movie ever made
   B. For being "kick ass"
   D. Because Christopher Lambert is the "greatest actor of all time"

995. Who was the first person to decline an Oscar?
   A. Dudley Nichols   **C.** Charlton Heston
   B. George C. Scott   **D.** Marlon Brando

996. Which of these Best Picture winners won no Oscars for acting or directing?
   A. *The Great Ziegfeld*   **C.** *The Life of Emile Zola*
   B. *Cavalcade*   **D.** *Chariots of Fire*

997.

998. For what film did Richard Dreyfuss win an Oscar?
   A. *Mr. Holland's Opus*   **C.** *Jaws*
   B. *The Goodbye Girl*   **D.** *American Graffiti*

999. For what film did co-directors win the Best Director Oscar for the first time in 1960?
   A. *The Nun's Story*   **C.** *The Diary of Anne Frank*
   B. *West Side Story*   **D.** *Four Frightened People*

1000. For which of these films was screenwriter Steven Zaillian *not* nominated for Best Screenplay?
   A. *Schindler's List*   **C.** *Gangs of New York*
   B. *Searching for Bobby Fischer*   **D.** *Awakenings*

CHAPTER FIVE:
THE DIRECTORS

1001. Which of these ghastly frights was directed by novelist Stephen King?
A. *Sleepwalkers*
B. *Sometimes They Come Back*
C. *Graveyard Shift*
D. *Maximum Overdrive*

1002. Which of these filmmakers directed the record-breaking blockbuster *Titanic*?
A. Oliver Stone
B. James Cameron
C. Steven Spielberg
D. Peter Jackson

1003. One of these films was *not* directed by George Lucas: which one?
A. *American Graffiti*
B. *Star Wars Episode One: The Phantom Menace*
C. *The Empire Strikes Back*
D. *THX 1138*

1004. What filmmaker was credited as the director of both *Gone with the Wind* and *The Wizard of Oz*?
A. Victor Fleming
B. George Cukor
C. Sam Wood
D. Mervyn LeRoy

1005. On which of these films did director Mike Nichols *not* collaborate with screenwriter Buck Henry?
A. *The Graduate*
B. *Carnal Knowledge*
C. *The Day of the Dolphin*
D. *Catch-22*

1006. What filmmaker is responsible for the films *Fitzcarraldo*, *Grizzly Man*, and *Nosferatu*?
A. Harmony Korine
B. Sidney Lumet
C. Zak Penn
D. Werner Herzog

1007. This filmmaker directed groundbreaking documentaries like *Harlan County, USA* before making the feature *Havoc*.
A. Albert Maysles
B. D. A. Pennebaker
C. Barbara Kopple
D. Errol Morris

OPPOSITE Director Spike Lee, 1990

1008. This director's credits include the films *His Girl Friday* and *Rio Bravo*.

A. Ernst Lubitsch

B. Howard Hawks

C. John Ford

D. William Wyler

1009. Who planned to direct *Reservoir Dogs* but wound up producing the film instead?

A. Harvey Keitel

B. Brian De Palma

C. Quentin Tarantino

D. Monte Hellman

1010. What filmmaker directed James Stewart in eight films including *The Naked Spur*?

A. Alfred Hitchcock

B. Budd Boetticher

C. Anthony Mann

D. John Ford

1011.

1012. Which of these John Cassavetes-directed films does *not* feature his wife Gena Rowlands?

A. *The Killing of a Chinese Bookie*

B. *Opening Night*

C. *A Woman Under the Influence*

D. *Love Streams*

1013. Which of these films directed by Jerry Lewis has never been released and has been wrapped up in litigation for several decades?

A. *Which Way to the Front?*

B. *Three on a Couch*

C. *The Day the Clown Cried*

D. *The Family Jewels*

1014. This director made the Nazi propaganda film *Triumph of the Will*.

A. Fritz Lang

B. Josef von Sternberg

C. Erich von Stroheim

D. Leni Riefenstahl

1015. Which of these bloody horror films was *not* directed by the "Godfather of Gore" Herschell Gordon Lewis?

A. *Blood Feast*

B. *Bucket of Blood*

C. *Color Me Blood Red*

D. *A Taste of Blood*

1016. What animator/director created the Road Runner and Wile E. Coyote?

A. David Hand

B. Chuck Jones

C. Joseph Barbera

D. Friz Freleng

1011.

After graduating from the Royal College of Art, Tony Scott was persuaded by his older brother Ridley to work for him at Ridley Scott Associates, his newly established commercial-production company. Ridley soon struck out for Hollywood, helming *The Duellists* and *Alien*, and Tony, who had by that point directed more than a thousand commercials for his brother, packed his bags and followed him.

In 1983, Tony made his directorial debut with the vampire thriller *The Hunger*. This David Bowie vehicle might have been a run-of-the-mill horror flick under another filmmaker's direction, but Tony crafted a sleek, stylish film with stunning visuals. While *The Hunger* failed to make an impact at the box office, it established Tony as an artistic talent with visual flair.

His subsequent efforts have included such films as *Top Gun*, *Revenge*, *Days of Thunder*, *The Last Boy Scout*, *True Romance*, *Crimson Tide*, *The Fan*, *Enemy of the State*, *Man on Fire*, *Domino*, and *Déjà Vu*. Today, Tony Scott is recognized as one of Hollywood's premiere directors.

Tony appeared as the lead in brother Ridley Scott's first short film in 1965.

What is the title of this film?

A. *Boy and Bicycle*

B. *In This Light*

C. *Loving Memory*

D. *Only the Daring*

1017. Who directed the film *Butch Cassidy and the Sundance Kid*?

A. Robert Redford

B. John Schlesinger

C. George Roy Hill

D. Paul Newman

1018. To what actor did Stanley Kubrick allegedly confide that he felt *Eyes Wide Shut* was no good due to interference by his lead actors?

A. R. Lee Ermey

B. Jack Nicholson

C. Malcolm McDowell

D. Keir Dullea

1019. What was the first feature-length film directed by Steven Spielberg?

A. *Jaws*

B. *Sugarland Express*

C. *Something Evil*

D. *Duel*

1020. What filmmaker was a professional bullfighter before directing such films as *Seven Men from Now*?

A. Anthony Mann

B. Budd Boetticher

C. John Ford

D. Orson Welles

1021. Which of these films does *not* feature director Ron Howard as an actor?

A. *The Music Man*

B. *Grand Theft Auto*

C. *The Shootist*

D. *The Arena*

1022. This filmmaker studied at UCLA before directing *Election* and *Sideways*.

A. Alexander Payne

B. Wes Anderson

C. David O. Russell

D. Roger Avary

1023. What noted filmmaker created the television series *Twin Peaks*?

A. Michael Mann

B. Tim Burton

C. Spike Jonze

D. David Lynch

1024. Which of these films was *not* directed by the legendary Orson Welles?

A. *The Magnificent Ambersons*

B. *The Third Man*

C. *The Stranger*

D. *F for Fake*

1025. This *House of Wax* helmer had only one eye.

A. Andre De Toth

B. Sergio Corbucci

C. Raoul Walsh

D. Jaume Collett-Serra

1026. What was the first film that Peter Bogdanovich directed under his real name?

A. *The Last Picture Show*

B. *Saint Jack*

C. *Voyage to the Planet of Prehistoric Women*

D. *Targets*

1027. Who directed the seminal "hood" film *Boyz n the Hood*?

A. Spike Lee

B. Rusty Cundieff

C. John Singleton

D. Ernest Dickerson

1028.

1029. This director made four films starring James Stewart, one of which is *Rope*.

A. Alfred Hitchcock

B. George Stevens

C. Anthony Mann

D. Frank Capra

1030. This director's wife, Sharon Tate, was murdered by the Manson clan. Who is this?

A. Peter Bogdanovich

B. Roman Polanski

C. John Schlesinger

D. William Friedkin

1031. Which of these films was directed by actor William Shatner?

A. *Star Trek: The Motion Picture*

B. *Showtime*

C. *Star Trek IV: The Voyage Home*

D. *Groom Lake*

1032. Which of these films was *not* directed by Oliver Stone?

A. *Wall Street*

B. *U Turn*

C. *Scarface*

D. *Salvador*

1033. Who directed *Night of the Living Dead*, *Dawn of the Dead*, and *Day of the Dead*?

A. Tom Savini

B. George Romero

C. Chris Watson

D. John Russo

1028.

Akira Kurosawa's 1954 masterpiece *The Seven Samurai* is one of only a handful of Japanese films to become widely known in the United States. It profoundly influenced Hollywood films, from its use of slow motion and panning shots during battle scenes to the now common plot element of recruiting a variety of heroes for a singular battle or mission. In 1957 Hollywood remade the film as the John Sturges western *The Magnificent Seven*.

The Seven Samurai tells the story of an impoverished village that is repeatedly attacked and robbed by bandits. The villagers enlist the services of an aged samurai, Kambei Shimada, who recruits a band of samurai to aid him in defending the village. The warriors bond with the villagers and when they learn that the villagers are giving them all of the best foods while they themselves go hungry, the samurai share their meals with them. Despite the fact that the samurai eventually defeat the bandits, the film ends unhappily with the remaining warriors realizing they have shed their own blood for the villagers but have nothing to show for it.

How is Toshiro Mifune's character Kikuchiyo killed?

A. Stabbed

B. Burned

C. Shot

D. Beaten

1034. Who produced *Goodfellas* and also directed *Guilty by Suspicion*?
- **A.** Irwin Winkler
- **B.** Frank Marshall
- **C.** Martin Scorsese
- **D.** John G. Avildsen

1035. Which of these films was directed by Sidney Poitier?
- **A.** *They Call Me Mister Tibbs!*
- **B.** *To Sir with Love II*
- **C.** *Buck and the Preacher*
- **D.** *Shoot to Kill*

1036. This filmmaker won a Directors Guild Award and an Oscar for *Rocky*.
- **A.** Sylvester Stallone
- **B.** George Roy Hill
- **C.** Peter Bogdanovich
- **D.** John G. Avildsen

1037. What auteur crafted the *Yojimbo*-inspired shoot-'em-up called *A Fistful of Dollars*?
- **A.** Sergio Corbucci
- **B.** Sergio Leone
- **C.** Mario Bava
- **D.** Dario Argento

1038. What filmmaker made *Marty* and later remade *All Quiet on the Western Front*?
- **A.** Lewis Milestone
- **B.** Delbert Mann
- **C.** Anthony Mann
- **D.** Martin Ritt

1039. This filmmaker was the Berlin correspondent for the *Chicago Tribune* before making *The Philadelphia Story* and *All About Eve*.
- **A.** Joseph L. Mankiewicz
- **B.** William A. Wellman
- **C.** Sam Wood
- **D.** Vincent Sherman

1040. Ed Wood is revered as the single worst filmmaker in the history of cinema. Which of these Wood-directed pictures does *not* feature actor Bela Lugosi?
- **A.** *Glen or Glenda*
- **B.** *Plan 9 from Outer Space*
- **C.** *Bride of the Monster*
- **D.** *Night of the Ghouls*

1041. This filmmaker cofounded DreamWorks with Jeffrey Katzenberg and David Geffen.
- **A.** Martin Scorsese
- **B.** George Lucas
- **C.** Steven Spielberg
- **D.** Stanley Kubrick

1042. Who directed *Ninotchka* and *To Be or Not to Be*?

A. Fritz Lang

B. Ernst Lubitsch

C. Michael Curtiz

D. Joseph L. Mankiewicz

1043. What is the name of the *cinema verite* pioneer who directed the Bob Dylan documentary *Don't Look Back*?

A. Richard Leacock

B. D. A. Pennebaker

C. Robert Drew

D. Albert Maysles

1044. Who directed Bogie and Hepburn in *The African Queen*?

A. Michael Curtiz

B. Preston Sturges

C. Howard Hawks

D. John Huston

1045. What country is *One Flew Over the Cuckoo's Nest* director Milos Forman from?

A. Czechoslovakia

B. Croatia

C. The Soviet Union

D. Ukraine

1046. What Ralph Bakshi animated film drew ire from the Congress of Racial Equality (CORE) and was ultimately pulled from theaters?

A. *Hey Good Looking*

B. *Heavy Traffic*

C. *Coonskin*

D. *Fritz the Cat*

1047. What filmmaker directed *Scarface* and *The Untouchables*?

A. Walter Hill

B. Brian De Palma

C. Martin Scorsese

D. Oliver Stone

1048. This legendary director's filmography includes *The Grand Illusion* and *The Rules of the Game*.

A. Claude Chabrol

B. Andrei Tarkovsky

C. Jean-Luc Godard

D. Jean Renoir

1049. What filmmaker established his own studio, American Zoetrope, with help from George Lucas?

A. Roger Corman

B. Francis Ford Coppola

C. James Cameron

D. Peter Jackson

1050. This filmmaker wrote the screenplays for *Awakenings* and *Schindler's List* before going on to direct films including *A Civil Action* and *All the King's Men*.

A. Steven Zaillian

B. David Veloz

C. Paul Haggis

D. Robert Towne

1051. What filmmaker directed the great love story *Casablanca*?
A. George Cukor
B. Frank Capra
C. Michael Curtiz
D. William Wyler

1052. What director's nickname was "Bloody Sam"?
A. Sam Peckinpah
B. Samuel Fuller
C. Sam Raimi
D. Sam Wood

1053.

1054. This French filmmaker wrote an analytical book on Alfred Hitchcock and also appears in Orson Welles's unfinished film *The Other Side of the Wind*.
A. François Truffaut
B. Eric Rohmer
C. Claude Chabrol
D. Jean-Luc Godard

1055. Which filmmaker studied at Brown University and the International Centre for Photography before directing films like *Swingers* and *Mr. and Mrs. Smith*?
A. Jon Favreau
B. Alexander Payne
C. Wes Anderson
D. Doug Liman

1056. Which of these women played Sergeant Lucy Bates on the television series *Hill Street Blues* before directing films like *Dr. Dolittle* and *Private Parts*?
A. Nora Ephron
B. Betty Thomas
C. Penny Marshall
D. Allison Anders

1057. This filmmaker was forty-five when he made his breakthrough with the film *M*A*S*H*.
A. Henry Jaglom
B. Sidney Pollack
C. Robert Altman
D. Hal Ashby

1058. What director started his career in television before making his big league directorial debut with *12 Angry Men*?
A. Stanley Kramer
B. Sidney Lumet
C. Blake Edwards
D. Robert Altman

1059. Which of these films was directed by Burt Reynolds?
A. *The Longest Yard*
B. *Modern Love*
C. *The End*
D. *Smokey and the Bandit II*

1053.

Prolific director Alfred Hitchcock had already made more than thirty films in his native England before relocating to the United States to work with producer David O. Selznick. (His British films include the gems *The 39 Steps* and *The Man Who Knew Too Much*, which he later remade in Hollywood.)

Rebecca was Hitchcock's first American film. The film was a success, and won Best Picture honors at the Academy Awards—the only Hitchcock film ever to do so. One of the films *Rebecca* beat out for Best Picture was Hitchcock's second Tinseltown feature, *Foreign Correspondent*. Subsequent Hitchcock films included *Spellbound*, *Notorious*, *Dial M for Murder*, *Rear Window*, *To Catch a Thief*, *Vertigo*, *North by Northwest*, *Psycho*, and *The Birds*.

Hitchcock's remarkable career spanned six decades and more than fifty films. He also hosted and produced the long-running television series *Alfred Hitchcock Presents*. Although he was seen as a commercial filmmaker in his day, Hitchcock is recognized today as one of the greatest directors in the history of film.

Hitchcock died in 1980. Which of these quirky pronouncements appears on his tombstone?

A. "This is what we do to bad little boys"
B. "I'm in on a plot"
C. "A mistake has been made—I'm not dead!"
D. "It's cold and dark in here"

1060. What filmmaker codirected *The Toxic Avenger* and established Troma Films with Michael Hertz?

A. Ted V. Mikels

B. Fred Olen Ray

C. Herschell Gordon Lewis

D. Lloyd Kaufman

1061. This *Conan the Barbarian* auteur also cowrote *Apocalypse Now*.

A. John Milius

B. Jonathan Demme

C. Francis Ford Coppola

D. Arthur Penn

1062. What filmmaker was responsible for the films *It's a Wonderful Life* and *It Happened One Night*?

A. George Cukor

B. William Wellman

C. Frank Capra

D. King Vidor

1063. Thirty-one years after crafting *All Quiet on the Western Front*, this filmmaker directed the Rat Pack in *Ocean's Eleven*.

A. Robert Wise

B. Steven Soderbergh

C. Randal Kleiser

D. Lewis Milestone

1064. What director was responsible for the classic western *Shane*?

A. George Stevens

B. Howard Hawks

C. Fred Zinnemann

D. Stanley Kramer

1065. What filmmaker edited *Citizen Kane* and later directed *The Sound of Music* and *West Side Story*?

A. Don Siegel

B. Blake Edwards

C. Orson Welles

D. Robert Wise

1066. The director of *When Harry Met Sally . . .* was once married to Penny Marshall. Who is this?

A. Sydney Pollack

B. Robert Zemeckis

C. Rob Reiner

D. Ron Howard

1067. Who directed *Dirty Harry* and *The Shootist*?

A. Don Seigel

B. John Milius

C. Clint Eastwood

D. Samuel Fuller

1068. What is the name of the crime novelist who directed *Eliot Ness: An Untouchable Life*?

A. Donald Westlake   **C.** Ed McBain

B. Elmore Leonard   **D.** Max Allan Collins

1069.

1069.

Orson Welles enjoyed successful careers working on stage and in radio—having already pulled off the most elaborate hoax in history with his *War of the Worlds* stunt—before coming to Hollywood. He wrote, directed, and starred in his first film, *Citizen Kane*, in 1941, when he was twenty-five years old. With this film, considered by many the single greatest motion picture ever made, Welles proved that his talents were not confined to any single medium.

There is a common misconception that *Citizen Kane* is Welles' only great work as director. This, of course, is false. While none of his subsequent works are as brilliant as *Citizen Kane*, films like *The Magnificent Ambersons*, *Touch of Evil*, *Mr. Arkadin*, *The Trial*, *Chimes at Midnight*, and *F for Fake* are masterworks by anyone's definition. And, judging from the completed footage we have from Welles' unfinished film *The Other Side of the Wind*, there is ample evidence to support a claim that this, too, would have been an equally exemplary effort had he completed it before his death.

Which of the following Welles films does *not* feature him onscreen?

A. *Mr. Arkadin*
B. *The Stranger*
C. *The Magnificent Ambersons*
D. *Touch of Evil*

1070. Who directed *Good Night and Good Luck*?

A. Jonathan Demme   **C.** Robert Redford

B. George Clooney   **D.** Steven Soderbergh

1071. Which of these films was *not* directed by actor Kevin Costner?

A. *Waterworld*   **C.** *The Postman*

B. *Dances with Wolves*   **D.** *Open Range*

1072. Who directed more than 500 films including the landmark 1902 film *Voyage to the Moon*?

A. Sergei Eisenstein   **C.** Georges Melies

B. Thomas Edison   **D.** D.W. Griffith

1073. This cult filmmaker made the indie smash *Clerks* on a budget of just $27,000.

A. Richard Linklater   **C.** Mike Judge

B. Gus Van Sant   **D.** Kevin Smith

1074. This director made his debut with 1958's *The Left-Handed Gun*. Nine years later he directed *Bonnie and Clyde*.

A. Sam Peckinpah   **C.** Robert Altman

B. Arthur Penn   **D.** Don Siegel

1075. Who directed *To Kill a Mockingbird*?

A. George Axelrod   **C.** Sidney Lumet

B. Clarence Brown   **D.** Robert Mulligan

1076. Which of these epic films was *not* directed by David Lean?

A. *Doctor Zhivago*   **C.** *Ryan's Daughter*

B. *The Man Who Would Be King*   **D.** *Lawrence of Arabia*

1077. Which of these Paul Newman–directed films also features Newman as an actor?

- **A.** Sometimes a Great Notion
- **B.** Rachel, Rachel
- **C.** The Effect of Gamma Rays on Man-in-the-Moon Marigolds
- **D.** The Shadow Box

1078. This filmmaker's production company is called Forty Acres & A Mule Filmworks.

- **A.** Craig Brewer
- **B.** Master P
- **C.** Forest Whitaker
- **D.** Spike Lee

1079. Stanley Kubrick's first film cost only $4,000 to make. What was this film?

- **A.** Fear and Desire
- **B.** The Killing
- **C.** Day of the Fight
- **D.** Killer's Kiss

1080. Marlon Brando directed only one film. What was its name?

- **A.** The Ugly American
- **B.** One-Eyed Jacks
- **C.** The Fugitive Kind
- **D.** The Appaloosa

1081. What filmmaker was responsible for the mega-flop Ishtar?

- **A.** Warren Beatty
- **B.** Peter Chelsom
- **C.** Walter Hill
- **D.** Elaine May

1082. Ida Lupino became one of the first successful female filmmakers ever after taking the reins of a film when director Elmer Clifton suffered a heart attack. What was this film?

- **A.** Red Rock Outlaw
- **B.** Marked for Murder
- **C.** Not Wanted
- **D.** The Trouble with Angels

1083. Which of these films was *not* directed by Bryan Singer?

- **A.** X-Men: The Last Stand
- **B.** X-Men
- **C.** The Usual Suspects
- **D.** Superman Returns

1084. Which actor portrayed *Nosferatu* director F. W. Murnau in the film *Shadow of the Vampire*?

- **A.** Udo Kier
- **B.** John Malkovich
- **C.** Willem Dafoe
- **D.** Cary Elwes

1085.

1085.

Ron Howard got his start as little Winthrop Paroo in the 1962 musical *The Music Man*, and went on to play Opie Taylor in the TV series *The Andy Griffith Show*. In 1974, he began a six-year run as fresh-faced teenager Richie Cunningham in the series *Happy Days*, opposite Henry Winkler as The Fonz. His big break as a director came two years after leaving *Happy Days*, when he directed the 1982 comedy *Night Shift*—a film that also spawned the song "That's What Friends Are For" and the career of Michael Keaton.

Since then, Howard has shattered the public's typically low expectations for child stars and built a reputation as one of Hollywood's major directors. His critically acclaimed films include *Apollo 13*, *Cinderella Man*, and *A Beautiful Mind*, the last of which won the Academy Award for Best Picture and Best Director in 2001.

In which of the following did Ron Howard direct himself?

- **A.** The Shootist
- **B.** Cinderella Man
- **C.** Grand Theft Auto
- **D.** Eat My Dust

1086. Which of these films was *not* directed by Tim Burton?

A. *Beetlejuice*

B. *Frankenweenie*

C. *Vincent*

D. *Big Top Pee-Wee*

1087. Oscar Micheaux established his own production company and made his first film, *The Homesteader*, in 1919, becoming the first African-American filmmaker. Which of Micheaux's films is significant because it features the debut of pioneering African-American actor Paul Robeson?

A. *The Spider's Web*

B. *Body and Soul*

C. *Deceit*

D. *The Broken Violin*

1088. Which of these films was directed by David Mamet?

A. *State and Main*

B. *The Lake Boat*

C. *Wag the Dog*

D. *Glengarry Glen Ross*

1089. With what film did Mel Gibson make his directorial debut?

A. *The Passion of the Christ*

B. *Braveheart*

C. *The Man Without a Face*

D. None of these

1090. Which of these films was *not* directed by Michael Moore?

A. *Canadian Bacon*

B. *Fahrenhype 9/11*

C. *Roger & Me*

D. *Bowling for Columbine*

1091. Who directed Marlon Brando in the films *On the Waterfront* and *A Streetcar Named Desire*?

A. John Huston

B. Nicholas Ray

C. Edward Dmytryk

D. Elia Kazan

1092. Who directed *Boogie Nights* and *Magnolia*?

A. Wes Anderson

B. Paul Thomas Anderson

C. Michel Gondry

D. Gus Van Sant

1093. Which of these films was *not* directed by Dennis Hopper?

A. *Chasers*

B. *The Last Movie*

C. *Colors*

D. *Mad Dog Morgan*

1094. Which of these films was directed by screenwriter Robert Towne?

A. *The Three Jakes*   C. *Tequila Sunrise*

B. *Frantic*   D. *Prefontaine*

1095. Director Roger Corman frequently appears in cameos in the films of others. Which of these films does *not* feature a cameo by Corman?

A. *The Godfather Part II*   C. *Silence of the Lambs*

B. *Scream 3*   D. *Little Shop of Horrors*

1096. Anthony Quinn only directed one feature film. Which of these is it?

A. *The Buccaneer*   C. *Zorba the Greek*

B. *Barabbas*   D. *Portrait in Black*

1097. In which of these films did Terrence Malick direct Richard Gere?

A. *The Thin Red Line*   C. *Days of Heaven*

B. *Badlands*   D. *The New World*

1098. On which of these classic films was Buster Keaton credited as director?

A. *Steamboat Bill, Jr.*   C. *College*

B. *The General*   D. *The Railrodder*

1099. Which of these Quentin Tarantino films was produced by *Two-Lane Blacktop* director Monte Hellman?

A. *Pulp Fiction*   C. *Kill Bill*

B. *Jackie Brown*   D. *Reservoir Dogs*

1100. All of these William Holden movies were directed by Billy Wilder except one. Which is it?

A. *Executive Suite*   C. *Sunset Boulevard*

B. *Fedora*   D. *Stalag 17*

1101.

1102. Which of these films was *not* directed by Sam Mendes?

A. *The Road to Perdition* C. *American Beauty*

B. *The Hours*   D. *Jarhead*

1101.

Robert Wise started his career in film as a sound effects editor at RKO, working on films like *Top Hat* and *The Informer*; he was then promoted to editor. Wise cut a handful of films, but his most significant achievement as an editor was Orson Welles' *Citizen Kane*. Wise also edited Welles' follow-up film, *The Magnificent Ambersons*, on which he also served as an uncredited co-director.

After Welles left the United States to work on another film, RKO ordered Wise to direct several new scenes. This led Wise to a career as a director. In 1944, he made his directorial debut with the stylish Val Lewton-produced *The Curse of the Cat People*.

Wise would ultimately direct forty films in a career spanning from 1944 to 2000. He displayed an uncanny ability to direct quality films in virtually every genre, from horror to musicals to drama. His stellar directorial credits include such standout entries as *The Set-Up*, *The Day the Earth Stood Still*, *Run Silent Run Deep*, *West Side Story*, *The Haunting*, *The Sound of Music*, and *The Sand Pebbles*.

Which of these films was *not* directed by Wise?

A. *Helen of Troy*

B. *The Andromeda Strain*

C. *Star Trek: The Motion Picture*

D. *Return to Paradise*

1103. This director, dubbed "King of the Nudies," made *Beyond the Valley of the Dolls*.
- **A.** Brad Paulson
- **B.** Al Adamson
- **C.** Russ Meyer
- **D.** A. C. Stephen

1104. What filmmaker fought in Vietnam and then later made the film *Platoon* about his experiences?
- **A.** Edward Zwick
- **B.** Oliver Stone
- **C.** John Milius
- **D.** John Badham

1105. What director's first film was the French production *The Story of a Three Day Pass*?
- **A.** Melvin Van Peebles
- **B.** Bernardo Bertolucci
- **C.** Woody Allen
- **D.** R.W. Fassbinder

1106. Which of these films was *not* directed by Wes Anderson?
- **A.** *The Royal Tenenbaums*
- **B.** *Rushmore*
- **C.** *Being John Malkovich*
- **D.** *Bottle Rocket*

1107. Who directed the film *Talk Radio*?
- **A.** Bryan Singer
- **B.** James L. Brooks
- **C.** Milos Forman
- **D.** Oliver Stone

1108. Which filmmaker studied to be a minister at a Calvinist college before eventually becoming a director?
- **A.** Paul Schrader
- **B.** Wes Craven
- **C.** Martin Scorsese
- **D.** Brian DePalma

1109. He directed music videos for Meat Loaf before helming films like *Bad Boys* and *Armageddon*.
- **A.** Tony Scott
- **B.** Michael Bay
- **C.** Roland Emmerich
- **D.** Joel Schumacher

1110. "I'm not a 'gay director,'" explained one filmmaker. "I'm an absolutely male director. Movies don't have any kind of sexuality." Who said this?
- **A.** Andy Warhol
- **B.** John Waters
- **C.** Bryan Singer
- **D.** Pedro Almódovar

1111. Which of these films was *not* directed by Nora Ephron?

A. *Sleepless in Seattle*
B. *You've Got Mail*
C. *When Harry Met Sally . . .*
D. *Mixed Nuts*

1112. Who directed Johnny Depp in *Dead Man*?

A. Jim Jarmusch
B. Tim Burton
C. Paul Thomas Anderson
D. Sam Mendes

1113. Who directed the landmark film *Battleship Potemkin*?

A. D.W. Griffith
B. Sergei Eisenstein
C. Georges Melies
D. Auguste Lumiére

1114. The director of *The French Connection* was married to actresses Jeanne Moreau and Lesley Anne Down. Who is this?

A. Roman Polanski
B. Sidney Lumet
C. John Schlesinger
D. William Friedkin

1115. This filmmaker famously remarked, "Give me any couple pages of the Bible and I'll give you a picture."

A. Charlton Heston
B. William Wyler
C. Cecil B. DeMille
D. Ernst Lubitsch

1116. From what country does Peter Weir hail?

A. Australia
B. Greenland
C. England
D. Hungary

1117.

1118. What director owns a production company called Malpaso Productions?

A. Sydney Pollack
B. Martin Scorsese
C. Clint Eastwood
D. Mel Brooks

1119. This filmmaker directed Buck Jones westerns before making more distinguished fare like *Adam's Rib* and *A Star Is Born*.

A. Howard Hawks
B. George Cukor
C. Nicholas Ray
D. William Wyler

1117.

To call Steven Spielberg one of the most successful filmmakers in history is an understatement. The three-time Academy Award—winning director has crafted many critically acclaimed films and is the most financially successful director of all time. Both *Premiere* and *Entertainment Weekly* have listed him as the most powerful man in Hollywood, and *Life* called him the single most influential individual of his generation.

Spielberg has received six Best Director Oscar nominations, winning twice. In addition, he has directed an astounding seven Best Picture contenders. (His sole Best Picture winner thus far has been *Schindler's List*.)

His most successful films include *Jaws*, *Close Encounters of the Third Kind*, *Raiders of the Lost Ark*, *E.T. the Extra-Terrestrial*, *Indiana Jones and the Temple of Doom*, *The Color Purple*, *Jurassic Park*, *Schindler's List*, *Amistad*, *Saving Private Ryan*, and *Munich*.

How many actors and actresses have been awarded Oscars for performing in a Spielberg-directed film?

A. Two
B. Zero
C. Six
D. Nine

1120. What director was quoted as saying, "Actors are like cattle"?

A. Alfred Hitchcock   C. Billy Wilder

B. Stanley Kubrick   D. John Ford

1121. Which of these classic films was directed by Ernest B. Schoedsack?

A. *The Four Feathers*   C. *Duck Soup*

B. *King Kong*   D. *Gaslight*

1122. How many films did George Cukor make with Katharine Hepburn?

A. Nine   C. Four

B. Six   D. Twelve

1123. Which of these films was *not* directed by Albert Brooks?

A. *The Muse*   C. *Mother*

B. *The Scout*   D. *Lost in America*

1124. What Steven Spielberg-helmed film features an uncredited cameo by Penny Marshall?

A. *E.T.*   C. *Always*

B. *The Sugarland Express*   D. *1941*

1125. Fred "the Hammer" Williamson has directed more than twenty films. Before working in film, Williamson played in the National Football League. Which of these teams did Williamson play for?

A. The Pittsburgh Steelers   C. The Kansas City Chiefs

B. The Minnesota Vikings   D. The Tampa Bay Buccaneers

1126. This filmmaker appeared as an actor in *Sunset Boulevard* and *Grand Illusion*.

A. Raoul Walsh   C. Erich von Stroheim

B. Buster Keaton   D. Josef von Sternberg

1127. Which of these films was *not* directed by D. W. Griffith?

A. *The Wind*   C. *Orphans of the Storm*

B. *The Birth of a Nation*   D. *Broken Blossoms*

1128. This filmmaker appeared as an actor in Stanley Kubrick's *Fear and Desire* sixteen years before directing *Bob & Carol & Ted & Alice*.

A. Henry Jaglom

B. Paul Mazursky

C. John Cassavetes

D. Hal Ashby

1129. This director made two different films about the famous OK Corral shoot-out: *Hour of the Gun* and *Gunfight at the OK Corral*.

A. Edward Dmytryk

B. John Sturges

C. Stanley Kramer

D. Preston Sturges

1130. This filmmaker was an assistant to Tod Browning before directing films like *Going My Way* and *Duck Soup*.

A. Fred Zinnemann

B. Lewis Milestone

C. Leo McCarey

D. Blake Edwards

1131. At what school did Martin Scorsese study film?

A. UCLA

B. Princeton

C. Starfleet Academy

D. NYU

1132. Who directed the films *Hell's Angels* and *The Outlaw*?

A. Howard Hughes

B. Budd Boetticher

C. Howard Hawks

D. Elia Kazan

1133.

1134. This experimental filmmaker also penned the notoriously naughty book *Hollywood Babylon*.

A. Andy Warhol

B. Kenneth Anger

C. Stan Brakhage

D. Peter Bogdanovich

1135. This filmmaker was Pier Paolo Pasolini's assistant director on *Accatone* before directing his own films, including *Last Tango in Paris*. Who is this?

A. Jean Renoir

B. Roberto Rossellini

C. Michelangelo Antonioni

D. Bernardo Bertolucci

1136. Which of these films was *not* directed by Baz Luhrman?

A. *Strictly Ballroom*

B. *Chicago*

C. *Moulin Rouge*

D. *Romeo and Juliet*

1133.

Quentin Tarantino was working as a clerk at Manhattan Beach video store Video Archives before he sold his first screenplay, *True Romance*. He then landed a deal with Live Entertainment to direct his script for *Reservoir Dogs*. The crime thriller, which stars Harvey Keitel, Lawrence Tierney, and Michael Madsen, garnered Tarantino great critical praise.

Tarantino then sold his script for *Natural Born Killers*, which was directed by Oliver Stone. Tarantino was so displeased with the final product, however, that he publicly disowned it.

In 1994, Tarantino directed his second feature, *Pulp Fiction*. This tour de force became a huge hit and propelled its director to levels of stardom he had not believed possible. The film was showered with awards around the world, including the Palme d'Or at Cannes. In addition, Tarantino and co-writer Roger Avary won the Oscar for Best Original Screenplay.

Tarantino has since directed *Jackie Brown*, *Kill Bill Vol. I and II*, and *Grindhouse*, which he co-directed with Robert Rodriguez.

On whose treatment was Tarantino's screenplay for *From Dusk Till Dawn* based?

A. Greg Nicotero

B. Robert Avary

C. Robert Kurtzman

D. Robert Rodriguez

1137. This director crafted music videos before making films like *Money Talks* and *Rush Hour*.
- **A.** Brett Ratner
- **B.** Tony Scott
- **C.** Mark Romanek
- **D.** Spike Jonze

1138. Which of these films was *not* helmed by a director using the pseudonym "Alan Smithee"?
- **A.** *Hellraiser: Bloodline*
- **B.** *Let's Get Harry*
- **C.** *An Alan Smithee Film: Burn, Hollywood, Burn!*
- **D.** *Leprechaun in the Hood*

1139. What filmmaker established Industrial Light and Magic?
- **A.** George Lucas
- **B.** Peter Jackson
- **C.** James Cameron
- **D.** Steven Spielberg

1140. This filmmaker worked as a film publicist before directing films like *The Best Years of Our Lives* and *Wuthering Heights*.
- **A.** Walter Wanger
- **B.** William Wyler
- **C.** William A. Wellman
- **D.** William Witney

1141. Who directed *My Dinner with Andre*?
- **A.** Joseph L. Mankiewicz
- **B.** Federico Fellini
- **C.** Rene Clement
- **D.** Louis Malle

1142. This *Straw Dogs* helmer started as a dialogue director on Don Siegel's *Riot in Cell Block 11*.
- **A.** Abraham Polonsky
- **B.** Arthur Penn
- **C.** Sam Peckinpah
- **D.** Sydney Pollack

1143. Who directed *Andy Warhol's Dracula* and *Andy Warhol's Frankenstein*?
- **A.** Paul Morrissey
- **B.** Andy Warhol
- **C.** A. C. Stephen
- **D.** Chris Watson

1144. Valerie Breiman's *Love & Sex* is about her relationship with which other filmmaker?
- **A.** Jon Favreau
- **B.** Adam Rifkin
- **C.** Richard Linklater
- **D.** Quentin Tarantino

1145. This person started working as a child actor in 1908, and later worked frequently as an assistant director on films directed by Josef von Sternberg. He eventually became a director, making such films as *The Sons of Katie Elder* and *Kiss of Death*.
   A. Howard Hawks
   B. William Wyler
   C. Henry Hathaway
   D. Stanley Kramer

1146. Who directed *In the Heat of the Night*?
   A. Sydney Poitier
   B. Stanley Kramer
   C. Otto Preminger
   D. Norman Jewison

1147. Which of these films was directed by actor Kevin Spacey?
   A. *Pay It Forward*
   B. *Beyond the Sea*
   C. *The Big Kahuna*
   D. *Swimming with Sharks*

1148. What was Alfred Hitchcock's first film?
   A. *The Mountain Eagle*
   B. *The Ring*
   C. *The Pleasure Garden*
   D. *The Lodger*

1149.

1150. Which of these films was *not* directed by Stanley Kubrick?
   A. *Eyes Wide Shut*
   B. *Spartacus*
   C. *A Clockwork Orange*
   D. *A.I.*

1151. Which of these films was *not* directed or codirected by Gene Kelly?
   A. *Singin' in the Rain*
   B. *Gigot*
   C. *An American in Paris*
   D. *Hello Dolly*

1152. This filmmaker made *ABBA: The Movie* before making a name for himself with such films as *The Cider House Rules* and *Chocolat*.
   A. Thomas Vinterberg
   B. Lars von Trier
   C. Anders Thomas Jensen
   D. Lasse Hallstrom

1153. Which of these films was directed by actor Steve Buscemi?
   A. *Albino Alligator*
   B. *Animal Factory*
   C. *American Buffalo*
   D. *Boondock Saints*

1149.

Cineast Peter Bogdanovich worked as a film writer for *Esquire* and as a movie programmer for New York's Museum of Modern Art before becoming a filmmaker. Through his work for *Esquire*, Bogdanovich established friendships with several legendary filmmakers, who would serve as mentors. These included Orson Welles, Howard Hawks, and John Ford.

In 1971, Bogdanovich directed his first mainstream film, *The Last Picture Show*. The film, starring Cybil Shepherd, Ben Johnson, and Cloris Leachman, received eight Academy Award nominations, including Best Director.

Bogdanovich has since directed such films as *What's Up, Doc?*, *Paper Moon*, *Nickelodeon*, and *The Cat's Meow*. In addition, he has written several highly respected volumes on cinema, including *This Is Orson Welles*, which he co-wrote with Welles.

Bogdanovich had a recurring role on a popular television series that aired from 1999 to 2007. What is this series?

   A. *The Sopranos*
   B. *Law and Order*
   C. *E.R.*
   D. *The West Wing*

1154. Which of these Bob Rafelson–directed films stars the music group the Monkees?

- **A.** *Stay Hungry*
- **B.** *Five Easy Pieces*
- **C.** *Head*
- **D.** *The King of Marvin Gardens*

1155. All of these Sydney Pollack films feature Sydney Pollack as an actor except one. Which one?

- **A.** *Tootsie*
- **B.** *Out of Africa*
- **C.** *Random Hearts*
- **D.** *The Interpreter*

1156. This man worked as a standup comic and also wrote for *The Carol Burnett Show* before directing *...And Justice for All* and *Rain Man*.

- **A.** Bob Fosse
- **B.** Joel Schumacher
- **C.** Barry Levinson
- **D.** Ulu Grosbard

1157. In how many films has Woody Allen directed Diane Wiest?

- **A.** Two
- **B.** Four
- **C.** Seven
- **D.** Five

1158. Which of these films was *not* directed by Philip Kaufman?

- **A.** *The Right Stuff*
- **B.** *The Outlaw Josey Wales*
- **C.** *Quills*
- **D.** *Rising Sun*

1159. Who directed the original 1974 version of *The Texas Chainsaw Massacre*?

- **A.** Wes Craven
- **B.** Steve Miner
- **C.** Tobe Hooper
- **D.** Stuart Rosenberg

1160. Which of the following Stanley Kramer films does *not* feature Spencer Tracy?

- **A.** *Judgment at Nuremberg*
- **B.** *Guess Who's Coming to Dinner*
- **C.** *It's a Mad, Mad, Mad, Mad World*
- **D.** *Ship of Fools*

1161. Monte Hellman directed Warren Oates in four films. Which of these is *not* one of them?

- **A.** *Bring Me the Head of Alfredo Garcia*
- **B.** *Four Lane Blacktop*
- **C.** *China 9, Liberty 37*
- **D.** *The Shooting*

1162. Which of these is a film directed by actor Peter Fonda?

- **A.** *The Wild Angels*
- **B.** *The Hired Hand*
- **C.** *Fighting Mad*
- **D.** *92 in the Shade*

1163. Who directed the great German war film *Das Boot*?

A. Uwe Boll

B. Werner Herzog

C. Wim Wenders

D. Wolfgang Petersen

1164. What is the name of the 1996 documentary with which Al Pacino made his directorial debut?

A. *Shakespeare in the Park*

B. *Screaming in Every Movie*

C. *Looking for Richard*

D. *The Performance*

1165.

1166. What director made the embarrassingly bad homophobic film *Cruising*?

A. William Friedkin

B. Roman Polanski

C. Jerry Schatzberg

D. Floyd Mutrux

1167. In which of these films does Oliver Stone make a cameo as a bum?

A. *Platoon*

B. *The Hand*

C. *U-Turn*

D. *Seizure*

1168. What filmmaker has directed William H. Macy in six films including *Spartan* and *Oleanna*?

A. Fred Schepisi

B. The Coen Brothers

C. David Mamet

D. Neil LaBute

1169. Which of the following is *not* a film directed by Sean Penn?

A. *The Assassination of Richard Nixon*

B. *The Pledge*

C. *The Crossing Guard*

D. *The Indian Runner*

1170. With what film did Tim Robbins make his directorial debut?

A. *The Player*

B. *Cradle Will Rock*

C. *Dead Man Walking*

D. *Bob Roberts*

1171. Which of these filmmakers has *not* directed a version of William Shakespeare's *Othello*?

A. Orson Welles

B. Tim Blake Nelson

C. Kenneth Branagh

D. Tony Richardson

1165.

Martin Scorsese considered being a priest, but instead opted to study film at New York University. After crafting several short films, he directed his first feature, *Who's That Knocking at My Door*, with actor Harvey Keitel. Scorsese was then hired by Roger Corman to direct the crime drama *Boxcar Bertha*. In 1973, Scorsese directed the classic film *Mean Streets*, which marked his first film with frequent collaborator Robert De Niro. The following year, Scorsese directed Ellen Burstyn in an Oscar-winning role in *Alice Doesn't Live Here Anymore*.

In 1976, Scorsese directed his first masterpiece, *Taxi Driver*. This gritty, iconic drama established him as a creative force to be reckoned with.

Subsequent Scorsese gems include *Raging Bull*, *The Color of Money*, *The Last Temptation of Christ*, *Goodfellas*, *Cape Fear*, *The Age of Innocence*, *Casino*, *Kundun*, *Gangs of New York*, *The Aviator*, and *The Departed*. Few filmmakers of the past thirty years, if any, have matched Scorsese's consistency in terms of artistic achievement.

In how many films has Scorsese directed actor Robert De Niro?

A. Four

B. Six

C. Ten

D. Eight

1172. What was the last film George Stevens directed before his death?

- **A.** *The Greatest Story Ever Told*
- **B.** *The Only Game in Town*
- **C.** *The Diary of Anne Frank*
- **D.** *Something to Live For*

1173. Which of these films was directed by legendary funnyman Richard Pryor?

- **A.** *Jo Jo Dancer, Your Life Is Calling*
- **B.** *Which Way Is Up?*
- **C.** *Wholly Moses!*
- **D.** *Bustin' Loose*

1174. What filmmaker served as an assistant director on Chaplin's *Limelight* before directing films like *Kiss Me Deadly*?

- **A.** Don Siegel
- **B.** Charles Lamont
- **C.** Robert Aldrich
- **D.** King Vidor

1175. Who directed John Wayne in *Sands of Iwo Jima*?

- **A.** Melville Shavelson
- **B.** Raoul Walsh
- **C.** Howard Hawks
- **D.** Allan Dwan

1176. Who directed the films *Alien*, *Blade Runner*, and *Gladiator*?

- **A.** Ridley Scott
- **B.** Tony Scott
- **C.** Ron Howard
- **D.** Oliver Stone

1177. What was the final film directed by the late great Japanese auteur Akira Kurosawa?

- **A.** *Ran*
- **B.** *Rhapsody in August*
- **C.** *Madadayo*
- **D.** *Yume*

1178. Which of these filmmakers was *not* the subject of an entire volume written by director Peter Bogdanovich?

- **A.** Orson Welles
- **B.** Otto Preminger
- **C.** John Ford
- **D.** Allan Dwan

1179. Which director made the transition from crafting Porky Pig cartoons to directing films like *Will Success Spoil Rock Hunter*?

- **A.** Chuck Jones
- **B.** Joseph Barbara
- **C.** Walt Disney
- **D.** Frank Tashlin

1180. What filmmaker enraged *Batman* fans with his not-so-popular 1997 film *Batman & Robin*?

A. Joel Schumacher

B. Tim Burton

C. Christopher Nolan

D. Bruce Wayne

1181.

1182. He directed the documentaries *35 Up* and *49 Up* before becoming the president of the Directors Guild of America.

A. Stephen Herek

B. Wayne Wang

C. Ken Burns

D. Michael Apted

1183. The director of the film *Detour* was later blacklisted after having an affair with the wife of a Universal Studios mogul. Who was this?

A. Abraham Polonsky

B. Edgar G. Ulmer

C. Fritz Lang

D. Laszlo Benedek

1184. Which of these is *not* a film codirected by Quentin Tarantino and Robert Rodriguez?

A. *From Dusk Till Dawn*

B. *Grindhouse*

C. *Four Rooms*

D. *Sin City*

1185. Which of these was Hong Kong action auteur John Woo's first American film?

A. *Bullet in the Head*

B. *Hard-Boiled*

C. *Broken Arrow*

D. *Hard Target*

1186. Which of these filmmakers directed the most films starring legendary actor John Wayne?

A. Raoul Walsh

B. John Ford

C. Howard Hawks

D. Andrew V. McLaglen

1187. This filmmaker was hired to shoot *Superman* and *Superman II* back-to-back, but was then replaced on the second film after a dispute with the producers.

A. Richard Lester

B. Sidney J. Furie

C. Richard Donner

D. Bryan Singer

1188. This filmmaker produced *Alien* and directed such films as *The Warriors*, *48 Hours*, and *Brewster's Millions*.

A. Sidney Lumet

B. Phil Joanou

C. David Mamet

D. Walter Hill

1181.

George Lucas attended the University of Southern California in the late 1960s. There he made many short films, including an early version of *THX 1138*, for which he won top honors at the 1967-68 National Student Film Festival. Lucas then expanded the film, which ultimately became his first feature.

In 1973 Lucas directed *American Graffiti*, an acclaimed film about one seminal night in the lives of several California teenagers. It wasn't until his 1977 film, *Star Wars*, however, that Lucas truly became a star. The sci-fi western, influenced heavily by Akira Kurosawa's *The Hidden Fortress*, became one of the biggest moneymakers in history. The film has since spawned five successful sequels and prequels. *Forbes* has estimated that Lucas himself has earned an inconceivable $20 billion from the franchise.

Lucas's other achievements include co-writing and producing the *Indiana Jones* films, establishing Industrial Light & Magic (ILM), and creating the revolutionary high-fidelity sound system known as THX.

In 2005, Lucas was named to the Discovery Channel's list of the all-time greatest Americans. At what number was he listed?

A. 7

B. 23

C. 100

D. 76

1189. Otto Preminger voiced a character in 1977's *The Hobbit*. What is the name of the character?

  A. Gollum   **C.** Gandalf

  B. Bilbo Baggins   **D.** Elvenking

1190. Eddie Murphy has only directed one film. Which of the following is it?

  A. *Showtime*   **C.** *Metro*

  B. *Harlem Nights*   **D.** *Life*

1191. What James Bond helmer was arrested for allegedly attempting to prostitute himself—while dressed as a woman—to an undercover police officer?

  A. Roger Spottiswoode   **C.** Martin Campbell

  B. John Glen   **D.** Lee Tamahori

1192. This filmmaker directed the cult favorite *Death Race 2000* and *Eating Raoul*.

  A. Roger Corman   **C.** Paul Bartel

  B. Buck Henry   **D.** Joe Dante

1193. *Scent of a Woman* is considered this filmmaker's best film; *Gigli* his worst.

  A. Paul Haggis   **C.** Edward Zwick

  B. Tony Scott   **D.** Martin Brest

1194. Which of these directors does *not* appear as an actor in Orson Welles's unfinished masterwork *The Other Side of the Wind*?

  A. François Truffaut   **C.** Claude Chabrol

  B. John Huston   **D.** Dennis Hopper

1195. This director's films include *Proof of Life* and *Ray*.

  A. Simon Wincer   **C.** Ridley Scott

  B. John Badham   **D.** Taylor Hackford

1196. Which of these films was directed by screen legend Gary Cooper?

  A. *Along Came Jones*   **C.** *Blowing Wild*

  B. None of these   **D.** *Casanova Brown*

1197. Accomplished director John Huston received many accolades for his acting performance in *Chinatown*. What is the name of the character he played?

A. Miles Adams

B. Ned Turner

C. Filmore Henry

D. Noah Cross

1198. Which of these directors has *not* helmed a John Steinbeck adaptation?

A. Howard Hawks

B. Lewis Milestone

C. John Ford

D. Elia Kazan

1199. Martin Scorsese appears in one film directed by Akira Kurosawa. What is the name of this film?

A. *Kagemusha*

B. *Ran*

C. *Dreams*

D. *Rhapsody in August*

1200.

1201. Who directed *Hell in the Pacific* and *Deliverance*?

A. John Boorman

B. Don Siegel

C. Richard Brooks

D. Buzz Kulik

1202. Who directed the *2001: A Space Odyssey* sequel, *2010*?

A. Stanley Kubrick

B. Curtis Harrington

C. Ronald Neame

D. Peter Hyams

1203. Which of these titles is *not* a part of François Truffaut's series of films about the life of a character named Antoine Doinel?

A. *The 400 Blows*

B. *Day for Night*

C. *Stolen Kisses*

D. *Love on the Run*

1204. Who directed the films *Scanners* and *A History of Violence*?

A. Paul Schrader

B. David Lynch

C. Tim Burton

D. David Cronenberg

1205. Which of these cities is the birthplace of Terry Gilliam?

A. Minneapolis, Minnesota

B. London, England

C. Toronto, Canada

D. Liverpool, England

1200.

After studying acting at New York's American Academy of Dramatic Arts, Robert Redford made appearances on a handful of television series, including *Dr. Kildare* and *The Twilight Zone*. He started acting in film in 1962, but did not become a bona fide star until his 1969 turn in *Butch Cassidy and the Sundance Kid*. With a career including such triumphs as *The Way We Were*, *The Sting*, *Three Days of the Condor*, and *All the President's Men*, Redford has made many lists of the all-time greatest actors.

In 1980, Redford established the Sundance Institute, designed to assist aspiring filmmakers. That same year he made his own directorial debut with *Ordinary People*, for which he won the Oscar for Best Director. He later received great acclaim for *A River Runs Through It*, starring Brad Pitt. In 1994, Redford solidified his status as one of the industry's most talented directors with *Quiz Show*. The film received four Oscar nominations, including Best Picture and Best Director.

On which of these 1960s television series did Redford *not* appear as an actor?

A. *Twilight Zone*

B. *Alfred Hitchcock Presents*

C. *Gunsmoke*

D. *Perry Mason*

1206. What was the budget for Robert Rodriguez's directorial debut *El Mariachi*?

A. $2,500

B. $7,000

C. $9,000

D. $12,000

1207. Complete this statement by director John Sayles: "Most of what I learned about style, I learned from . . ."

A. Roberto Clemente

B. Muhammad Ali

C. Charles Chaplin

D. Orson Welles

1208. In which of these films did Michael Schultz *not* direct Richard Pryor?

A. *Car Wash*

B. *Greased Lightning*

C. *Cooley High*

D. *Which Way Is Up?*

1209. Which of these Nora Ephron–penned screenplays did Mike Nichols direct?

A. *Hanging Up*

B. *Mixed Nuts*

C. *This Is My Life*

D. *Heartburn*

1210. Brian DePalma directed his first film while still an undergraduate at Columbia University. What is this film?

A. *Greetings*

B. *Imitating Hitchcock*

C. *The Wedding Party*

D. *Hi, Mom!*

1211. Who directed the 1927 silent masterpiece *Napoleon*?

A. Abel Gance

B. D.W. Griffith

C. Sergei Eisenstein

D. F.W. Murnau

1212. He produced *To Kill a Mockingbird* and later directed *All the President's Men*. Who is this?

A. Stanley Kramer

B. George Axelrod

C. Robert Mulligan

D. Alan J. Pakula

1213. He was the lead in *Christine* before directing films like *The Chocolate War* and *Mother Night*.

A. Keith Gordon

B. Mark Romanek

C. John Stockwell

D. Ethan Hawke

1214. This Clint Eastwood protégé directed *The Deer Hunter* and *Heaven's Gate*.

A. John Milius

B. Hal Ashby

C. Michael Cimino

D. Sondra Locke

1215. Which of these films was *not* directed by Paul Verhoeven?

- **A.** *Showgirls*
- **B.** *The Running Man*
- **C.** *Starship Troopers*
- **D.** *Hollow Man*

1216. Which of these John Landis–directed films features cameos by directors Costa-Gavras and Robert Wise?

- **A.** *Spies Like Us*
- **B.** *Kentucky Fried Movie*
- **C.** *Animal House*
- **D.** *The Stupids*

1217. Which of David Lynch's films was originally filmed as a television pilot, but then revived with newly shot scenes and expanded into a feature film?

- **A.** *Lost Highway*
- **B.** *Twin Peaks: Fire Walk with Me*
- **C.** *Mulholland Dr.*
- **D.** *The Straight Story*

1218. Which of these Francis Ford Coppola films does *not* feature daughter Sofia Coppola as an actress?

- **A.** *The Godfather Part II*
- **B.** *Jack*
- **C.** *Rumble Fish*
- **D.** *The Cotton Club*

1219. Which of these filmmakers did *not* direct a segment for *Twilight Zone: The Movie*?

- **A.** Ridley Scott
- **B.** George Miller
- **C.** Joe Dante
- **D.** Steven Spielberg

1220. For which of these films did Stephen Frears receive a Best Director Oscar nomination?

- **A.** *Dirty Pretty Things*
- **B.** *Dangerous Liaisons*
- **C.** *Mrs. Henderson Presents*
- **D.** *The Grifters*

1221. Who directed the films *Women in Love*, *Altered States*, and *Tommy*?

- **A.** Robert Altman
- **B.** Nicolas Roeg
- **C.** Ken Russell
- **D.** Julien Temple

1222. James Cameron was discovered while working on *Battle Beyond the Stars*. What was his job on that picture?

- **A.** Miniature set builder
- **B.** Gaffer
- **C.** Craft services
- **D.** Production assistant

1228.

Francis Ford Coppola got his start in Hollywood directing the 1963 "B" horror movie *Dementia 13* for American International Pictures under producer Roger Corman. In 1968, Coppola directed Petula Clark and Fred Astaire in the musical *Finian's Rainbow*. His first Oscar, for the *Patton* screenplay, came in 1971.

The following year, Coppola directed his first masterpiece, *The Godfather*. The film received eleven Oscar nominations, including nods for Coppola's screenplay and direction. (He won for the screenplay.) This was the first of four classic films Coppola directed in the 1970s. The other three masterworks were *The Godfather Part II* (the first truly respected sequel), *The Conversation*, and *Apocalypse Now*. All four of these films were nominated for Best Picture.

Subsequent directorial efforts include *The Cotton Club*, *The Godfather Part III*, and *Bram Stoker's Dracula*. Coppola also remains busy as a producer, working on such standout films as *American Graffiti*, *Lost in Translation*, and *The Good Shepherd*.

Coppola's father was a musician who scored many of his greatest films. What was his name?

A. Alan Coppola
B. Roman Coppola
C. Giancarlo Coppola
D. Carmine Coppola

1223. Brother-sister directors Garry and Penny Marshall played husband and wife in which movie?
  A. *Orange County*
  B. *Runaway Bride*
  C. *Beaches*
  D. *Hocus Pocus*

1224. Which of these Phillip Noyce films tells a story that had been filmed previously by Orson Welles, but never released?
  A. *The Bone Collector*
  B. *Dead Calm*
  C. *Patriot Games*
  D. *The Quiet American*

1225. In which of these films did Steven Soderbergh *not* direct actor Don Cheadle?
  A. *Ocean's Eleven*
  B. *Traffic*
  C. *Solaris*
  D. *Out of Sight*

1226. Which of these films was directed by Keenan Ivory Wayans?
  A. *Blankman*
  B. *A Low Down Dirty Shame*
  C. *Hollywood Shuffle*
  D. *Most Wanted*

1227. In which of these films did Vincente Minelli *not* direct Gene Kelly?
  A. *Brigadoon*
  B. *An American in Paris*
  C. *The Pirate*
  D. *The Devil Makes Three*

1228.

1229. All of these filmmakers, except one, co-directed the anthology film *New York Stories*. Which one did *not*?
  A. Woody Allen
  B. Paul Schrader
  C. Francis Ford Coppola
  D. Martin Scorsese

1230. Who directed the Kansas scenes for *The Wizard of Oz*?
  A. King Vidor
  B. Mervyn LeRoy
  C. Richard Thorpe
  D. Victor Fleming

1231. What filmmaker portrayed John Wilkes Booth in *The Birth of a Nation*?
  A. D.W. Griffith
  B. Howard Hawks
  C. Fred Niblo
  D. Raoul Walsh

1232. What is the title of the 1933 film whose negatives were allegedly destroyed by Charles Chaplin?

- **A.** *The Floorwalker*
- **B.** *Return of the Tramp*
- **C.** *The Sea Gull*
- **D.** *Gypsy Life*

1233. Which of these war films was *not* directed by Samuel Fuller?

- **A.** *The Big Red One*
- **B.** *Battleground*
- **C.** *Fixed Bayonets!*
- **D.** *Merrill's Marauders*

1234. Which United States president presented John Ford with the Medal of Freedom?

- **A.** Richard Nixon
- **B.** Dwight Eisenhower
- **C.** Franklin Roosevelt
- **D.** Gerald Ford

1235. How many features did Stanley Kubrick direct in his lifetime?

- **A.** Seven
- **B.** Twenty
- **C.** Seventeen
- **D.** Thirteen

1236. In which of these films did Billy Wilder appear as an actor?

- **A.** *The Apartment*
- **B.** *What Women Dream*
- **C.** *Hell of a Reporter*
- **D.** *Ocean's Eleven*

1237. Which of these films was directed by actor Ethan Hawke?

- **A.** *Chelsea Walls*
- **B.** *Reality Bites*
- **C.** *The Jimmy Show*
- **D.** *The Newton Boys*

1238. What actor directed *The Greatest Game Ever Played*?

- **A.** Kurt Russell
- **B.** Bill Paxton
- **C.** Billy Bob Thornton
- **D.** William Sadler

1239. What is the only feature film directed by rapper and actor Ice Cube?

- **A.** *Friday*
- **B.** *Barbershop*
- **C.** *I Got the Hook Up*
- **D.** *The Players Club*

1240. Which of these Michael Curtiz–directed films feature Curtiz as an actor?

- **A.** He appeared in all of his movies
- **B.** *The Comancheros*
- **C.** He never appeared in any of his movies
- **D.** *Yankee Doodle Dandy*

1244.

Roger Corman studied engineering before breaking into the film industry, first as a messenger and later as a producer. Corman became a director for American International Pictures in 1955, directing four low-budget features and co-directing a fifth. This began a prolific directorial career that includes more than fifty features. He is most frequently remembered as a director for a series of lush Edgar Allan Poe adaptations he made. Corman directed other films, including *Machine Gun Kelly*, *The Little Shop of Horrors*, *Bucket of Blood*, *The St. Valentine's Day Massacre*, and *Bloody Mama*.

Corman has also produced nearly four hundred features and discovered many extraordinarily talented filmmakers and actors, including Francis Ford Coppola, Martin Scorsese, Jack Nicholson, Monte Hellman, Peter Bogdanovich, Jonathan Demme, James Cameron, Ron Howard, and Joe Dante.

Corman took a long hiatus from directing after 1971's *The Red Baron*. With what 1990 film did Corman return to the director's chair?

A. *To Die Standing*
B. *Schweitzer*
C. *Frankenstein Unbound*
D. *Play Murder for Me*

1241. What is the name of the character director Kevin Smith plays in several of his films, including *Clerks* and *Chasing Amy*?
A. Randal
B. Silent Bob
C. Jay
D. Dante

1242. Which of these Michael Winner-helmed films does *not* star Charles Bronson?
A. *Lawman*
B. *Chato's Land*
C. *The Mechanic*
D. *Death Wish*

1243. This filmmaker directed thirteen actors in Oscar-nominated performances. His directorial credits include *The Long, Hot Summer*, *Hud*, and *Norma Rae*.
A. None of these
B. Mike Nichols
C. Bob Rafelson
D. Martin Ritt

1244.

1245. Jodie Foster was a celebrated actress before she stepped behind the camera. With what film did Foster make her directorial debut?
A. *Home for the Holidays*
B. *Little Man Tate*
C. *Nell*
D. *Panic Room*

1246. What animator is sometimes referred to as the "Walt Disney of Japan"?
A. Hayao Miyazaki
B. Yoshifumi Kondo
C. Isao Takahata
D. Hiroyuki Morita

1247. *Dangerous Game*, directed by Abel Ferrara, depicts the making of a film. What actor plays the film's director, Eddie Israel?
A. Christopher Walken
B. Harvey Keitel
C. David Caruso
D. Vincent Gallo

1248. Which of these films was *not* directed by horror maven John Carpenter?
A. *Elvis*
B. *Starman*
C. *The Thing*
D. *The Eyes of Laura Mars*

1249. Which of these adaptations from the work of playwright Neil Simon was *not* directed by the late Herbert Ross?
A. *I Ought to Be in Pictures*
B. *Seems Like Old Times*
C. *The Goodbye Girl*
D. *The Sunshine Boys*

1250. Alfred Hitchcock directed more than fifty feature films in his long and glorious career. What was his final directorial effort?
A. *Frenzy*
B. *Topaz Plot*
C. *Family Plot*
D. *Torn Curtain*

CHAPTER SIX:

NAME THAT FILM

1251. Robert Redford plays a CIA researcher who discovers a deadly secret in which film?
A. *Sneakers*
B. *3 Days of the Condor*
C. *The Hot Rock*
D. *Brubaker*

1252. This 1942 musical stars Fred Astaire and Bing Crosby and is best known for the song "White Christmas."
A. *White Christmas*
B. *Holiday Inn*
C. *High Society*
D. *Bells Are Ringing*

1253. Katharine Hepburn and Spencer Tracy are husband-and-wife lawyers on opposing sides in this film.
A. *Adam's Rib*
B. *Pat and Mike*
C. *Desk Set*
D. *State of the Union*

1254. George Lazenby walked a proverbial mile in Sean Connery's shoes in this, his one and only James Bond film.
A. *Thunderball*
B. *From Russia with Love*
C. *On Her Majesty's Secret Service*
D. *Casino Royale*

1255. Bill Murray is a weatherman forced to relive the same day over and over in this comedic romp.
A. *Stripes*
B. *Where the Buffalo Roam*
C. *Groundhog Day*
D. *Same Time Tomorrow*

1256. In this offbeat comedy, a health food restaurant owner is cryogenically frozen.
A. *Forever Young*
B. *While You Were Sleeping*
C. *Sleeper*
D. *Cryo*

1257. John Garfield assists Lana Turner in killing her hubby in this 1946 James M. Cain adaptation.
A. *Strangers on a Train*
B. *Detour*
C. *The Postman Always Rings Twice*
D. *The Big Heat*

OPPOSITE John Travolta and Karen Lynn Gorney in
Saturday Night Fever, 1977

1258. This Marx Brothers farce takes place in the mythical land of Freedonia.
- **A.** *A Night at the Opera*
- **B.** *Duck Soup*
- **C.** *Animal Crackers*
- **D.** *A Day at the Races*

1259. Two male musicians dress up like women to "skirt" the mob in this gender-bending comedy.
- **A.** *Some Like It Hot*
- **B.** *Riff Raff*
- **C.** *Lost In America*
- **D.** *Tootsie*

1260. This movie about the birth of hip-hop stars local Queens artists Run-DMC with the Fat Boys and Sheila E.
- **A.** *Wild Style*
- **B.** *Krush Groove*
- **C.** *Tougher Than Leather*
- **D.** *Disorderlies*

1261.

1262. Brother and sister Ray Milland and Ruth Hussey have some "grave" concerns about their new haunted mansion in this horror flick.
- **A.** *The Haunting*
- **B.** *The Uninvited*
- **C.** *House on Haunted Hill*
- **D.** *Black Sunday*

1263. James Stewart plays a gunless lawman in this classic western directed by Anthony Mann.
- **A.** *The Naked Spur*
- **B.** *Winchester '73*
- **C.** *The Man from Laramie*
- **D.** *Destry Rides Again*

1264. Pretty boy Warren Beatty plays a gambler in this Robert Altman-helmed western.
- **A.** *The Only Game in Town*
- **B.** *All Fall Down*
- **C.** *McCabe & Mrs. Miller*
- **D.** *The Fortune*

1265. In this 1936 oddity, Katharine Hepburn disguises herself as a boy.
- **A.** *Alice Adams*
- **B.** *A Woman Rebels*
- **C.** *Sylvia Scarlett*
- **D.** *Quality Street*

1261.

This 1959 film directed by François Truffaut was the first of five films to revolve around recurring character Antoine Doinel (played by Jean-Pierre Leaud). In this film, one of the watershed entries of the French New Wave movement, young Antoine continually gets into trouble. He is eventually sent to a work camp for stealing a typewriter from his stepfather's workplace.

Truffaut's classic character study was met with great critical acclaim. The film received award nominations around the world. Truffaut won Best Director honors at Cannes, and the film was nominated for the prestigious Palme d'Or Award. In addition, Truffaut received a Best Original Screenplay nod at the Academy Awards.

Through the years Truffaut's coming-of-age story has influenced many filmmakers, and was reportedly the inspiration for Miramax founders Bob and Harvey Weinstein's entrance into the film industry.

What is the title of this film?

- **A.** *Bed and Board*
- **B.** *Antoine and Colette*
- **C.** *The 400 Blows*
- **D.** *Stolen Kisses*

1266. An uppity church organist dies in an automobile accident, but doesn't know she's dead in this film.

  A. *Near Dark*
  B. *I Woke Up Early the Morning I Died*
  C. *Carnival of Souls*
  D. *Suspiria*

1267. A mentally unbalanced judge is institutionalized after becoming convinced he is Sherlock Holmes. What is the name of this film?

  A. *Trouble In Mind*
  B. *They Might Be Giants*
  C. *Nuts*
  D. *The Gods Must Be Crazy*

1268. Clint Eastwood directed this biopic about the life of late great sax man Charlie Parker.

  A. *All That Jazz*
  B. *Mo' Better Blues*
  C. *Bird*
  D. *King of Jazz*

1269. George Segal plays the unlikely father of Denzel Washington in this silly 1981 comedy directed by Michael Shultz.

  A. *Dad*
  B. *Critical Condition*
  C. *Carbon Copy*
  D. *Black Like Me*

1270. A band of National Guardsmen is systematically hunted down by ragin' Cajuns in this 1981 thriller.

  A. *Deliverance*
  B. *Southern Comfort*
  C. *Death at Dawn*
  D. *The Warriors*

1271. Jack Nicholson is a concert pianist turned oil rig laborer in this 1970 Bob Rafelson drama.

  A. *Five Easy Pieces*
  B. *A Safe Place*
  C. *Studs Lonigan*
  D. *Carnal Knowledge*

1272. Steve Martin hopes to nose out the competition and win the love of Daryl Hannah in this 1987 comedy.

  A. *Pennies from Heaven*
  B. *Roxanne*
  C. *The Lonely Guy*
  D. *L.A. Story*

1273. Emma Thompson tosses and turns with nightmares about a murder committed before she was born in this film.

  A. *Blood Simple*
  B. *Dead Ringers*
  C. *Dead Again*
  D. *Jacob's Ladder*

1274. John Wayne, Dean Martin, and Ricky Nelson star in this Howard Hawks-helmed jailhouse siege film.

A. The Sons of Katie Elder
B. Rio Bravo
C. Rio Grande
D. El Dorado

1275. Jack Benny and Carole Lombard are Polish actors attempting to outsmart the Gestapo in this 1942 comedy.

A. The Great Dictator
B. The General
C. To Be or Not to Be
D. Triumph of the Will

1276.

1277. Investigating cop Glenn Ford's wife is killed by a mob-planted car bomb intended for him in this 1953 Fritz Lang thriller.

A. Gun Crazy
B. Kiss Me Deadly
C. The Big Heat
D. The Lodger

1278. Woody Allen plays Fielding Mellish, a product tester who ultimately becomes a fascist dictator in this wacky comedy.

A. Play It Again, Sam
B. Bananas
C. Zelig
D. Everything You Always Wanted to Know About Being a Dictator But Were Afraid to Ask

1279. Craig T. Nelson's family is terrorized by the ghosts inhabiting their home in this flick.

A. The Changeling
B. Poltergeist
C. The Shining
D. The Amityville Horror

1280. Serial killer lovers Mickey and Mallory slay their way across the country in this shocking Oliver Stone film.

A. Natural Born Killers
B. True Romance
C. Love and a .45
D. Badlands

1281. This is the film in which Peter Finch announces that he's "mad as hell and not going to take this anymore" during a live news broadcast.

A. Broadcast News
B. The Last Broadcast
C. Network
D. Stay Tuned

1276.

This 1999 crime film, written and directed by Troy Duffy, tells the story of brothers Connor (Sean Patrick Flanery) and Murphy (Norman Reedus). The brothers are vigilantes who believe they are doing God's work by killing Mobsters and street thugs. Willem Dafoe makes a turn as a conflicted FBI agent hot on their trail.

After writer-director Troy Duffy was infamously awarded a deal to make this film at Miramax, he soon lost the deal when he disrespected studio chiefs Harvey and Bob Weinstein and acted irrationally on numerous occasions. (These events are depicted in the behind-the-scenes documentary *Overnight*.) As a result, Duffy was unable to find decent distribution for the project, and the film played in only five theaters. After its release on video and DVD, however, the film developed a massive following and is now considered a cult classic.

What is this film?

A. Suicide Kings
B. Memento
C. Requiem for a Dream
D. The Boondock Saints

1282. Ashton Kutcher and Bernie Mac star in this occasionally funny exploration of racial boundaries.

- **A.** Black and White
- **B.** Mixed Nuts
- **C.** Zebrahead
- **D.** Guess Who

1283. Federal agent Samuel L. Jackson finds himself pitted against coldblooded killers while escorting a witness overseas in this film.

- **A.** Freedomland
- **B.** Snakes on a Plane
- **C.** Kiss of Death
- **D.** Amos & Andrew

1284. A family gets lost and finds itself terrorized by half-crazed atomic bomb survivors in this horror movie.

- **A.** The Texas Chainsaw Massacre
- **B.** House of 1000 Corpses
- **C.** The Hills Have Eyes
- **D.** Wrong Turn

1285. Miami Vice star Don Johnson gets to display his acting talent in this strange apocalyptic Harlan Ellison adaptation.

- **A.** Death Race 2000
- **B.** The Road Warrior
- **C.** A Boy and His Dog
- **D.** The Postman

1286. John Travolta plays an angel who smells of cookie dough in this quirky, offbeat film costarring William Hurt and Andie MacDowell.

- **A.** Michael
- **B.** Who Knew There Were Scientologist Angels?
- **C.** City of Angels
- **D.** Phenomenon

1287. Humphrey Bogart appears as a broken-down seaman named Charlie Allnut in this endearing film.

- **A.** Passage to Marseilles
- **B.** The African Queen
- **C.** Dark Passage
- **D.** Key Largo

1288. A reporter hopes to find out exactly who a dead man was by uncovering the meaning of his dying words in this film.

- **A.** Sunset Boulevard
- **B.** Citizen Kane
- **C.** The Front Page
- **D.** Rebecca

1289. A dying rich man offers Chevy Chase an exorbitant amount of money to kill him in this attempt at comedy.

- **A.** Cops & Robbersons
- **B.** Modern Problems
- **C.** Fletch
- **D.** Man of the House

1290. In which of these films does a novelist on vacation in Vienna investigate the "death" of his old chum Harry Lime?

A. *Detour*

B. *The Third Man*

C. *A Night in Vienna*

D. *The Man Who Knew Too Much*

1291. Surveilance and bugging expert Harry Caul finds himself in hot water when he unknowingly stumbles across something he shouldn't have. Which film is this?

A. *Taps*

B. *I See You*

C. *The Conversation*

D. *Peeping Tom*

1292. Ben Gazzara plays an American pimp in Singapore in this flick.

A. *Trick Baby*

B. *Dollars and Sense*

C. *Saint Jack*

D. *The Mack*

1293.

1294. There's no horsing around in this film when a band of thieves that includes Elisha Cook, Jr. and Sterling Hayden pulls off a grand heist at a racetrack.

A. *The Taking of Pelham One Two Three*

B. *Straight Time*

C. *The Killing*

D. *A Day at the Races*

1295. In which film do bad guys Robert Ryan, Lee Marvin, and Ernest Borgnine try to thwart one-armed Spencer Tracy from discovering their town's dirty little secret?

A. *Our Town*

B. *Burn!*

C. *Bad Day at Black Rock*

D. *Riding Shotgun*

1296. Michael Moriarty stars in this whacked-out 1982 Larry Cohen film about a monster that wreaks havoc on an unsuspecting Manhattan.

A. *I, Monster*

B. *Q—The Winged Serpent*

C. *The Terror*

D. *Manhattan Melodrama*

1297. Hired guns Steve McQueen, Charles Bronson, and Yul Brynner defend a small Mexican village against a band of banditos in this John Sturges western.

A. *A Minute to Pray, A Second to Die*

B. *7 Men from Now*

C. *The Magnificent Seven*

D. *Ride the High Country*

1293.

This David Lean war film was adapted from a novel by French author Pierre Boulle. The film, which stars Alec Guinness, Sessue Hayakawa, and William Holden, tells the story of Allied prisoners in a Japanese prison camp in Burma during World War II. Stubborn British officer Colonel Nicholson (Guinness) makes the camp's commandant, Colonel Saito (Hayakawa), irate when he refuses to obey his commands. Eventually Nicholson not only agrees to obey Saito's instructions, but also orders his men to assist the Japanese in building the best railroad bridge possible. American Commander Shears (Holden) pulls off a daring escape, but is ultimately forced to lead a squad back to the camp to destroy the bridge.

The film was nominated for eight Oscars, and collected all but one. Among the statuettes it won were prizes for Best Picture, Best Director, and Best Adapted Screenplay. The film is ranked at number thirteen on the American Film Institute's list of the one hundred greatest American films.

What is this film?

A. *A Bridge Too Far*

B. *King Rat*

C. *The Bridge on the River Kwai*

D. *The Bridges at Toko-Ri*

1298. Dustin Hoffman is the sole surviving paleface at Custer's Last Stand in this Thomas Berger adaptation.

A. *Little Big Horn*

B. *Straw Dogs*

C. *Little Big Man*

D. *Custer's Last Ride*

1299. Tamara Dobson goes to war with Shelley Winters in this action-packed 1973 blaxploitation flick.

A. *Foxy Brown*

B. *Cleopatra Jones*

C. *Switchblade Sisters*

D. *Coffy*

1300. Nicolas Cage and Holly Hunter go shopping for a baby in this hilarious kidnapping comedy crafted by the Coen Brothers.

A. *Miller's Crossing*

B. *Baby's Day Out*

C. *Raising Arizona*

D. *Barton Fink*

1301. For this trippy psychedelic 1968 film, Bob Rafelson directed, Jack Nicholson cowrote the screenplay, and the not-quite-Fab Four rockers the Monkees star.

A. *Head*

B. *The Trip*

C. *Heart and Soul*

D. *Poodle Springs*

1302. This 1979 thriller about an incident at a nuclear power plant features Jane Fonda as an investigative reporter.

A. *The Andromeda Strain*

B. *The Stuff*

C. *The China Syndrome*

D. *Meltdown*

1303. Robert De Niro is a baseball-obsessed stalker who attempts to assist the San Francisco Giants by killing one of their players and helping their newest star, Wesley Snipes, get his favorite jersey number back.

A. *Game 6*

B. *The Fan*

C. *For Love of the Game*

D. *Fear Strikes Out*

1304. Ex-Nazi Laurence Olivier decides to practice dentistry without a license on Dustin Hoffman, the brother of a dead CIA agent, in this film.

A. *The Boys from Brazil*

B. *Straight Time*

C. *Marathon Man*

D. *The Conversation*

1305. An American is imprisoned in Turkey for attempting to smuggle hash back to the states in this grueling Oliver Stone-scripted prison flick.

A. *Return to Paradise*

B. *Midnight Express*

C. *Hash Train to Clarksville*

D. *Brokedown Palace*

1306. Warren Oates is a trigger-happy bank robber pursued by G-man Ben Johnson in this 1973 crime drama.

A. *Public Enemies*
B. *Dillinger*
C. *Melvin Purvis, G-Man*
D. *Pretty Boy Floyd*

1307. Samurai Toshiro Mifune and gunslinger Charles Bronson join forces in this East-meets-West action movie.

A. *El Cid*
B. *Red Sun*
C. *The Stranger and the Gunfighter*
D. *Six-String Samurai*

1308.

1309. In this film, a group of surviving humans sets up a base of operations in an underground missile silo in hopes of keeping safe from the zombies that have taken over the earth.

A. *Dawn of the Dead*
B. *Zombiegeddon*
C. *Day of the Dead*
D. *Zombie*

1310. Lee Marvin leads a squad of condemned military prisoners on a deadly World War II mission.

A. *Merrill's Marauders*
B. *The Guns of Navarone*
C. *The Devil's Brigade*
D. *The Dirty Dozen*

1311. Mafia chieftain Robert Loggia is bitten by a vampire. He then becomes a vampire himself, and immediately goes to work assembling a family of undead Mafiosi. What movie is this?

A. *Blood In, Blood Out*
B. *Bloodletting*
C. *Innocent Blood*
D. *Bloodthirsty*

1312. An eighteenth-century composer becomes obsessed with a rival composer in this film, and begins plotting his demise.

A. *Amadeus*
B. *The Pianist*
C. *Whom the Gods Love*
D. *The Piano*

1313. Schoolteacher Geena Davis overcomes amnesia and learns that she was an assassin in her previous life in this Shane Black-scripted action film.

A. *Kiss Kiss Bang Bang*
B. *Way of the Gun*
C. *The Long Kiss Goodnight*
D. *Revenge*

1308.

This 1997 film was Kevin Smith's third film as writer and director. It tells the story of successful comic book artist Holden McNeil (Ben Affleck) and his relationship with lesbian artist Alyssa Jones (Joey Lauren Adams). As the two become good friends, Holden finds himself falling in love with the one woman he cannot have. He then tells Alyssa how he feels, and convinces her to walk away from the lifestyle she's chosen so she can be with him. Confused, Alyssa attempts to (ahem) go straight. Her struggle to come to grips with her own sexual identity coupled with Holden's own jealous nature ultimately causes problems in this compelling character study.

This film won two prizes at the Independent Spirit Awards (Best Supporting Male for Jason Lee and Best Screenplay for Smith). The film also received a Golden Globe nomination, for Best Performance by an Actress in a Motion Picture—Comedy or Musical, for Adams' impressive turn.

Can you name this film?

A. *Love & Sex*
B. *Relax . . . It's Just Sex!*
C. *Jersey Girl*
D. *Chasing Amy*

1314. Con man James Woods teams up with professional fighter Louis Gossett, Jr. to hustle bad guy Bruce Dern in this film.

- **A.** *Dirty Dingus Magee*
- **B.** *The Squeeze*
- **C.** *Diggstown*
- **D.** *The Fix*

1315. In which film do Bill Cosby and Sidney Poitier travel to New Orleans hoping to rig a boxing match and winning a nice chunk of money for their lodge?

- **A.** *Hickey & Boggs*
- **B.** *A Piece of the Action*
- **C.** *Let's Do It Again*
- **D.** *Uptown Saturday Night*

1316. Glenn Close is a nurse who impregnates herself with the sperm of a dying patient, and later becomes a role model for women's liberation. Robin Williams plays her son in this film.

- **A.** *The Survivors*
- **B.** *The World According to Garp*
- **C.** *Skylark*
- **D.** *Maxie*

1317. Husband and wife Sam Neill and Nicole Kidman are alone on their yacht in the middle of the Pacific. But when they lend a helping hand to the stranded Billy Zane, trouble ensues. What is this film?

- **A.** *The Deep*
- **B.** *Dangerous Water*
- **C.** *Dead Calm*
- **D.** *Murder in the Pacific*

1318. When rock star Kris Kristofferson is busted for drugs, dirty cop Gene Hackman persuades the singer to sell pot for him in this film.

- **A.** *Me and Bobby McGee*
- **B.** *One Trick Pony*
- **C.** *Cisco Pike*
- **D.** *Night Moves*

1319. After his wife is murdered and his daughter raped, Charles Bronson takes the law into his own hands in this action flick.

- **A.** *Vigilante*
- **B.** *Death Hunt*
- **C.** *Death Wish*
- **D.** *Mr. Majestyk*

1320. In what movie does single dad Cary Grant hire Sophia Loren to clean his house and watch his three children?

- **A.** *The Pride and the Passion*
- **B.** *Kiss Them for Me*
- **C.** *Houseboat*
- **D.** *Dream Wife*

1321. Al Pacino is a good cop who exposes corruption within the New York City Police Department in this 1973 Sidney Lumet drama.

- **A.** *. . . And Justice for All*
- **B.** *One Good Cop*
- **C.** *Bobby Deerfield*
- **D.** *Serpico*

1322. Bounty hunter Robert De Niro must dodge mob bullets while transporting criminal Charles Grodin in this 1988 comedy.

A. *Jacknife*
B. *We're No Angels*
C. *Midnight Run*
D. *Born to Win*

1323. As Denzel Washington and Gene Hackman fight for control of a nuclear submarine, the fate of the world hangs in the balance in this drama.

A. *Crimson Tide*
B. *U-571*
C. *The Hunt for Red October*
D. *Das Boot*

1324. Steve McQueen is a wealthy businessman who masterminds an elaborate heist. Paul Burke and Faye Dunaway are the investigators attempting to trap him in which film?

A. *The Great St. Louis Bank Robbery*
B. *The Cincinnati Kid*
C. *The Thomas Crown Affair*
D. *The Getaway*

1325. A struggling female boxer convinces an aging trainer to show her the ropes—no pun intended—and he does. She later becomes injured and paralyzed, turning this film into a euthanasia debate.

A. *Girlfight*
B. *Million Dollar Baby*
C. *Right Cross*
D. *The Opponent*

1326.

1327. Clarence Darrow argues for a jury to spare the lives of murderers Nathan Leopold, Jr. and Richard Loeb in this classic courtroom drama.

A. *Inherit the Wind*
B. *12 Angry Men*
C. *Compulsion*
D. *Anatomy of a Murder*

1328. In this film, the crew of the USS *Enterprise* travels through time, searching for a humpback whale to reply to an alien probe.

A. *Star Trek: Generations*
B. *Star Trek IV: The Voyage Home*
C. *Star Trek: Insurrection*
D. *Star Trek II: The Wrath of Khan*

1329. Woody Allen and Diane Keaton attempt to assassinate Napoleon in this wacky comedy.

A. *The Purple Rose of Cairo*
B. *Interiors*
C. *Don't Drink the Water*
D. *Love and Death*

1330. A con man in the Midwest during the Depression takes on a nine-year-old-girl as his new partner.

A. *Nickelodeon*
B. *Targets*
C. *Paper Moon*
D. *They All Laughed*

1326.

Roberto Benigni wrote, directed, and stars in this 1997 Italian film about a Jewish man named Guido Orefice (Benigni). Guido finds the girl of his dreams, Dora (Nicoletta Braschi), convinces her to marry him, and they have a child together. For a while Guido lives a dream existence. When the Nazis arrive in Italy, however, things change. Guido and his young son Giosue are imprisoned in a concentration camp. Surrounded by death, doom, and despair, Guido shields Giosue from the realities of their situation, convincing him that they are in fact willing participants in a grand game.

Benigni's film was released to critical accolades. The film took home the Grand Prix trophy at Cannes and was named the Best Foreign Film at the César Awards. The film received seven Academy Award nominations, including Best Picture, Best Director, and Best Original Screenplay. It was awarded three Oscars, including Best Actor (Benigni) and Best Foreign Film.

What is the title of this film?

A. *Jakob the Liar*
B. *Life Is Beautiful*
C. *The Great Dictator*
D. *The Tiger and the Snow*

1331. Harrison Ford escapes the hustle and bustle of metropolitan life by moving with his wife and four children to a remote island in this film.

A. *Heroes*

B. *The Island*

C. *Cast Away*

D. *The Mosquito Coast*

1332. In this '80s classic, five very different high school students spend their Saturday together in detention, where they learn that they're more alike than they thought.

A. *Heathers*

B. *The Breakfast Club*

C. *Sixteen Candles*

D. *Some Kind of Wonderful*

1333. It is revealed that John Coffey, a nearly retarded death row inmate, has the ability to heal people in this heartwarming prison flick.

A. *American Me.*

B. *The Green Mile*

C. *The Shawshank Redemption*

D. *Dead Man Walking*

1334. A pair of career criminal siblings and the family they've abducted fight off vampires in a Mexican biker bar in this horror flick.

A. *Twins of Evil*

B. *Bloodrayne*

C. *From Dusk Till Dawn*

D. *Slayers*

1335. John Cassavetes and Sidney Poitier become friends while working together in a railroad yard in this 1957 drama.

A. *Crime in the Streets*

B. *No Way Out*

C. *Edge of the City*

D. *Pressure Point*

1336. Three soldiers return home after World War II and find difficulty adapting to civilian life in this William Wyler drama.

A. *The Children's Hour*

B. *From Here to Eternity*

C. *The Best Years of Our Lives*

D. *Friendly Persuasion*

1337. American Harrison Ford's wife Betty Buckley disappears without a trace in Paris in this 1988 Roman Polanski thriller.

A. *Frantic*

B. *Tess*

C. *Repulsion*

D. *The Streets of Paris*

1338. Hong Kong cop Jackie Chan teams up with motormouthed Los Angeles detective Chris Tucker in this lively action comedy.

A. *Rush Hour*

B. *Police Story*

C. *Double Impact*

D. *Big Trouble in Little China*

1339. A group of old college pals reunites for the funeral of their friend Alex, who killed himself. Together they ponder their pasts, futures, and Alex's reasoning for ending his own life.

A. *The Big Chill*

B. *Fandango*

C. *We Don't Live Here Anymore*

D. *That Championship Season*

1340. U.S. Army Captain Willard is given a top secret mission to locate a Green Beret colonel and terminate him with extreme prejudice.

A. *Platoon*

B. *Apocalypse Now*

C. *Hamburger Hill*

D. *Casualties of War*

1341.

1342. A former gangster is released from prison. He vows to live a crime-free life, but finds it exceedingly difficult to do so in this drama.

A. *This Thing of Ours*

B. *A Bronx Tale*

C. *Carlito's Way*

D. *Bluehill Avenue*

1343. In this film Anthony Hopkins reveals that he is . . . black.

A. *Proof*

B. *Shadowlands*

C. *August*

D. *The Human Stain*

1344. This musical was directed by Martin Scorsese and stars Robert De Niro and Liza Minnelli.

A. *Cabaret*

B. *Falling in Love*

C. *New York, New York*

D. *True Confessions*

1345. Samuel L. Jackson and Eugene Levy team up in this incredibly unfunny action comedy.

A. *Amos & Andrew*

B. *The Man*

C. *The Great White Hype*

D. *Loaded Weapon 1*

1346. The government recruits an extreme sports athlete to infiltrate a Russian crime ring in this action film.

A. *A Man Apart*

B. *xXx*

C. *The Fast and the Furious*

D. *Stealth*

1347. Bob Jones discovers that he has cancer. His wife is pregnant and he now fears that he may never live to see their baby. He prepares for his death by filming a series of messages to document his remaining days so his child will know who its father was. Which film is this?

A. *Marvin's Room*

B. *The Hours*

C. *My Life*

D. *Last Days*

1341.

This Stanley Kubrick–directed Stephen King adaptation tells the story of an out-of-work teacher and struggling writer named Jack Torrance (Jack Nicholson) who agrees to work as the winter caretaker of a hotel in the mountains of Colorado. He soon relocates his wife, Wendy (Shelley Duvall), and six-year-old son, Danny (Danny Lloyd), to the remote hotel. Jack hopes to complete a novel during his winter stay at the hotel, but instead finds himself involved in a series of events that are worthy of a novel themselves. Unfortunately for Jack, it's a horror novel.

The Overlook Hotel, it seems, is filled with all kinds of ghosts. Young Danny, who possesses some psychic abilities, senses that something is wrong, but there's nothing he can do to stop the horrific chain of events that have been put into motion. Soon Jack goes mad and attempts to murder his family.

This movie was released to lukewarm reception in 1980, but is generally viewed as a masterwork of the horror genre today.

Can you name this film?

A. *Ghost Story*

B. *The Changeling*

C. *The Amityville Horror*

D. *The Shining*

1348. In this film, an unseen omnipotent crime leader named Keyser Soze coerces five criminals to work for him. It later turns out that one of these men is actually Soze himself.

A. Kiss Kiss Bang Bang

B. The Usual Suspects

C. Things to Do in Denver When You're Dead

D. Way of the Gun

1349. Thieves Pierce Brosnan and Salma Hayek have just completed their last big score, and now they're retiring to a tropical island. The only problem is that FBI agent Woody Harrelson won't leave them alone. Which film is this?

A. The Thomas Crown Affair

B. After the Sunset

C. Laws of Attraction

D. Before Sunset

1350. A young boy has an unusual aging disorder which causes him to age four times as fast as a normal human being. Because of this, the fifth-grader looks like he's forty in this comedy.

A. Big

B. Billy Madison

C. Jack

D. 13 Going on 30

1351. A mother and son flee from a disastrous relationship with an abusive boyfriend to Seattle. Once there, the mother meets a new abusive boyfriend, played by Robert De Niro in this film.

A. Jacknife

B. A Bronx Tale

C. This Boy's Life

D. Falling in Love

1352. This film tells the comedic life story of a fictitious jazz guitarist named Emmet Ray.

A. Johnny Guitar

B. Sweet and Lowdown

C. Up at the Villa

D. Duke of Groove

1353. A college dropout lands a big-money job as a broker for an investment firm, but later concludes that he may be involved in an illegal operation in this drama.

A. Wall Street

B. The Prime Gig

C. Boiler Room

D. Glengarry Glen Ross

1354. This is the true story of George Jung, an entrepeneur who established the cocaine market in the United States in the 1970s.

A. Jung

B. The Salton Sea

C. Blow

D. Spun

1355. Convict James Cole volunteers to be sent back in time to gather information about a deadly virus that will kill billions of humans in the future. However, he's accidentally sent back too far and is institutionalized as a crazy man in this sci-fi drama.

- **A.** *The Jacket*
- **B.** *12 Monkeys*
- **C.** *Blade Runner*
- **D.** *The Andromeda Strain*

1356. In which film does a gangster return home for his brother's funeral, investigate his brother's death, then learn that it may not have been an accident?

- **A.** *Get Carter*
- **B.** *Point Blank*
- **C.** *Revenge*
- **D.** *Hard Boiled*

1357.

1358. An unfriendly and compulsive writer agrees to take care of his artist neighbor's dog when he is hospitalized in which of these films?

- **A.** *As Good As It Gets*
- **B.** *Pay It Forward*
- **C.** *Imaginary Heroes*
- **D.** *My Dog Skip*

1359. This movie stars Chuck Barris, host of TV's *The Gong Show*, doubling as a covert operative for the CIA.

- **A.** *No Place to Hide*
- **B.** *Safe Men*
- **C.** *Confessions of a Dangerous Mind*
- **D.** *Going All the Way*

1360. A Los Angeles detective sent to assist a murder investigation in Alaska accidentally shoots his partner while attempting to apprehend a suspect in this film.

- **A.** *Sea of Love*
- **B.** *Insomnia*
- **C.** *Bobby Deerfield*
- **D.** *Scarecrow*

1361. Actor Sam Street portrays author Truman Capote in this film.

- **A.** *Capote*
- **B.** *Isn't She Great*
- **C.** *The Hoax*
- **D.** *Infamous*

1362. Richard Gere stars in this courtroom thriller about a cocky lawyer who takes on the case of an altar boy accused of murdering a priest.

- **A.** *Final Analysis*
- **B.** *Primal Fear*
- **C.** *Intersection*
- **D.** *The Honorary Consul*

1357.

Hot off the success of the previous year's *The Last Picture Show*, Peter Bogdanovich directed this 1972 screwball comedy. The film, scripted by Buck Henry, David Newman, and Robert Benton, focuses on four identical bags and the confusion caused when they are mistaken for one another. The first bag contains igneous rocks, and is owned by Dr. Howard Bannister (Ryan O'Neal). The second bag contains the wardrobe of one Judy Maxwell (Barbra Streisand). A third bag contains confidential government reports, and the fourth contains a wealthy widow's valuable jewels. The film contains many movie in-jokes, including a humorous reference to actor O'Neal's famous "love means never having to say you're sorry" line from *Love Story*.

Henry, Newman, and Benton took home Writer's Guild Awards for their efforts, and Madeline Kahn, who made her debut in this film, received a nomination for New Star of the Year at the Golden Globes.

What is the name of this film?

- **A.** *Paper Moon*
- **B.** *Nickelodeon*
- **C.** *What's Up, Doc?*
- **D.** *They All Laughed*

1363. This film depicts the true story of Vince Papale, a Philadelphia Eagles fan who tried out for the team—and made it.

A. *Invincible*
B. *The Replacements*
C. *The Longest Yard*
D. *Any Given Sunday*

1364. This film is about Andrew Beckett, a talented young lawyer infected with AIDS. Upon learning that Andrew has the deadly disease, his employers fire him.

A. *It's My Party*
B. *Philadelphia*
C. *And the Band Played On*
D. *Angels in America*

1365. William Hurt has a torrid affair with married Kathleen Turner in this drama. The two of them then conspire to kill her hubby, Richard Crenna.

A. *Blood Simple*
B. *Body Heat*
C. *The Man Who Wasn't There*
D. *Fatal Instinct*

1366. This Edna Ferber adaptation tells the tale of a Texas rancher named Bick Benedict, his wife Leslie, and an oil baron named Jett Rink.

A. *Raintree County*
B. *Giant*
C. *The Earth Is Mine*
D. *All That Heaven Allows*

1367. In this film, a high-profile lawyer survives a shooting, but walks away with brain damage. As he starts to unravel the mystery of who he was, he begins to find that he lived a life filled with secrets.

A. *Spellbound*
B. *I Love You Again*
C. *Regarding Henry*
D. *The English Patient*

1368. Con men Lawrence and Freddy make a wager to see who can take a wealthy woman for $50,000 in this film.

A. *Penthouse*
B. *The Sting*
C. *Dirty Rotten Scoundrels*
D. *The Grifters*

1369. This film stars Michael J. Fox as a young soldier who's just arrived in Vietnam. There he sees a group of corrupted soldiers rape and kill innocent people. He vows to see that justice is served, even if it costs him his life.

A. *Casualties of War*
B. *A Bright Shining Lie*
C. *The Killing Fields*
D. *The Boys in Company C*

1370. In this film, Miami loan shark Chili Palmer goes to Hollywood to collect on a gambling debt. While he's there, he has a change of heart and decides to become a film producer.

A. *Death Collector*
B. *Get Shorty*
C. *Be Cool*
D. *Sharky's Machine*

1371. Desperate car salesman Jerry Lundegaard comes up with a poorly planned scheme that involves the kidnapping of his own wife in this black comedy.

- **A.** High and Low
- **B.** Ransom
- **C.** Fargo
- **D.** Abduction

1372. A cartoonist is sucked into the world of his own creations in this 1992 film which meshes animation with live action.

- **A.** Monkeybone
- **B.** Cool World
- **C.** Who Framed Roger Rabbit
- **D.** Evil Toons

1373. In what film does Charlize Theron play a miner who successfully sues for sexual harrassment?

- **A.** Norma Rae
- **B.** Trapped
- **C.** North Country
- **D.** The Yards

1374. Math teacher Mr. Escalante attempts to transform the gangbanging knuckle-heads in his class into top algebra students in what film?

- **A.** Teachers
- **B.** Dangerous Minds
- **C.** Lean on Me
- **D.** Stand and Deliver

1375. A group of Allied prisoners must play a game of soccer against the Nazis in this 1981 John Huston drama.

- **A.** The Mean Machine
- **B.** Champions Again
- **C.** Victory
- **D.** Hooligans

1376. What is the name of the film that recounts the real-life murders of an entire rural Kansas family by two men in 1959?

- **A.** The Executioner's Song
- **B.** In Cold Blood
- **C.** Anatomy of a Murder
- **D.** Shot Through the Heart

1377.

1378. This film is the mostly-true story of Rubin Carter, a middleweight boxing contender who was later imprisoned for murder.

- **A.** Raging Bull
- **B.** The Hurricane
- **C.** Fat City
- **D.** On the Ropes

1377.

This under-appreciated Steven Soderbergh gem is an adaptation of a science-fiction novel by Stanislaw Lem and a remake of a critically acclaimed 1972 film by Soviet director Andrei Tarkovsky. The film tells the story of Chris Kelvin, a psychologist sent to a remote space station that is orbiting a mysterious planet to investigate the mental collapse of its crew. While he is there, Kelvin, still reeling from the recent demise of his wife, Rheya, learns a strange truth about the planet. Somehow it is able to reproduce the dead friends and relatives of the crew members. When Kelvin's wife Rheya shows up, he is faced with a dilemma; even though he knows the "woman" he sees is not his wife, he must consider the chance to rebuild his life as it once was.

Like *2001: A Space Odyssey* before it, this atmospheric film's meditative nature made it a tough sell at the box office, especially in the post-*Star Wars* era. Further complicating matters, many critics were unable to see past the film's differences from the Tarkovsky original.

Do you know the title of this film?

- **A.** A Scanner Darkly
- **B.** Solaris
- **C.** Schizopolis
- **D.** Eros

1379. This film's main character, Elwood P. Dowd, is a mild-mannered man who claims to have an invisible six-foot rabbit as a pal.

A. Donnie Darko
B. My Friend
C. Harvey
D. What's Up, Doc?

1380. Luke Perry portrays world-class bullrider Lane Frost in this John G. Avildsen–directed biopic.

A. Cowboys Don't Cry
B. Electric Cowboy
C. 8 Seconds
D. The Cowboy Way

1381. In this drama, Death comes to visit media mogul Bill Parrish on his sixty-fifth birthday—in the form of a man. Death then allows Bill extra time as he falls in love with his victim's daughter.

A. Meet Joe Black
B. The Visitor
C. Death Takes a Holiday
D. He Comes Without Calling

1382. This film tells the true story of FBI agent Joe Pistone, who went undercover and infiltrated the New York Mafia.

A. Witness to the Mob
B. Kiss of Death
C. Donnie Brasco
D. Getting Gotti

1383. A fortune teller informs William H. Macy that he's not where he's supposed to be. This "revelation" causes him to leave his wife and embark upon an aimless journey through the streets of New York in this David Mamet-scripted drama.

A. The Cooler
B. Edmond
C. Focus
D. Hit Me

1384. When French soldiers refuse to follow through with an attack during World War I, their commander is forced to make an example out of them in this bold antiwar film.

A. No Man's Land
B. Paths of Glory
C. Breaker Morant
D. Dishonored

1385. In this film, an ophthalmologist seeks to end a long affair, but his mistress insists that he marry her or she will inform his wife of their relationship. In despair, he finally decides to have her whacked.

A. Match Point
B. Crimes and Misdemeanors
C. Shadows and Fog
D. Husbands and Wives

1386. Warren Beatty is an overzealous reporter who recognizes a pattern in the deaths of several of his colleagues in this 1974 Alan J. Pakula thriller.

A. All Fall Down
B. Kaleidoscope
C. The Parallax View
D. Blow Out

1387. Big-money publicist Eli Wurman manages the images of the rich and famous in this drama. One night he is asked by award-winning actor Cary Launer to babysit a woman with whom he's been having an affair. While the woman is in his care, however, she's murdered.

- A. Two Bits
- B. The Insider
- C. People I Know
- D. Chinese Coffee

1388. When the President's daughter is kidnapped, Special Ops agent Scott (Val Kilmer) is assigned the case in this action film.

- A. Kiss Kiss Bang Bang
- B. The Missing
- C. Thunderheart
- D. Spartan

1389. A millionaire offers six people a million dollars each if they stay inside a haunted house for one night.

- A. The Haunting
- B. The House on Haunted Hill
- C. Hell House
- D. Rose Red

1390. Gene Hackman's wife Candice Bergen is kidnapped by Oliver Reed and his gang in this bloody western. Hackman then hunts them down and kills them one by one.

- A. The Hunting Party
- B. Zandy's Bride
- C. Night of the Hunter
- D. Bite the Bullet

1391. This film examines a quadruple homicide committed in 1981 and porn star John Holmes' possible involvement in the crime.

- A. Wonderland
- B. Rated X
- C. Boogie Nights
- D. Porn Star

1392.

1393. A Nazi officer played by Paul Scofield is transporting stolen artwork out of France before the Americans liberate Paris. Burt Lancaster is a French railway worker trying to stop him in this film.

- A. The General
- B. The Train
- C. The Last Train
- D. The Railrodder

1394. Charlie, a New York City police officer, promises to share the winnings of his lottery ticket with a waitress should he win in this heartwarming romantic comedy.

- A. Just the Ticket
- B. It Could Happen to You
- C. Lucky Number
- D. Long Life, Happiness and Prosperity

1392.

Fred Zinnemann directed this 1953 James Jones adaptation one year after helming *High Noon*. The film focuses on soldiers stationed at Schofield Barracks in Hawaii just before the Japanese attack on Pearl Harbor. Private Robert E. Lee Prewitt (Montgomery Clift) has just been reassigned there. When his new captain learns that Prewitt had once been a standout boxer, he urges him to fight for the unit's team. Prewitt, however, has vowed never to box again after blinding a sparring opponent, and refuses to join the team. This angers the captain, who "needs a win this year," and he begins to devise methods of punishing Prewitt. At the same time all of this is happening, the wife of the sadistic captain is falling in love with 1st Sergeant Warden (Burt Lancaster).

This film, ranked at number fifty-two on the American Film Institute's list of the one hundred greatest American films, was nominated for thirteen Academy Awards. The film won eight Oscars, including Best Picture and Best Adapted Screenplay.

What is this film?

- A. From Here to Eternity
- B. The Winds of War
- C. In Harm's Way
- D. Tora! Tora! Tora!

1395. Alicia Silverstone plays a spoiled rich girl named Cher Horowitz in Amy Heckerling's revision of Jane Austen's *Emma*.
- A. *The Truth About Cats and Dogs*
- B. *Excess Baggage*
- C. *Love's Labour's Lost*
- D. *Clueless*

1396. This faux documentary follows a chameleon-like man who has the uncanny ability to make himself look and act like those around him.
- A. *Zelig*
- B. *Behind the Mask*
- C. *Bob Roberts*
- D. *Changes*

1397. William A. Wellman's biopic of war correspondent Ernie Pyle's exploits with Company C, 18th Infantry in North Africa during World War II.
- A. *Battleground*
- B. *The Story of G.I. Joe*
- C. *War Correspondent*
- D. *Reach for Glory*

1398. In what film is Rod Steiger a concentration camp survivor living in New York?
- A. *The Hangman*
- B. *The Pianist*
- C. *The Pawnbroker*
- D. *The Man in the Glass Booth*

1399. Burt Reynolds is an ex-con who agrees to help the Feds stop a band of moonshiners in this film.
- A. *Hooper*
- B. *White Lightning*
- C. *Gator*
- D. *Greased Lightning*

1400. A Louisiana mob lawyer gives a young boy important information regarding murder evidence before killing himself in this John Grisham adaptation.
- A. *Witness*
- B. *The Chamber*
- C. *The Rainmaker*
- D. *The Client*

1401. A spin doctor and a big-shot Hollywood producer join forces at election time to distract the media from a potential scandal involving the President's inappropriate conduct with a young girl in this political satire.
- A. *Man of the Year*
- B. *Wag the Dog*
- C. *The American President*
- D. *Deterrence*

1402. In this drama, the parents of a young boy with a rare life-threatening illness educate themselves on the disease in the hopes of saving his life.
- A. *I'll Do Anything*
- B. *One True Thing*
- C. *The Prince of Tides*
- D. *Lorenzo's Oil*

1403. In what movie does a vengeful girl spread a nasty rumor that two headmistresses at her school are a bit more than just friends and coworkers?
- A. *The L-Shaped Room*
- B. *Rumor Has It . . .*
- C. *The Children's Hour*
- D. *If These Walls Could Talk*

1404. In this film, Detroit cop Axel Foley is visited by childhood pal Mikey Tandino. When Mikey is murdered at his apartment, Foley goes searching for the killer himself.

A. *Metro*

B. *Beverly Hills Cop*

C. *Eddie Murphy Shemale Prostitute Scandal: The Movie*

D. *Showtime*

1405. In what film does lonely bank clerk Terence Stamp kidnap a woman and hold her hostage in his country house?

A. *The Mind of Mr. Soames*

B. *Blue*

C. *The Collector*

D. *Obsession*

1406. When a newspaper reporter believes that an innocent liquor warehouse owner knows more than he's letting on, she prints a story saying that he's the target in an investigation involving the murder of a union boss. This false report ruins the man's life. What film is this?

A. *Ace in the Hole*

B. *Absence of Malice*

C. *House of Cards*

D. *Presumed Innocent*

1407.

1408. A group of criminals led by convicted murderer Humphrey Bogart find refuge in the suburban home of Fredric March and his family in this William Wyler thriller.

A. *High Sierra*

B. *The Desperate Hours*

C. *Beat the Devil*

D. *The Harder They Fall*

1409. This biopic on renowned composer Cole Porter stars Kevin Kline, Ashley Judd, and Jonathan Pryce.

A. *Nite and Day*

B. *De-Lovely*

C. *Love for Sale*

D. *Beyond the Sea*

1410. A single mother and her daughter are forced to share quarters with a moody thespian who sublet their apartment from the woman's ex-boyfriend in this comedy based on a play by Neil Simon.

A. *California Suite*

B. *I Ought to Be in Pictures*

C. *The Goodbye Girl*

D. *Only When I Laugh*

1411. A Vietnam veteran who's not all there is pushed beyond his breaking point by abusive rural cops in this film. He then snaps and goes on a rampage, waging his own personal war.

A. *Stryker's War*

B. *A Force of One*

C. *The Hunted*

D. *First Blood*

1407.

This film is a 1979 comedy directed by Carl Reiner. Steve Martin, in his first starring role, plays dim-witted Navin R. Johnson. Navin is the white son of black sharecroppers. Navin has long questioned his lack of rhythm and dislike for the blues. One day he hears a Lawrence Welk tune on the radio, and finally feels like dancing. His family then informs him that he is not black.

With a dog named Shithead for a traveling partner, Navin sets out for St. Louis (where the Welk song was broadcast from). He soon finds himself being tracked down by a serial killer who chose his name randomly from a telephone book. He then bumbles into inventing an eyeglasses handle, which ultimately makes him a fortune. (Said fortune is later lost after his invention causes its users to become cross-eyed.)

This film was listed at number twenty on Bravo's list of the one hundred funniest movies. *Total Film* magazine listed the film as the forty-eighth funniest movie ever made.

What is the name of this film?

A. *Dumb and Dumber*

B. *The Jerk*

C. *Pennies from Heaven*

D. *Dead Men Don't Wear Plaid*

1412. In this film, Michael Caine is an womanizer who experiences some bad luck. He makes an offer to a woman who turns him down for a younger, newer model.

A. *Play Dirty*

B. *Alfie*

C. *Male of the Species*

D. *Blame It on Rio*

1413. In this drama, a criminal named Porter is shot in the back by his wife and partner, survives, and goes searching for revenge and his money.

A. *Revenge*

B. *Parker's Back*

C. *Payback*

D. *Sin*

1414. John Wayne's estranged wife asks him to track down the men who kidnapped their eight-year-old grandson and bring him home in this lively western.

A. *Big Jim McLain*

B. *Chisum*

C. *Cahill, U.S. Marshal*

D. *Big Jake*

1415. A New York attorney has a one-night stand with an apparently sane woman. Later she wreaks havoc on the man, his family, and their pet bunny.

A. *Basic Instinct*

B. *Swimfan*

C. *Rabbit Stew*

D. *Fatal Attraction*

1416. A group of college buddies attempt to briefly outrun the realities of their lives—Vietnam, graduation, and marriage—for a few days by driving to Mexico for one last adventure in this film.

A. *Chasing Dreams*

B. *Fandango*

C. *American Flyers*

D. *Stacy's Knights*

1417. Gene Hackman is a soldier assigned to escort prisoner Tommy Lee Jones from Germany to the United States. The prisoner, an assassin, gets loose and Hackman must track him down. What film is this?

A. *Company Business*

B. *The Package*

C. *Loose Cannons*

D. *Under Fire*

1418. In this survival film, an aged billionaire and the younger photographer who's sleeping with his wife become involved in a dangerous game when they are lost in the woods together after a plane crash. The photographer wants to kill the rich hubby, but they must work together to stay alive.

A. *Hunted Past Reason*

B. *The Edge*

C. *Surviving the Game*

D. *Alive*

1419. In what film does depressed suburbanite Lester Burnham find a new lease on life after losing his job and discovering that his wife is cheating on him?

A. *Slums of Beverly Hills*

B. *Welcome to the Dollhouse*

C. *American Beauty*

D. *The War of the Roses*

1420. A bank robber breaks out of prison and becomes romantically attached to a beautiful U.S. marshal in this Elmore Leonard adaptation.

A. *Gold Coast*

B. *Out of Sight*

C. *Glitz*

D. *The Big Bounce*

1421. In which film does Edward G. Robinson track a Nazi war criminal who's now living a mundane life in rural Connecticut?

A. *Mother Night*

B. *The Stranger*

C. *Marathon Man*

D. *A Time to Die*

1422.

1423. A Russian official defects to the United States and promptly informs the government that a group of French spies have been selling information to the Russians in this Alfred Hitchcock thriller.

A. *The Paradine Case*

B. *Frenzy*

C. *Topaz*

D. *Family Plot*

1424. In this romantic comedy, a handsome, wealthy man finds the perfect woman for him: a hooker.

A. *Whore*

B. *Pretty Woman*

C. *Hooker with the Heart of Gold*

D. *True Romance*

1425. This biopic tells the story of Ron Kovic, a paralyzed Vietnam veteran who later becomes an antiwar activist.

A. *The Ron Kovic Story*

B. *Article 99*

C. *Paths of Glory*

D. *Born on the Fourth of July*

1426. A minor league baseball player is left an enormous sum of money by a deceased relative he never knew he had. But there's a catch: in order to collect the money, he must dispose of $30 million in thirty days and have absolutely no assets to show for it. What film is this?

A. *Mr. Deeds Goes to Town*

B. *Next of Kin*

C. *Brewster's Millions*

D. *Thirty Days*

1427. Kirk Douglas' Vincent van Gogh keeps an ear out for opportunities to gain the respect of peers like Paul Gauguin in this Vincente Minnelli biopic.

A. *Vincent & Theo*

B. *Lust for Life*

C. *Vincent*

D. *Van Gogh*

1422.

This dark musical from Danish director Lars von Trier tells the story of Selma Jezkova (Björk), a Czech immigrant working at a factory in the United States. Selma suffers from a degenerative hereditary disease that is slowly causing her to lose her eyesight. Rather than focus on her own handicap, Selma chooses instead to be happy and save her money so she can pay for an operation to prevent her son from losing his eyesight.

One day Selma is fired from her job. She then goes home to find that her landlord and presumed friend, Bill, has stolen the money she has worked so hard to save. When Selma goes to get her money back, things go horribly wrong and she finds herself wanted for murder.

This film won the Palme d'Or at Cannes. It received nominations and won awards around the world, including the Best Foreign Film prize at the Independent Spirit Awards and an Academy Award nomination for Best Original Song.

Name this film.

A. *Shades of Gray*

B. *Manderlay*

C. *Dancer in the Dark*

D. *The Long Darkness*

1428. In this film, Al Pacino is released from prison and goes to work in a diner. There he meets and falls for an unhappy waitress.

A. *Sea of Love*

B. *Frankie & Johnny*

C. *The Local Stigmatic*

D. *Falling in Love*

1429. John Wayne's Colonel John Marlowe and William Holden's regimental surgeon Major Hank Kendall don't see eye to eye in this Civil War drama.

A. *She Wore a Yellow Ribbon*

B. *The Horse Soldiers*

C. *Fort Apache*

D. *Rio Grande*

1430. Aspiring TV anchor Suzanne Stone enlists a group of teens to kill her hubby in this 1995 drama.

A. *Circle of Friends*

B. *The Last Seduction*

C. *To Die For*

D. *Wild Things*

1431. A career-minded woman quits her job and moves back home to take care of her dying mother in this family drama. While there, she finally sees her English professor father for the adulterous failure he is.

A. *Marvin's Room*

B. *One True Thing*

C. *Anywhere But Here*

D. *Children of a Lesser God*

1432. An ambitious young attorney defends a black man accused of murdering the two white men who raped his daughter in this racially-charged southern drama.

A. *Trial by Jury*

B. *A Time to Die*

C. None of these

D. *The Rainmaker*

1433. Big-money ad man Roger O. Thornhill is mistaken for a spy in this Alfred Hitchcock thriller.

A. *The Wrong Man*

B. *North by Northwest*

C. *The Man Who Knew Too Much*

D. *Secret Agent*

1434. In this film, a band of veteran outlaws led by Pike Bishop plans one last job. Meanwhile, a former member of their clan leads bounty hunters to them.

A. *The Great Train Robbery*

B. *The Hellbenders*

C. *The Outlaws*

D. *The Wild Bunch*

1435. A washed-up fighter during the Depression is given another chance to box. He wins, becomes a national hero and symbol for the working man, and ultimately fights the heavyweight champion of the world. What film is this?

A. *Raging Bull*

B. *Requiem for a Heavyweight*

C. *Cinderella Man*

D. *Palooka*

1436. Teenager Joel is allowed to stay home alone for a few days while his parents go away on vacation in this comedy. He winds up dancing in his underwear and getting into all kinds of trouble, including a party where he makes a lot of cash selling the wares of prostitutes to other teens.

A. *The Girl Next Door*   C. *All the Right Moves*

B. *Risky Business*   D. *Losin' It*

1437.

1438. In what film does Barbra Streisand, as a streetwise prostitute and commercial actress, find herself first at odds with unpublished author George Segal, and later in love?

A. *For Pete's Sake*   C. *Up the Sandbox*

B. *The Owl and the Pussycat* D. *On a Clear Day You Can See Forever*

1439. A thief finds his life in danger after witnessing the President of the United States murder the woman he was sleeping with. What film is this?

A. *Power*   C. *The Quiet American*

B. *Absolute Power*   D. *No Way Out*

1440. Robin Williams is a robot named Andrew Martin who becomes aware of his own existence and longs to be human in this futuristic drama.

A. *Robots*   C. *Robot Stories*

B. *A.I.: Artificial Intelligence* D. *Bicentennial Man*

1441. A politician named Blake Pellarin is campaigning to become president when he finds himself confronted with his own past in this film.

A. *The Distinguished Gentleman* C. *The Last Party*

B. *Primary Colors*   D. *The Big Brass Ring*

1442. In this Ridley Scott–directed film, serial killer and cannibal Hannibal Lecter hides from the authorities in Italy, posing as an art expert. Soon a wealthy and disfigured victim of Hannibal pays to track him down.

A. *Red Dragon*   C. *Hannibal*

B. *Manhunter*   D. *The Silence of the Lambs*

1443. Dakota Fanning convinces her father Kurt Russell to save an injured race horse rather than having it put down. The two of them mend the horse's injured leg and the horse eventually races again. What is the name of this film?

A. *All the Pretty Horses*   C. *Dreamer*

B. *Flicka*   D. *Black Beauty*

1437.

This thriller directed by Martin Scorsese is a remake of the Hong Kong film *Infernal Affairs*. The film, which stars Matt Damon, Leonardo DiCaprio, and Jack Nicholson, follows two police officers. One of them, Billy Costigan, is a cop who goes undercover to infiltrate the Irish mob. The other, Colin Sullivan, is a bad cop who's on the payroll of local crime chieftain Frank Costello. Things become interesting when both the criminals and the police begin searching for the mole who has infiltrated their respective organizations. Further complicating things, both Costigan and Sullivan become romantically involved with the same woman. As the film speeds towards its climactic finale, each man knows he must uncover the identity of the other if he wants to survive this deadly game.

What is the name of this film?

A. *Training Day*

B. *The Departed*

C. *Dark Blue*

D. *Gangs of New York*

1444. Scott Glenn and Kevin Costner play brothers in this light-hearted comedic oater, which also stars Kevin Kline, Danny Glover, and John Cleese.

A. *Wyatt Earp*
B. *Open Range*
C. *Silverado*
D. *Tombstone*

1445. A fictional British metal band is featured in this Rob Reiner-helmed faux documentary.

A. *Hard Core Logo*
B. *Take the Money and Run*
C. *CB4*
D. *This Is Spinal Tap*

1446. In what film does Whoopi Goldberg play a savvy businesswoman who gets ahead by pretending to be an old white man named Cutty?

A. *Here Comes Mr. Cutty*
B. *Made in America*
C. *The Associate*
D. *Boys on the Side*

1447. Buddy Amaral thinks he's doing a good deed by switching plane tickets with a man so he can get home to see his son. However, the plane crashes. Furthermore, Buddy falls in love with the man's widow. What film is this?

A. *Reindeer Games*
B. *Bounce*
C. *The Ticket*
D. *Forces of Nature*

1448. In this suspense film, a Moscow detective investigates a triple homicide, but finds that his superiors don't want him to find the killer.

A. *Red Corner*
B. *Gorky Park*
C. *Telefon*
D. *The Kremlin Letter*

1449. A band of jewel thieves is assigned colors as code names before a big score in this movie. Later, after the heist, the remaining members of the team wait for their boss in a warehouse.

A. *Heist*
B. *Reservoir Dogs*
C. *The Taking of Pelham One, Two, Three*
D. *Point Blank*

1450. A priest played by Linus Roache grapples with his own homosexuality in this drama.

A. *The Crimes of Padre Amaro*
B. *Priest*
C. *The Dangerous Lives of Altar Boys*
D. *Saint Ralph*

1451. Jan is left paralyzed after an accident on an oil rig snaps his neck in this film. Unable to sleep with his wife, he convinces her to let him watch her have sex with another man for his entertainment.

A. *The Idiots*
B. *Dear Wendy*
C. *Breaking the Waves*
D. *Unconditional Love*

1452. Lieutenant John Dunbar is assigned to an abandoned army camp in this drama. While waiting for the reinforcements he believes are coming, he makes friends with the local Indians, and ultimately joins the tribe.

A. *Drums Along the Mohawk*
B. *Little Big Man*
C. *The Last of the Mohicans*
D. *Dances with Wolves*

1453. After six years the drunk driver who killed Freddy Gale's daughter is being released from the slammer. Now Freddy plans to get even. What film is this?

A. *Rolling Thunder*
B. *The Crossing Guard*
C. *The Indian Runner*
D. *The Pledge*

1454. In what film is Marlon Brando, a bounty hunter who occasionally dresses in women's clothes, hired to track down and kill a band of horse thieves?

A. *Burn!*
B. *The Appaloosa*
C. *Morituri*
D. *The Missouri Breaks*

1455. Driven to madness by childhood observational experimentation by his father, Mark Lewis murders women and films their dying expressions in this movie.

A. *Peeping Tom*
B. *Camera*
C. *The Projectionist*
D. *The Watcher*

1456.

1457. Luke Skywalker loses his hand and learns that Darth Vader is his father in this Ewok-inhabited episode of the *Star Wars* series.

A. *The Empire Strikes Back*
B. *Return of the Jedi*
C. *Attack of the Clones*
D. *The Phantom Menace*

1458. George Raft and Humphrey Bogart play brothers in this film. Bogie loses a hand in an automobile accident.

A. *High Sierra*
B. *They Drive By Night*
C. *The Hand*
D. *The Harder They Fall*

1459. In what film does the life of Wall Street wizard Sherman McCoy hit a snag when his mistress Maria runs into a young man—with Sherman's automobile?

A. *Wall Street*
B. *Detour*
C. *The Bonfire of the Vanities*
D. *Short Cuts*

1460. In this film, a New York City doctor walks through the city and gets himself into trouble after his wife confides she once fantasized about cheating on him.

A. *After Hours*
B. *Fear and Desire*
C. *Scenes from a Marriage*
D. *Eyes Wide Shut*

1456.

This 1940 John Steinbeck adaptation about Okies in the Dust Bowl was scripted by Nunnally Johnson and directed by John Ford. The story centers around Tom Joad (Henry Fonda), a newly freed convict who returns home to find that the bank has foreclosed on his family's farm, which is now deserted. He locates his family and learns that they are about to embark upon a cross-country journey to California in search of employment and better living conditions. Along the way the Joad family encounters numerous hardships that test their bonds and endurance.

Ford's film is ranked at number twenty-one on the American Film Institute's list of the one hundred greatest American films. At the time of its release, it received seven Academy Award nominations, including Best Picture, Best Adapted Screenplay, and Best Actor (Fonda). These nominations yielded two statuettes, awarded for Best Direction and Best Supporting Actress (Jane Darwell).

What is the title of this film?

A. *The Grapes of Wrath*
B. *Of Mice and Men*
C. *East of Eden*
D. *The Winter of Our Discontent*

1461. In what film do Bill Pullman and Nicole Kidman find their lives turned upside down when Kidman is operated on by a doctor with a God complex played by Alec Baldwin?

A. *Intolerable Cruelty*   **C.** *Domestic Disturbance*

B. *Malice*   **D.** *The Doctor*

1462. The first rule is you don't talk about it. The second rule is you don't talk about it. "It" refers to the title of which film?

A. *The Joy Luck Club*   **C.** *The Monster Club*

B. *Fight Club*   **D.** *The First Wives Club*

1463. This flm stars Marlon Brando as a latent homosexual Army major with a cheating wife who never misses an opportunity to belittle him. One memorable scene finds Brando abusing her horse with a riding crop.

A. *Latent Homosexual Army Major: The Musical*   **C.** *Reflections in a Golden Eye*

B. *The Nightcomers*   **D.** *The Ugly American*

1464. The president of the United States hopes to improve the nation's economy and his own polling numbers by going to war with Canada in this comedy.

A. *The American President*   **C.** *Canadian Bacon*

B. *Wag the Dog*   **D.** *South Park: Bigger, Longer & Uncut*

1465. Two lipstick lesbians take on the mob in this heist movie, stealing $2 million in cash from a gangster named Caesar.

A. *Bound*   **C.** *Big Doll House*

B. *Caged*   **D.** *Heavenly Creatures*

1466. Two prisoners become unlikely friends on the penal colony known as Devil's Island. One of them, Henri, endures years of abuse before finally escaping. What is the name of this film?

A. *We're No Angels*   **C.** *Terminal Island*

B. *Papillon*   **D.** *No Escape*

1467. In what film does hitman Jeffrey Chow accidentally cause a woman to lose her sight, and then later befriend her?

A. *Bullet in the Head*   **C.** *Hard Boiled*

B. *The Killer*   **D.** *A Better Tomorrow*

1468. In what film does a country music star make a wager that she can transform an average New York cabbie into a bonafide country singer?

A. *Honkytonk Man*
B. *Pure Country*
C. *Rhinestone*
D. *Electric Cowboy*

1469. A band of U.S. soldiers goes behind enemy lines to steal $16 million worth of gold bars from the Nazis in this action comedy.

A. *Three Kings*
B. *Kelly's Heroes*
C. *The Dirty Dozen*
D. *Inglorious Bastards*

1470.

1471. Ashley Judd believes her husband, supposedly dead for the past six years, is still alive in this thriller.

A. *Twisted*
B. *Double Jeopardy*
C. *Eye of the Beholder*
D. *High Crimes*

1472. Bad man Jack Nicholson is about to be hanged in this western, but then learns of a law that states that he can be freed if he finds a local woman to marry him.

A. *Carnal Knowledge*
B. *The King of Marvin Gardens*
C. *Goin' South*
D. *Shotgun Wedding*

1473. American RAF pilot in Jerusalem Tom Hanks meets a Jewish girl of Spanish descent while mending his injured leg. The two of them like one another, but her family disapproves of his being a Gentile. What film is this?

A. *The Razor's Edge*
B. *The Bonfire of the Vanities*
C. *Every Time We Say Goodbye*
D. *Always*

1474. Aging hitman Charles Bronson takes the young Jan-Michael Vincent under his wing and teaches him the ropes in this 1972 thriller.

A. *Mr. Majestyk*
B. *The Mechanic*
C. *The Stone Killer*
D. *Hard Times*

1475. In this drama, a naïve Texas cowboy relocates to New York City to become a prostitute. Once there, he befriends a homeless crippled man.

A. *Urban Cowboy*
B. *The Cowboy Way*
C. *Drugstore Cowboy*
D. *Midnight Cowboy*

1476. Dying Edwina has her soul transferred into another body in this film. However, something goes wrong, and she winds up sharing the body of a man.

A. *The Man with Two Brains*
B. *All of Me*
C. *Braindead*
D. *Seconds*

1470.

This poignant examination of racial tensions in Los Angeles, co-written and directed by Paul Haggis, divided critics and moviegoers in a way that few movies have before or since. Famed *Chicago Sun-Times* critic Roger Ebert immediately dubbed it the best film of the year, while *LA Weekly*'s Scott Foundas called it the worst film of the year.

The film's intersecting story lines focus on several different characters over the course of a thirty-six-hour period. These diverse characters include carjackers, a sadistic bigoted cop, a television producer and his wife, the Los Angeles district attorney and his racist wife, and a Latino locksmith, among others.

When awards season came, the controversy surrounding the film only became louder. The film was awarded numerous prizes at too many awards ceremonies to mention. Perhaps the most significant honor the film received was an Oscar for Best Picture. (Once again, the film's detractors cried foul and protested this.)

What is the name of this controversial film?

A. Do the Right Thing
B. Everyday People
C. Crash
D. Monster's Ball

1477. In which Superman movie does the hero take on computer genius Gus Gorman (played by Richard Pryor) before Kryptonite turns him evil?

A. Superman

B. Superman III

C. Superman II

D. Superman IV: The Quest for Peace

1478. This film's tagline is: "Colonel Frank Slade has a very special plan for the weekend. It involves travel, women, good food, fine wine, the tango, chauffeured limousines and a loaded forty-five. And he's bringing Charlie along for the ride."

A. Two for the Money

B. Scent of a Woman

C. American Gun

D. Sidewalks of New York

1479. A comic book store employee marries a hooker, kills her pimp, and travels to Hollywood to sell the mob's cocaine in this 1993 film.

A. Take the Money and Run

B. Badlands

C. True Romance

D. Truth or Consequences, N.M.

1480. James Bond's assignment is to retrieve a missing encryption device known as ATAC in this film.

A. A View to a Kill

B. For Your Eyes Only

C. The Spy Who Loved Me

D. Live and Let Die

1481. In this comedy, Ray opens a bakery two doors down from a bank so he can slowly tunnel his way into the bank and rob it. However, the bakery is a huge success and he soon becomes wealthy from his wife's cookies.

A. Take the Money and Run

B. Small Time Crooks

C. Criminal

D. The Cookie Thief

1482. In this comedy, Will Smith plays a professional date doctor who's assisted many men in landing their dream girl. However, he finds his own methods lacking when trying to land a gossip columnist played by Eva Mendes.

A. Breakin' All the Rules

B. The Legend of Bagger Vance

C. Confessions of a Date Doctor

D. Hitch

1483. This film tells the story of Leonard, an insurance investigator who suffered head trauma and, as a result, has lost his ability to make new memories. He's trying to track down the man who did this to him (and killed his wife), if only he can remember his mission.

A. Following

B. Memento

C. Clean Slate

D. The Memory of a Killer

1484. Johnny Depp stars as an accountant named William Blake in this haunting western directed by Jim Jarmusch.

A. *Slow Burn*   C. *Arizona Dream*

B. *Dead Man*   D. *The Brave*

1485. A dim fashion model is brainwashed in this comedy and given an implausible mission: to assassinate a world leader.

A. *Mind Over Murder*   C. *Zoolander*

B. *Fair Game*   D. *The Man Who Knew Too Little*

1486. World War III begins with a bang in this film as Russians overtake a small midwestern town. Soon a band of rebels, made up of local high school students, pick up rifles and start fighting back.

A. *Russkies*   C. *The Russians Are Coming, The Russians Are Coming*

B. *Red Dawn*   D. *Red Sun*

1487. This 2003 South Korean thriller concerns a businessman who is kidnapped and held captive for fifteen years. When he's released, he sets out to find his captors and exact revenge.

A. *Audition*   C. *Oldboy*

B. *Sympathy for Mr. Vengeance*   D. *Ichi the Killer*

1488. A late night talk show host runs for president as a publicity stunt, and is shocked when he actually wins in this political comedy.

A. *Head of State*   C. *Bulworth*

B. *Primary Colors*   D. *Man of the Year*

1489. Dustin Hoffman and Susan George play an American couple who move to England. After they are bullied by locals and the wife is raped, hubby Hoffman flips out and goes to war with them in this bloody thriller.

A. *Agatha*   C. *Straw Dogs*

B. *John & Mary*   D. *Straight Time*

1490.

1491. A man comes forward to inform the FBI that his brother may be a serial killer in this drama. This is a result of their father, who murdered people because he believed they were demons in human form.

A. *The Gift*   C. *Frailty*

B. *Identity*   D. *Asylum*

1490.

This pop-culture romance was adapted from a novel by British author Nick Hornby—but while the book is set in London, the film makes a nearly seamless switch to Chicago.

Compulsive list maker and record store owner Rob Gordon gets dumped by his girlfriend Laura and decides to revisit his top five breakups. He tracks down each of his ex-girlfriends to find out what went wrong and learn how to win Laura back. Helped along by his two socially inept, music-obsessed employees and their endless lists (Top Five Elvis Costello Songs, Top Five Songs About Death), he tries to decide whether he listens to pop music because he's miserable or he's miserable because he listens to pop music. Along the way, the soundtrack's obscure gems heighten the mood: the Kinks, the Velvet Underground, Stereolab, and the Beta Band, among others.

What movie is this?

A. *Love Stinks*

B. *High Fidelity*

C. *Backbeat*

D. *About a Boy*

1492. In this film, an American movie actor and the lonely wife of a fashion photographer meet and form an unlikely connection in Tokyo.

- **A.** The Dreamers
- **B.** Lost in Translation
- **C.** The Last Kiss
- **D.** Swimming Pool

1493. This movie could be described as Steven Seagal versus Tommy Lee Jones and Gary Busey.

- **A.** Exit Wounds
- **B.** Hard to Kill
- **C.** Under Siege
- **D.** The Glimmer Man

1494. When a member of the Travis family commits suicide in this drama, each of the remaining members must come to grips with this death and their own lives.

- **A.** The Ice Storm
- **B.** The Upside of Anger
- **C.** Off the Map
- **D.** Imaginary Heroes

1495. In this 1997 film, a small-town teacher starts to examine his sexuality when he is "outed" by a former student on national television.

- **A.** Angels in America
- **B.** In & Out
- **C.** First Kiss
- **D.** Normal

1496. A seaman in the British Royal Navy is tried for the murder of a sadistic officer in this Herman Melville adaptation.

- **A.** Last of the Pagans
- **B.** Bartleby
- **C.** The Sea Beast
- **D.** Billy Budd

1497. Rupert Pupkin aspires to be a comic and dreams of one day appearing on a particular late night show. He then begins stalking the show's host, Jerry Langford. What is the title of this film?

- **A.** They All Laughed
- **B.** The Day the Laughter Died
- **C.** The King of Comedy
- **D.** The Jimmy Show

1498. Alan Ladd is the good guy and Jack Palance the bad guy in this classic oater.

- **A.** High Noon
- **B.** Red River
- **C.** Winchester '73
- **D.** Shane

1499. In which of these movies do drug smugglers terrorize a blind woman while attempting to obtain a doll?

- **A.** Wait Until Dark
- **B.** Night Falls on the City
- **C.** Terror
- **D.** A Shot in the Dark

1500. Which horror flick stars John Cassavetes and Mia Farrow?

- **A.** It's Alive
- **B.** Basket Case
- **C.** Repulsion
- **D.** Rosemary's Baby

CHAPTER SEVEN:
THE CHARACTERS

1501. What is the soon-to-be-floating-corpse Joe Gillis' occupation in *Sunset Boulevard*?
- **A.** Novelist
- **B.** Buoy
- **C.** Journalist
- **D.** Screenwriter

1502. In what city does *The Departed's* Billy Costigan reside?
- **A.** Chicago
- **B.** Newark
- **C.** Boston
- **D.** Kansas City

1503. In the submarine thriller *Crimson Tide*, Denzel Washington plays Ron Hunter. What is Hunter's rank?
- **A.** Captain
- **B.** Lieutenant Commander
- **C.** Lieutenant
- **D.** Bosun's Mate

1504. What is the name of the book store chain owned by Joe in *You've Got Mail*?
- **A.** Everything Books
- **B.** Book World
- **C.** Books & Things
- **D.** Fox Books

1505. For what team does *For Love of the Game's* pro baseballer Billy Chapel play?
- **A.** San Francisco Giants
- **B.** Detroit Tigers
- **C.** Chicago Cubs
- **D.** Boston Red Sox

1506. Clint Eastwood plays "Gunny" Highway in *Heartbreak Ridge*. What is Gunny's real name?
- **A.** Tom
- **B.** Jim
- **C.** Edward
- **D.** Joe

1507. In *The Wizard of Oz*, what is the name of Dorothy's uncle (played by Charlie Grapewin)?
- **A.** Buck
- **B.** Charlie
- **C.** Henry
- **D.** Edward

OPPOSITE Ray Bolger, Jack Haley, Judy Garland, and Bert Lahr in *The Wizard of Oz*, 1939

1508. Bonasera comes to *The Godfather* to plead for vengeance against a man who threatened to rape his daughter. What is Bonasera's occupation?

A. Funeral director

B. Pawnbroker

C. Bus driver

D. Manager of a deli

1509. In *True Romance*, Clarence Worley is obsessed with a deceased musical icon. Who is this?

A. Jim Morrison

B. Elvis Presley

C. Jimi Hendrix

D. John Lennon

1510. In what city does *Anchorman* Ron Burgundy reside?

A. Los Angeles

B. San Francisco

C. Palm Beach

D. San Diego

1511. What illegal substance do Billy the Kid and Wyatt purchase at the beginning of *Easy Rider*?

A. Heroin

B. Marijuana

C. Cocaine

D. Acid

1512. *Cast Away*'s Chuck Noland is an executive working for a major U.S. company. What is this company?

A. Kentucky Fried Chicken

B. UPS

C. Microsoft

D. FedEx

1513. Samuel L. Jackson plays an FBI agent named Flynn who must fight off slithering baddies in *Snakes on a Plane*. What is Flynn's first name?

A. Neville

B. Tyson

C. Carl

D. Maurice

1514.

1515. At what university does Charles W. Kingsfield Jr. teach in *The Paper Chase*?

A. Yale

B. Harvard

C. Stanford

D. Princeton

1516. What organization employs Avner and company in the Steven Spielberg drama *Munich*?

A. KGB

B. Mossad

C. PLO

D. Israelis for World Freedom

1514.

The Shawshank Redemption is a 1994 Stephen King adaptation written and directed by Frank Darabont. The film tells the story of Andy Dufresne (Tim Robbins), an innocent man framed for the murder of his wife and her lover. Andy is sentenced to serve two consecutive life sentences in a maximum-security prison. Inside, Andy faces a number of hardships, not the least of which are repeated rapes and beatings. Andy soon finds a friend in Red (Morgan Freeman), a man who "knows how to get things." Two of the items Andy acquires from Red are a rock hammer and a poster. He then begins the slow process of tunneling through the wall, using the poster to conceal what he's done.

Before being sent to prison, Andy was the vice-president of a bank. In what city was this bank located?

A. Bangor, Maine

B. Portland, Maine

C. Seattle, Washington

D. Baltimore, Maryland

1517. For what NFL team does former teacher Vince Papale play in *Invincible*?

A. Washington Redskins
B. New York Jets
C. Philadelphia Eagles
D. San Diego Chargers

1518. Michael Douglas plays the leader of the free world in *The American President*. What is the president's name?

A. Bill Mitchell
B. Jed Bartlett
C. Andrew Shepard
D. Bob Rumson

1519. What was Sean Thornton's occupation before relocating to Ireland in *The Quiet Man*?

A. Boxer
B. Saloon owner
C. Soldier
D. Gunrunner

1520. What was the occupation of Alicia Huberman's father in Alfred Hitchcock's *Notorious*?

A. Nazi spy
B. Gestapo officer
C. Propagandist
D. Bootlegger

1521. Yo, what was Adrian's last name before she married Rocky Balboa in *Rocky*?

A. Graffanino
B. Caselotti
C. Pennino
D. Tataglia

1522. In *Crash*, Lieutenant Dixon has a framed photograph of a politician hanging in his office. Who is this?

A. Arnold Schwarzenegger
B. George H.W. Bush
C. Gray Davis
D. George W. Bush

1523. What is the name of the newspaper of which Charles Foster Kane was editor and publisher in *Citizen Kane*?

A. *Daily Examiner*
B. *Globe*
C. *Inquirer*
D. *Herald*

1524. *The Graduate's* Mrs. Robinson has only one daughter. What is the name of this daughter?

A. Anne
B. Elaine
C. Theresa
D. Katharine

1525. Just-married Will Kane is the lawman of a small town awaiting the imminent arrival of outlaws in *High Noon*. What is the name of the town over which Kane presides?

A. Hadleyville
B. Rayville
C. Hays
D. Lordsburg

1526. Gil Renard is a die-hard baseball junkie/stalker in *The Fan*. Over what Major League baseball team does Gil obssess?

A. San Diego Padres
B. Kansas City Royals
C. Oakland Athletics
D. San Francisco Giants

1527. The newscaster Michelle Pfeiffer plays in *Up Close & Personal* was loosely modeled after real-life anchor Jessica Savitch. What is the name of Pfeiffer's character?

A. Sally Savitch
B. Tally Atwater
C. Marcia McGrath
D. Veronica Corningstone

1528. Dustin Hoffman plays a young American named David Sumner in *Straw Dogs*. What is David's occupation?

A. Mathematician
B. Engineer
C. Novelist
D. Architect

1529.

1530. J. J. Gittes is a private detective investigating an adultery case in *Chinatown*. By what name is Gittes known?

A. Jack
B. Jay
C. Jake
D. John

1531. In *Clerks II* we find that Dante Hicks and sidekick Randal Graves have relocated from the convenience store where they worked previously. Name the restaurant where they are now employed.

A. The Shake Shack
B. Mooby's
C. The Pie Hole
D. Banky's

1532. Jim Williams is a wealthy homosexual art dealer in *Midnight in the Garden of Good and Evil*. In what city does Williams reside?

A. Savannah
B. Tupelo
C. New Orleans
D. Atlanta

1533. Ted Stryker is briefly institutionalized at the beginning of *Airplane II: The Sequel*. After whom is the mental institution where Stryker stays named?

A. Zsa Zsa Gabor
B. Vivien Leigh
C. Liberace
D. Ronald Reagan

1529.

Schindler's List is the 1993 adaptation of Thomas Keneally's book *Schindler's Ark*. The Steven Spielberg—directed film tells the true story of Oskar Schindler, a Czech businessman who arrives in Krakow, Poland, just as the Jews are being relocated to "population centers." At first Schindler is oblivious to the horrors of the Holocaust, but later employs as many of the Jews in his factory as he can in order to keep them out of harm's way. When the Nazis begin "liquidating" the Jews, Schindler forfeits his fortune to save their lives by having them shipped back to his original home in Zwittau-Brinnlitz.

Schindler's List received twelve Academy Award nominations. These nominations yielded seven statuettes, including Best Picture, Best Director, and Best Adapted Screenplay. The film is consistently included on just about every all-time greatest films list, and is ranked at number nine on the American Film Institute's list of the one hundred greatest American films.

What is the name of Oskar Schindler's wife?

A. Greta
B. Helen
C. Emilie
D. Victoria

1534. What fixture loomed over *Annie Hall* character Alvy Singer's childhood home?

A. A giant statue of Christopher Columbus

B. A roller coaster

C. The Space Needle

D. A billboard advertising tampons

1535. Tom Hanks plays a lonely widower in *Sleepless in Seattle*. What is the name of this character?

A. Paul Edgecomb

B. Andrew Beckett

C. Sam Baldwin

D. Jimmy Dugan

1536. *Taxi Driver* Travis Bickle was a member of the armed forces before relocating to New York City. In which branch did he serve?

A. Army

B. Navy

C. Marines

D. Air Force

1537. *Superman* doubles as mild-mannered reporter Clark Kent. For what newspaper does Clark write?

A. *The New York Times*

B. *The Daily Planet*

C. *The Daily Bugle*

D. *New York Post*

1538. In *Goodfellas*, Tommy Conway, Henry Hill, and Tommy DeVito are mobsters. Who is their boss?

A. Richie Aprile

B. Paul Cicero

C. Frankie Carbone

D. Billy Bats

1539. Kevin Costner plays aging baseballer Crash Davis in *Bull Durham*. Davis holds the dubious distinction of having hit more homers in the minors than anyone else. What position does he play?

A. First Base

B. Shortstop

C. Catcher

D. Third Base

1540. Martin Brody is the police chief of Amity Island in *Jaws*. Prior to his relocating to the island, Brody had been a police officer in a major U.S. city. Where was this?

A. New York City

B. San Francisco

C. Chicago

D. Boston

1541. Louis Jourdan plays Stefan Brand in *Letter from an Unknown Woman*. What is Brand's occupation?

A. Violinist

B. Pianist

C. Saxophone player

D. Politician

1542. In *Modern Times*, Charles Chaplin's Tramp is a factory worker. Do you know the name of the factory in which he works?

A. Acme Steel Company

B. The ABC Corporation

C. Electro Steel Corporation

D. Allied Cabinet Manufacturers

1543. In *Ferris Bueller's Day Off*, the lead character concocts a plan to keep himself and his friends out of school for a day. In what city does Ferris reside?

A. St. Louis

B. San Diego

C. Chicago

D. New York City

1544. Sean Connery plays reclusive author William Forrester in *Finding Forrester*. What is the name of the aspiring writer to whom Forrester serves as mentor?

A. Jamal Wallace

B. Rashid Wallace

C. Ben Wallace

D. Terrell Wallace

1545. Where is Mookie employed in *Do the Right Thing*?

A. *Pizza by Sal*

B. *Sal's Place*

C. *Sal's Famous Pizzeria*

D. *Sal's World Famous Pizzeria*

1546. In *The General*, we are told that Johnnie had two loves: his engine and his girlfriend. What is the name of his girlfriend?

A. Clara

B. Annabelle Lee

C. Estelle Marie

D. Laruvia

1547. Seth Davis goes to work for a new investment firm in *Boiler Room*. What is the name of this firm?

A. J.D. Macklin

B. J.T. Macklin

C. J.D. Marlin

D. J.T. Marlin

1548. George Sanders plays the cynical Addison DeWitt in *All About Eve*. What is DeWitt's occupation?

A. Critic

B. Acting coach

C. Director

D. Actor

1549. Peter Warne is the name of Clark Gable's reporter character in *It Happened One Night*. What is the name of Warne's editor?

A. Jack Gideon

B. Tom Lampley

C. Joe Gordon

D. John Darrow

1550. *The King of Comedy*'s Rupert Pupkin believes himself a comedian at heart and longs to one day be like his late-night talk show host hero. Who is this?

A. Jerry Langford

B. Johnny Carson

C. Carl Brown

D. Carl Burrows

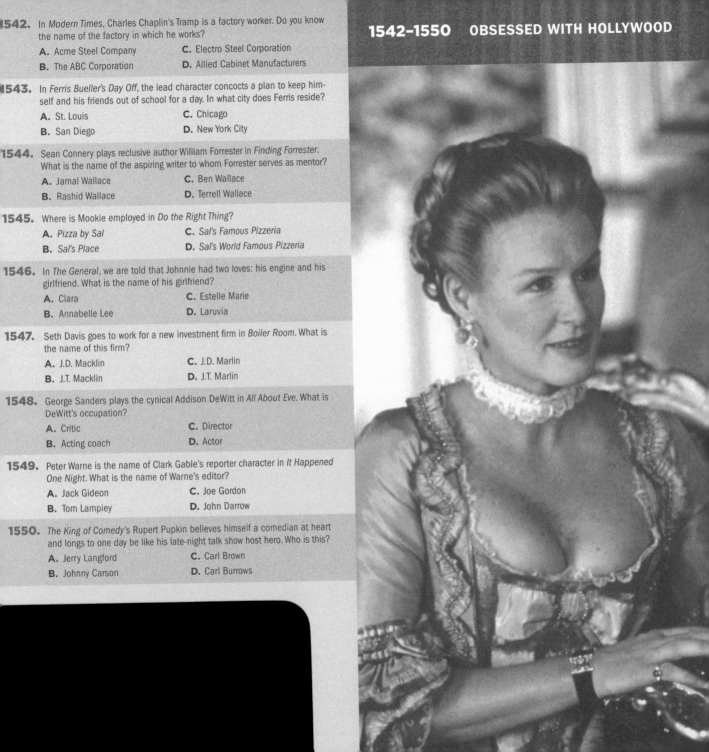

1554.

Glenn Close was born in Greenwich, Connecticut, in 1947, and spent part of her childhood in the Belgian Congo, where her surgeon father operated a clinic. Close majored in drama and anthropology at Virginia's College of William and Mary. After receiving her BA, she began working on stage. While performing on Broadway in the musical *Barnum*, Close was discovered by director George Roy Hill. This led to her breakout role in *The World According to Garp*.

Close has since appeared in such films as *The Big Chill*, *The Natural*, *Fatal Attraction*, *Dangerous Liaisons*, *Hook*, *Mars Attacks!*, and *Air Force One*. The gifted actress has received many awards and nominations throughout her storied career, including five Academy Award nominations. Unfortunately, these nominations have yet to yield a single Oscar. She has also received ten Emmy nominations, which have resulted in one award.

In what film does Close play a character named Iris Gaines?

A. *The Paper*
B. *The Natural*
C. *The Big Chill*
D. *Fatal Attraction*

1551. Professional football player turned convict Paul Crewe is persuaded to lead a team of criminals against a team of guards in *The Longest Yard*. What is the name of Crewe's team?

A. White Lightning
B. The Mean Machine
C. The Panthers
D. The Killers

1552. In *The Lady Eve*, Charles Pike is said to be an ophiologist. What does this mean?

A. Snake expert
B. Antiques expert
C. Bird expert
D. None of these

1553. In which of her films does Bette Davis play a character named Hannah Loftin?

A. *Death on the Nile*
B. *Madame Sin*
C. *Where Love Has Gone*
D. *As Summers Die*

1554.

1555. When bad guys take over a battleship in *Under Siege*, they are stopped by a former Navy SEAL named Casey Ryback. What is Ryback's occupation on the ship?

A. Security coordinator
B. Cook
C. Janitor
D. Captain's assistant

1556. What is the name of the department store where *Army of Darkness* hero Ash mops floors and stocks shelves?

A. S-Mart
B. J-Mart
C. D-Mart
D. L-Mart

1557. Detective Mitch Preston is assigned a new partner in the comedy *Showtime*. What is the name of his new partner?

A. Chase Renzi
B. Ceasar Vargas
C. Trey Sellars
D. Kit Ramsey

1558. In *Raging Bull*, Jake performs a one-man show entitled (appropriately enough) "An Evening with Jake La Motta." What is the name of the establishment where he performs this?

A. The Barbizon Plaza Hotel Theater
B. Jake's Place
C. The Shoreline Theater
D. The Italian Sandwich Grill

1559. The Othello character is named Odin in Tim Blake Nelson's stylish Shakespeare update *O*. What is Odin's surname?

A. Harris
B. Freemont
C. Jenkins
D. James

1560. The Big Kahuna is the story of Larry, Phil, and Bob, three salesmen at a convention. What type of product do they sell?

A. Industrial lubricant   C. Industrial bulk hand sanitizer

B. Industrial cleaning solvent   D. Industrial deodorizer

1561. While injured and homebound, L.B. Jefferies begins to spy upon his neighbors in *Rear Window*. What is Jefferies' occupation?

A. Sportswriter   C. Salesman

B. Photographer   D. Newspaper editor

1562. Rap artist Eminem made his acting debut in 2002's *8 Mile* playing a character known as B-Rabbit. What is B-Rabbit's real name?

A. Greg Buehl, Jr.   C. Jimmy Smith, Jr.

B. David Porter, Jr.   D. Jimmy Porter, Jr.

1563.

1564. *The Limey* tells the story of an ex-con named Wilson who tears Los Angeles apart looking for his daughter's killer. What was the name of his daughter?

A. Tammy   C. Lizzie

B. Kelly   D. Jenny

1565. *Capote* follows novelist/personality Truman Capote as he works on one of his books. Which book is he writing?

A. *Breakfast at Tiffany's*   C. *The Grass Harp*

B. *Remembering Tennessee*   D. *In Cold Blood*

1566. One of the criminals in *Bonnie and Clyde* is named C.W. Moss. Who is Moss' favorite movie star?

A. Douglas Fairbanks   C. Clara Bow

B. Myrna Loy   D. Mae West

1567. Seven old college pals gather together for the death of a friend in *The Big Chill*. One of these friends, played by Tom Berenger, is a TV star. Do you know his name?

A. Nick Carlton   C. Sam Weber

B. Michael Gold   D. Harold Cooper

1568. Like the James Stewart character in *Harvey*, title character *Donnie Darko* also has an invisible rabbit for a friend. What is the rabbit's name?

A. Frank   C. Clyde

B. Bugsy   D. Eddie

1563.

The Best Years of Our Lives is William Wyler's examination of the lives of three American servicemen who return home after the conclusion of World War II. These three men, Fred Derry (Dana Andrews), Homer Parrish (Harold Russell), and Al Stephenson (Fredric March), each find it difficult to reacclimate themselves to the life they knew before.

Bank loan manager Al's problem is that he now has a newfound trust in others and begins giving loans to people with insufficient collateral. Homer is the most affected, though, as he lost both hands to burns, and now finds himself a social outcast.

During the war, Fred was an officer who made important decisions that affected the lives of many soldiers. In the "real world," however, Fred works in a demeaning low-paying job as a soda jerk. His new wife enjoyed being married to an officer, but now has little interest. As a result, Fred falls in love with Al's daughter, Peggy.

What is the name of Fred's wife?

A. Wilma

B. June

C. Marie

D. Eleanor

1569. Peter Sellers plays three characters in *Dr. Strangelove or: How I Learned to Stop Worrying and Love the Bomb*. These are Dr. Strangelove, Group Captain Lionel Mandrake, and the President of the United States. What is the president's name?

A. Merkin Muffley

B. T.J. Kong

C. Buck Turgidson

D. "Bat" Guano

1570. *Double Indemnity* is the story of an insurance agent named Walter Neff who helps a woman murder her husband so they can split the insurance money. What is the name of the insurance company for which Neff works?

A. Allied Pacific All-Risk Insurance

B. United Alliance All-Risk Insurance Company

C. Pacific All-Risk Insurance Company

D. American Eagle All-Risk Premium Insurance

1571. What is the name of Tony Camonte's sister in the 1932 version of *Scarface*?

A. Isabella

B. Francesca

C. Caroline

D. Gina

1572. Mark Wahlberg plays a porn star known to the world as Dirk Diggler in *Boogie Nights*. What is Diggler's real name?

A. Jack Horner

B. Eddie Adams

C. Floyd Gondolli

D. Andy Richards

1573. Steve, Diane, Dana, Robbie, and Carol Anne are the names of the family that's terrorized in *Poltergeist*. What is the surname of the family?

A. Robeson

B. Zeitmeyer

C. Freeling

D. Elliot

1574. In *No Way Out*, Kevin Costner plays Tom Farrell, a Navy officer who witnesses a murder by the secretary of defense. What is Farrell's rank in the film?

A. Lieutenant Commander

B. Lieutenant

C. Major

D. Captain

1575. What is the name of the preacher played by John Carradine in *The Grapes of Wrath*?

A. Andy Levine

B. Muley

C. Jeremiah Anderson

D. Jim Casy

1576. What is the name of the casino Ace Rothstein operates in the Martin Scorsese film *Casino*?

A. Riviera

B. Stardust

C. Tangiers

D. Mirage

1577. *The Player* is the story of a slimy Hollywood studio exec who finds himself mixed up in a web of deceit. What is the name of the exec?

  A. Buddy Ackerman

  B. Larry Levy

  C. Josh Martin

  D. Griffin Mill

1578. Cary Grant plays Dr. David Huxley in the screwball comedy *Bringing Up Baby*. What type of doctor is Huxley?

  A. Paleontologist

  B. Ophthalmologist

  C. Zoologist

  D. Etymologist

1579. Burt Reynolds plays a moonshiner nicknamed Bandit who agrees to transport beer across state lines in *Smokey and the Bandit*. What is Bandit's real name?

  A. Cledus Snow

  B. Enos Burdette

  C. Bo Darville

  D. Gator McClusky

1580. Harvey Keitel plays patriarch Jacob Fuller in the horror romp *From Dusk Till Dawn*. Keitel is retired in the film. What was his previous occupation?

  A. Minister

  B. Rabbi

  C. Priest

  D. Scientologist couch-jumper

1581. James Cagney portrays George M. Cohan in *Yankee Doodle Dandy*. What is Cohan's "triumphal return to the stage" with which the film opens?

  A. *The Orphans*

  B. *I'd Rather Be Right*

  C. *Four of a Kind*

  D. *The Irish Darlings*

1582. Sidney Deane and Billy Hoyle are basketball hustlers in *White Men Can't Jump*. Billy has a girlfriend, Gloria, and Sidney is married. What is the name of Sidney's wife?

  A. Wanda

  B. Tyra

  C. Chalise

  D. Rhonda

1583. In *Heaven Can Wait*, pro football quarterback Joe Pendleton dies and is given a chance to return to earth in someone else's body. What NFL team did Joe play for?

  A. New York Jets

  B. Los Angeles Rams

  C. Oakland Raiders

  D. San Francisco 49ers

1584. Harry Caul is a professional surveillance operative in *The Conversation*. In what city does Harry reside?

  A. New York City

  B. Los Angeles

  C. San Francisco

  D. San Diego

1585. Jack Nicholson plays concert-pianist-turned-oil-rig-worker Robert Eroica Dupea in *Five Easy Pieces*. He lives with his girlfriend, Rayette Dipesto. What is Rayette's occupation?

A. Waitress

B. Sales clerk

C. Maid

D. She is unemployed

1586. Alex DeLarge is the leader of a gang in *A Clockwork Orange*. By what term does he refer to the other gang members?

A. Dorfs

B. Dargels

C. Droogs

D. Dragoos

1587. At the beginning of *Raiders of the Lost Ark*, Indiana Jones escapes Peruvian natives by seaplane. What is the name of Indy's English pilot friend who flies the plane?

A. Chick

B. Jock

C. Dink

D. Jank

1588. What is the name of the highest paid star at the *Moulin Rouge!* club?

A. Christian

B. Satine

C. Satie

D. China Doll

1589. What is the name of *Mildred Pierce's* hubby (played by Zachary Scott) who is murdered in the film's opening scene?

A. Monte Beragon

B. Thomas Beragon

C. Edmond Beragon

D. Wilmer Beragon

1590.

Magnolia, the 1999 film written and directed by Paul Thomas Anderson, intertwines the stories of eight very different San Fernando Valley inhabitants. These characters include author T.J. Mackey (Tom Cruise), former child quiz show winner Donnie Smith (William H. Macy), a woman facing her guilt for cheating on her dying husband (Julianne Moore), a nurse taking care of a dying old man (Philip Seymour Hoffman), game show host Jimmy Gator (Philip Baker Hall), a dying television producer (Jason Robards), cocaine addict Claudia (Melora Waters), and a current gameshow contestant (Jeremy Blackman).

Author T.J. Mackey is the creator of a self-help system that helps men sleep with women. What is the name of this system?

A. *Seduce and Destroy*

B. *Seek and Destroy*

C. *Make Her Want It*

D. *Seducing Women for Dummies*

1591. Teddy Gammell assists the memory-impaired Leonard in finding his wife's killer in *Memento*. What is Teddy's real name?

A. Jim

B. John

C. Jeff

D. Jack

1592. Will Hunting is a janitor at a college in *Good Will Hunting*. At what college is he employed?

A. Harvard

B. MIT

C. University of Nevada, Las Vegas

D. Princeton

1593. In *Dead Man*, William Blake relocates to Machine for a job that's already gone when he gets there. From where did Blake relocate?

A. Cleveland

B. Chicago

C. Philadelphia

D. Pawtuckett

1594. In which of these films did the late great Mae West play a character named Lady Lou?

A. *She Done Him Wrong*

B. *My Little Chickadee*

C. *Myra Breckinridge*

D. *I'm No Angel*

1595. Longfellow Deeds inherits a great sum of money in *Mr. Deeds Goes To Town*. One of Deeds' hobbies is playing what musical instrument?

A. Harmonica

B. Tuba

C. Trumpet

D. Banjo

1596. In *Being John Malkovich*, Schwartz, a puppeteer, discovers a portal that leads into the head of actor John Malkovich. What is Schwartz's first name?

A. Greg

B. Jeff

C. Craig

D. Gary

1597. *Clerks'* Dante Hicks becomes jealous when he learns that his ex-girlfriend is getting married. What is her name?

A. Veronica

B. Alyssa

C. Heather

D. Caitlin

1598. The John Cassavetes character Guy Woodhouse is unemployed in *Rosemary's Baby*. What is Woodhouse's trade?

A. Actor

B. Playwright

C. Screenwriter

D. Director

1599. Which *Indiana Jones* film features a sidekick named Short Round?

A. *Indiana Jones and the Philosopher's Stone*

B. *Indiana Jones and the Temple of Doom*

C. *Indiana Jones and the Secret of the Sphinx*

D. *Indiana Jones and the Last Crusade*

1600. What is Mickey's occupation when he meets Mallory in *Natural Born Killers*?

A. Grocery store delivery boy

B. Pizza delivery boy

C. Bartender at Cheers

D. Meat market delivery boy

1601. *Smoke's* Auggie Wren photographs what each day?

A. His customers

B. The sidewalk outside his store

C. Feet

D. Clouds

1602. Where is George employed in *A Place in the Sun*?

A. Eastman Industries

B. B & B Imports

C. Windlow Industries

D. Mo-Con Tec

1606.

No one breathes life into a character like Jack Nicholson. In his capable hands, characters become more than just living, breathing entities — they become iconic fixtures of our pop culture awareness. Among his most memorable scenes: lamenting on the troubles of the world in *Easy Rider*; banging away on a piano in the back of a moving truck in *Five Easy Pieces*; discovering the not-so-pretty truth about a pretty woman in *Chinatown*; staging a momentary coup when he doesn't get his way in *One Flew Over the Cuckoo's Nest*; peering maniacally through the splintered bathroom door in *The Shining*; the irresistibly over-the-top Joker in *Batman*; the "you can't handle the truth" monologue in *A Few Good Men*; the compulsive gay-bashing writer in *As Good As It Gets*; singing show tunes on a congested freeway in *Anger Management*; playing a joke in a porn theater in *The Departed*.

In what film does Nicholson play a character named Garrett Breedlove?

A. *The Postman Always Rings Twice*
B. *Prizzi's Honor*
C. *Terms of Endearment*
D. *The Last Detail*

1603. Dennis and Brian McCaffrey are sibling firefighters in *Backdraft*. In what city do they fight fires?
A. Minneapolis
B. Philadelphia
C. San Francisco
D. Chicago

1604. Fred MacMurray plays Lieutenant Tom Keefer in *The Caine Mutiny*. What does Keefer dream of one day being?
A. A novelist
B. A Broadway performer
C. A radio personality
D. Court-martialed

1605. Rod Steiger plays Sheriff Bill Gillespie in the film *In the Heat of the Night*. What is the name of the small Mississippi town where Gillespie enforces the law?
A. Upton
B. Algoma
C. Sparta
D. Marietta

1606.

1607. Brad Majors and Janet Weiss spend a night inside the home of mad scientist Dr. Frank N. Furter in *The Rocky Horror Picture Show*. Furter dreams of creating a man with blond hair and a tan. What does he plan to name him?
A. Dexter
B. Rocky
C. Adolf
D. Margaret

1608. Miles Monroe is a geeky health food store owner who has himself cryogenically frozen in *Sleeper*. Monroe plays a musical instrument: which one is it?
A. Pan flute
B. Trumpet
C. Clarinet
D. Guitar

1609. Jack Burden is a news writer covering politician Willie Stark in *All the King's Men*. What is the name of the newspaper for which Burden writes?
A. *The Post*
B. *The Gazette*
C. *The Sun*
D. *The Chronicle*

1610. Christian Slater appears in *Windtalkers* as Sergeant Pete Anderson. By what nickname is Anderson known to his fellow soldiers?
A. Hoot
B. Slick
C. Big Pete
D. Ox

1611. Alice Bowman assists a negotiator in getting back her kidnapped husband in *Proof of Life*. What is the name of Alice's missing hubby?
A. Terry
B. Peter
C. David
D. Michael

1612. Josh Baskin is a twelve-year-old boy trapped inside the body of an adult man in *Big*. Josh lands a job working as a consultant for a toy company. What is the name of this company?

A. Indestructo Toys

B. MacMillan Toys

C. Willeford Toy Company

D. Geiger Toy Company

1613. Charles Van Doren is a recurring winner on the rigged show *Twenty-One* in *Quiz Show*. What is the name of the previous winner Van Doren defeated to begin his reign?

A. Dick Goodwin

B. Dan Enright

C. Robert Kintner

D. Herbert Stempel

1614. Ronny Cox plays Drew Ballinger in the 1972 drama *Deliverance*. What musical instrument does Ballinger play?

A. Guitar

B. Violin

C. Harmonica

D. Banjo

1615. *Showgirls'* Nomi Malone gets her big break when she is cast in a Stardust Casino production. What is the name of this production?

A. *Glamorous*

B. *Goddess*

C. *Dreamgirls*

D. *Heaven*

1616. PFC Edward Garlick is Adrian Cronhauer's sidekick of sorts in Barry Levinson's *Good Morning, Vietnam*. What is Edward Garlick's middle name?

A. Bellmondo

B. Tiberius

C. Montesque

D. Percy

1617. *Eyes Wide Shut's* Bill Harford is a doctor. What is his wife Alice's occupation?

A. Advertising executive

B. Fashion designer

C. Art curator

D. Interior decorator

1618. Cal and Aron Trask fight for their father's affection in the John Steinbeck adaptation *East of Eden*. What is their father's name?

A. Adam

B. Andrew

C. Jacob

D. Joseph

1619. What is the name of Jett Rink's oil company in the classic film *Giant*?

A. Jetexas Oil

B. Jett Rink Oil

C. Rink Oil

D. None of these

1626.

With his live-action directorial debut *Office Space*, Mike Judge examines the everyday horrors inside the cubicles of an average corporate office. The film follows three burned-out computer programmer friends and coworkers who can no longer take the day-to-day routine of their jobs. Soon after consultants are brought in to downsize the corporation, one of the friends, Peter Gibbons, is hypnotized and then left in a permanent state of relaxation when the hypnotist suffers a heart attack and dies. The end result is that Peter no longer cares about losing his job. His new-found easygoing demeanor somehow impresses the downsizing consultants, who now consider him "management material." After the other two friends, Michael and Samir, are fired, the friends cook up a half-baked scheme to embezzle a fortune from the corporation.

What is the name of the corporation where the three friends work?

A. Cal-Tech
B. Initech
C. Dytech
D. Comtech

1620. *Billy Madison* is a lazy buffoon who must go back to school so that he may one day run his father's business. What is Billy's age?
A. Twenty-five   C. Twenty-eight
B. Twenty-six   D. Twenty-seven

1621. O'Ren Ishii is a former member of the Deadly Viper Assassination Squad in *Kill Bill Vol. 1*. What was her code name?
A. Copperhead   C. Sidewinder
B. Cottonmouth   D. California Mountain Snake

1622. Emperor Marcus Aurelius is slain by his own son for not selecting him as his successor in *Gladiator*. What is the name of Marcus Aurelius' murderous son?
A. Maximus   C. Gracchus
B. Commodus   D. Proximo

1623. Leonard is a bumbling private nicknamed "Gomer Pyle" in the Stanley Kubrick war film *Full Metal Jacket*. What is Leonard's surname?
A. Maltin   C. Lawrence
B. Davis   D. Hartman

1624. *Napoleon Dynamite* is a weird high school kid who lives with his grandmother and his older brother. What is the name of Napoleon's uncle who comes to take care of him while his grandmother is in the hospital?
A. Ed   C. Rico
B. Kip   D. Pedro

1625. Band members Chazz, Rex, and Pip take over a radio station so they can finally get some attention in *Airheads*. What is the name of their band?
A. Metal Detector   C. Mistuh Rogers
B. Airheads   D. The Lone Rangers

1626.

1627. What is the name of the newspaper that publishes Peter Parker's photographs in *Spider-Man*?
A. *Daily Bugle*   C. *Daily Planet*
B. *Daily Post*   D. *Daily Examiner*

1628. In what country is *Roman Holiday's* Princess Ann a member of the royal family?
A. This is never revealed   C. Paraguay
B. Bolivia   D. Hugary

1629. Jerry Welbach is an errand boy for the Mob who is sent to Mexico to bring back an antique rare pistol in *The Mexican*. What is the name of Jerry's girlfriend?

A. Tess

B. Darian

C. Elizabeth

D. Samantha

1630. Mac and Pat McBeth murder their boss in the 2001 Shakespeare adaptation *Scotland, PA*. What is their boss' name?

A. McDuff

B. Anthony Banconi

C. Norm Duncan

D. Douglas McKenna

1631. *Dazed and Confused* documents the last day of the school year for a group of Texas students. What is the name of the high school they attend?

A. John F. Kennedy High School

B. Robert E. Lee High School

C. Jeb Stuart High School

D. Roosevelt High School

1632. Retired *Commando* John Matrix vows to make terrorists pay dearly after they kidnap his daughter. What is her name?

A. Katie

B. Theresa

C. Beth

D. Jenny

1633. Robert De Niro plays a spin doctor brought in to distract the media from a scandal involving the president in *Wag the Dog*. What is the spin doctor's name?

A. Conrad Brean

B. Fad King

C. Johnny Dean

D. William Schumann

1634. A team of six Allied and Greek soldiers are sent to dismantle two powerful guns in *The Guns of Navarone*. What is the name of the captain who leads them?

A. Andrea Stavros

B. Keith Mallory

C. Butcher Brown

D. Roy Franklin

1635. Terry Malloy unwittingly helps lure an informant to the rooftop to be dealt with at the beginning of *On the Waterfront*. What is the name of the informant?

A. Johnny Friendly

B. Joey Doyle

C. Charley Malloy

D. Kayo Dugan

1636. What is the name of Burt Lancaster's powerful *Globe* columnist in *Sweet Smell of Success*?

A. Steve Dallas

B. Sidney Falco

C. J.J. Hunsecker

D. Frank D'Angelo

1641.

Iconic Hollywood actor William Holden was born William Franklin Beedle Jr. in O'Fallon, Illinois, in 1918.

While attending Pasadena Junior College, he began performing in local radio shows; Paramount Pictures discovered the fledgling actor in 1937.

Two years later Holden appeared in his first starring role in the boxing drama *Golden Boy*. Holden's career didn't really take off, however, until his unforgettable turn in Billy Wilder's 1950 black comedy *Sunset Boulevard*. Holden received a Best Actor Academy Award nomination for his effort. After this triumph, there was no stopping the charismatic performer.

Other standout entries from his filmography include *Stalag 17*, *Executive Suite*, *Sabrina*, *The Bridges at Toko-Ri*, *Love Is a Many-Splendored Thing*, *Picnic*, *The Bridge on the River Kwai*, *The Horse Soldiers*, *Alvarez Kelly*, *The Wild Bunch*, *The Towering Inferno*, *Network*, and *S.O.B.*

In what film does Holden play a character named Richard Thorn?

A. *Damien: Omen II*
B. *Executive Suite*
C. *Sabrina*
D. *Casino Royale*

1637. Coworkers Klara and Alfred are in love with each other, but they don't know it yet. What is the name of *The Shop Around the Corner* where they work?
A. Matuschek's
B. Kralik's
C. Kazcek's
D. Tessio's

1638. In which film does Tom Hanks play a character named Robert Langdon?
A. *Road to Perdition*
B. *Cast Away*
C. *The Ladykillers*
D. *The Da Vinci Code*

1639. In *The Apartment*, Jack Lemmon plays C.C. Baxter, a man determined to climb to the top of the business world no matter what it takes. By what name is C.C. Baxter known?
A. Ed
B. Clyde
C. Ralph
D. Bud

1640. Two friends, Captain Rafe McCawley and Captain Danny Walker, are caught in a romantic triangle with a nurse in *Pearl Harbor*. What is her name?
A. Doris Miller
B. Evelyn Johnson
C. Betty Bayer
D. Beth Grant

1641.

1642. Captain Dana Holmes is the base commander in *From Here to Eternity*. What is the name of the base he commands?
A. Schofield Barracks
B. Fort Dix
C. Carlisle Barracks
D. Fort Lee

1643. Wilma Dean Loomis and Bud Stamper fall in love in *Splendor in the Grass*. What is Wilma's nickname?
A. Willie
B. Candy
C. Wildy
D. Deanie

1644. *Patch Adams* is a physician who establishes his own clinic and treats patients with unorthodox methods. Prior to this, he attends a medical school where he finds himself in complete disagreement with the policies taught there. What is the name of this medical school?
A. Maryland Medical College
B. Medical College of Virginia
C. Washington Medical College
D. Tennessee Medical College

1645. *Tombstone* is a retelling of the events that transpired at the O.K. Corral in Tombstone, Arizona. Of the following, who is *not* one of the Earp brothers?
A. Morgan
B. Wyatt
C. Earl
D. Virgil

1646. Harrison Ford plays the president of the United States in *Air Force One*. What is the name of his character?

A. James Marshall
C. Jed Bartlet
B. Walter Emerson
D. Andrew Shepard

1647. *Mr. Smith Goes to Washington* is the story of a naïve and idealistic man named Jefferson Smith who becomes a junior senator. From what state does Smith hail?

A. Oregon
C. Mississippi
B. Montana
D. Virginia

1648. Which of these is *not* the name of one of the innocent men wrongly lynched in *The Ox-Bow Incident*?

A. Donald Martin
C. Halva Harvey
B. Juan Martinez
D. Art Croft

1649. Thirty-four-year-old butcher Marty Piletti still lives with his mother in *Marty*. What is his mother's name?

A. Ellen
C. Theresa
B. Betty
D. Anita

1650. John Book is a Philadelphia cop trying to protect a young Amish boy who saw a murder in *Witness*. While doing this, Book falls in love with the boy's mother. What is her name?

A. Rachel
C. Elaine
B. Marilyn
D. Ellen

1651. *Glory* tells the story of the first all-black volunteer company. What is the name of the colonel who leads them?

A. John Rawlins
C. Robert Gould Shaw
B. Thomas Searles
D. Charles Fessenden Morse

1652. *When Harry Met Sally . . .* follows the friendship and romance of Harry Burns and Sally Albright. What college does Harry attend when they meet?

A. University of Chicago
C. University of Kansas
B. Cornell University
D. New York University

1653. John Fiedler plays Juror #2 in *12 Angry Men*. What is his occupation?

A. High school basketball coach
C. Stockbroker
B. Factory laborer
D. Bank teller

1654. What is the occupation of Vada Sultenfuss's father, Harry, in *My Girl*?

A. Shop owner
C. Police officer
B. Undertaker
D. Mechanic

1657.

Vincent Price attended Yale, where he studied art history and fine art. In 1935, Price began acting on stage, and three years later made his film debut in *Service de Luxe*. Over the next few years, Price appeared in several films, including Otto Preminger's *Laura* and Henry King's *The Song of Bernadette*.

In the 1950s, Price found great success when he reinvented himself as a horror player in such memorable films as *House of Wax*, *The Fly*, and *House on Haunted Hill*. His image now cemented as a master of horror, Price appeared in a series of stylish Edgar Allan Poe adaptations directed by Roger Corman. These included *The Fall of the House of Usher*, *The Pit and the Pendulum*, *Tales of Terror*, *The Raven*, *The Haunted Palace*, *The Masque of the Red Death*, and *The Tomb of Ligeia*.

Subsequent Price films include *The Abominable Dr. Phibes*, *Theatre of Blood*, *The Whales of August*, *Vincent*, and *Edward Scissorhands*.

In what film does Price play a character named Dr. Robert Morgan?

A. *Twice-Told Tales*
B. *Diary of a Madman*
C. *The Last Man on Earth*
D. *House on Haunted Hill*

1655. Elderly Rose Dawson Calvert revisits the site of the famous ship's sinking in *Titanic*. How old is Rose at this time?
A. 100   **C.** 103
B. 101   **D.** 102

1656. In what city does Henry of *Henry: Portrait of a Serial Killer* fame reside and do his dirty work?
A. Chicago   **C.** Los Angeles
B. New York City   **D.** Detroit

1657.

1658. Mitch McDeere is a lawyer employed by a high-profile law firm that's a front for the Mob in *The Firm*. What is the name of this firm?
A. Lambert, Locke, and Bendini   **C.** Bendini, Lambert & Locke
B. Bendini & Locke   **D.** Lambert & Locke

1659. Casey Brodsky decides to divorce her parents, Albert and Lucy, in *Irreconcilable Differences*. What is Albert Brodsky's occupation?
A. Movie director   **C.** Journalist
B. Weatherman   **D.** Film producer

1660. Melanie Daniels asks pet shop clerk Mrs. MacGruder if she's ever seen anything like the strange phenomenon in *The Birds*. What is the name of the shop where Mrs. MacGruder works?
A. Davidson's Pet Shop   **C.** O'Brien's Pet Shop
B. MacGruder's Pet Shop   **D.** Westhoff's Pet Shop

1661. Jack Torrance and his family experience supernatural occurrences in *The Shining*. What kind of automobile does Jack drive?
A. A pick-up truck   **C.** A station wagon
B. A Volkswagen   **D.** A van

1662. Katherine Watson finds herself at odds with the teachings of the new college at which she works in *Mona Lisa Smile*. What is the name of this college?
A. Willoughby   **C.** Willeford
B. Wellington   **D.** Wellesley

1663. *American Me* tells the story of a Los Angeles gangbanger named Santana who goes to prison for a long stretch. To what prison is Santana sent?
A. Riker's Island   **C.** Mid-State Correctional
B. Folsom State   **D.** Adirondack Correctional

1664. *Cadillac Man's* Joey O'Brien is a car salesman who must sell a predetermined number of cars in two days or he will lose his job. How many cars must Joey sell?

A. Eight
B. Twelve
C. Ten
D. Twenty

1665. *In Love and War* is a wartime romance picture starring Sandra Bullock and Chris O'Donnell. What literary figure does O'Donnell portray in this film?

A. William Faulkner
B. Ernest Hemingway
C. Gabriel García Márquez
D. John Dos Passos

1666. Bruce Lee plays a martial artist and member of the Shaolin temple who is recruited as a spy in the chop-socky action film *Enter the Dragon*. What is the name of his character?

A. Lee
B. Bruce
C. Chen
D. Tang

1667. What actor appears as secretary Bob Rolland in the classic Marx Brothers comedy *Duck Soup*?

A. Groucho Marx
B. Harpo Marx
C. Chico Marx
D. Zeppo Marx

1668. In *Marathon Man*, Thomas Levy's brother, Henry, was a member of a covert government team. By what name is this team known?

A. The Force
B. The Squad
C. The Division
D. The Team

1669. Vietnam vet Joseph Megessey pays a visit to old war buddy David Flannigan in *Jacknife*. He then meets David's sister, Martha, and sparks fly. What does Martha do for a living?

A. Prostitute
B. Teacher
C. Firefighter
D. Sales clerk

1670. Poet Charlie Mackenzie falls for a butcher named Harriet in *So I Married an Axe Murderer*. As the title implies, he later discovers that this woman with the killer body may actually be a killer. In what city does Charlie reside?

A. San Francisco
B. Denver
C. Baltimore
D. Philadelphia

1671. In *The Killers*, John Cassavetes makes the mistake of falling for Ronald Reagan's gal and pays dearly for having done so. What is the occupation of Cassavetes' character, Johnny North?

A. Hitman
B. Gambler
C. Race car driver
D. Professional thief

1677.

The Thin Red Line is director/screenwriter Terrence Malick's meditative 1998 adaptation of a World War II novel by James Jones. The film, which received seven Academy Award nominations, follows various members of C Company during the invasion of Guadalcanal. Among them are the rebellious Private Witt (Jim Caviezel), the sensitive and overly-conscious Captain Staros (Elias Koteas), the tired 1st Sergeant Welsh (Sean Penn), the over-eager Lieutenant Colonel Tall (Nick Nolte), the lovesick Private Bell (Ben Chaplin), the ambitious young Captain Gaff (John Cusack), and a handful of other soldiers and officers played by the likes of Adrien Brody, George Clooney, John C. Reilly, John Travolta, Woody Harrelson, Thomas Jane, Jared Leto, and Nick Stahl.

What is Captain James Staros's nickname?

A. Starstruck
B. Bugger
C. Killer
D. The Greek

1672. *Diner* is about a group of friends in their early twenties who must face the fact that their lives are changing. What is the name of the diner?
  A. The Hilltop Diner   **C.** Harpers Ferry Diner
  B. Reistertown Road Diner   **D.** Fells Point Diner

1673. Preston Waters crosses paths with career criminal Quigley in the 1994 *Home Alone* imitator *Blank Check*. What is Preston's age?
  A. Ten   **C.** Twelve
  B. Eleven   **D.** None of these

1674. Sally Field and James Garner fall in love in the heartfelt comedy *Murphy's Romance*. Field's character, Emma, is a divorced mother and horse trainer. What does Garner's character, Murphy, do for a living?
  A. Pharmacist   **C.** Podiatrist
  B. Bus driver   **D.** Radio deejay

1675. Housewife Lucy Chadman returns from beyond the grave in the comedy *Hello Again*. How did Lucy die in the first place?
  A. Choking   **C.** Suicide
  B. Automobile accident   **D.** Drowning

1676. Barbara Jean is the queen of the country music scene in Robert Altman's *Nashville*. What is the name of her selfish husband and manager?
  A. Delbert   **C.** Barnett
  B. Buddy   **D.** Haven

1677.

1678. Filmmaker John L. Sullivan pretends to be a bum in order to learn about the troubles of the poor so he can make a film about the problems of society in *Sullivan's Travels*. What is the title of the film he wants to make?
  A. *Tales of the Down and Out*   **C.** *The Life of a Beggar*
  B. *Lonely Are the Weary*   **D.** *O Brother, Where Art Thou?*

1679. A man named James falls in love with an attractive hearing-impaired girl named Sarah in *Children of a Lesser God*. What is James's occupation?
  A. Teacher   **C.** Novelist
  B. Maintenance man   **D.** Photographer

1680. American Mark Elliott and Chinese Han Suyin fall in love, but find this interracial relationship difficult in *Love Is a Many-Splendored Thing*. Mark is a war correspondent. What is Han's occupation?
  A. Doctor   **C.** Politician
  B. Waitress   **D.** Teacher

1681. Housewife Laura Jesson and Dr. Alec Harvey meet by chance at the train station and fall rather quickly for one another in *Brief Encounter*. The two then continue meeting at a café. On what day do they meet each week?

A. Monday
B. Tuesday
C. Thursday
D. Wednesday

1682. Three divorced women hatch a plan to get even with their ex-husbands in *The First Wives Club*. What event initially brings the three women together?

A. Chance encounter in the waiting room at the lawyer's office
B. The death of a friend
C. Chance encounter in the waiting room at the hospital
D. A class reunion

1683. Warren Schmidt is forced to reevaluate his life after the death of his wife in *About Schmidt*. What is the name of his wife?

A. Edna
B. Barbara
C. Claire
D. Helen

1684.

1685. Leo Holland blackmails a rock star into selling drugs for him in *Cisco Pike*. What is Leo Holland's occupation?

A. Record executive
B. Cop
C. DEA agent
C. Attorney

1686. Madonna's Rebecca Carlson is tried for the murder of a man who leaves her a significant amount of money in his will in *Body of Evidence*. How much money does she inherit?

A. $5 million
B. $3 million
C. $6 million
D. $8 million

1687. A man named Jefferson Reed is struck by a piece of meteor and turned into a superhero in *The Meteor Man*. In what city does Jefferson reside?

A. Lincoln, Nebraska
B. San Jose, California
C. Washington, D.C.
D. St. Louis, Missouri

1688. Clyde Williams and Billy Foster set out to win money for their fraternal order in *Let's Do It Again*. What is the name of this fraternal order?

A. Brothers and Sisters Under Allah
B. The Brothers and Sisters of Shaka
C. The Brothers and Sisters of Ali
D. The Brothers and Sisters of Khan

1689. George and Nina Banks' lives are turned upside down when their daughter decides to get married in *Father of the Bride*. What is their daughter's name?

A. Annie
B. Diane
C. Kimberly
D. Matty

1684.

By the age of twenty-five, Kevin Costner had already given up on his dream of becoming an actor. Instead, he was working in a mundane job at a marketing firm. Everything changed, however, after Costner had a chance encounter with legendary actor Richard Burton, who convinced him to drop everything else and pursue acting. Costner did, and soon began acting in film. His breakout came with 1983's *The Big Chill*, a film in which all of his scenes were cut. Lawrence Kasdan, who had directed that film, cast him in a larger role in his next film, *Silverado*.

In 1987, Costner finally started receiving recognition with *The Untouchables*. This led to an impressive five-year run as one of Hollywood's premiere players, with such films as *No Way Out*, *Bull Durham*, *Field of Dreams*, *Dances with Wolves*, which he himself directed, *Robin Hood: Prince of Thieves*, *JFK*, and *The Bodyguard*.

Costner's subsequent films include *A Perfect World*, *Wyatt Earp*, *Waterworld*, *Tin Cup*, *The Postman*, *Message in a Bottle*, *For Love of the Game*, *Thirteen Days*, *Open Range*, *The Upside of Anger*, and *Rumor Has It . . .*

In what film does Costner play a character named Roy McAvoy?

A. *Tin Cup*
B. *The Guardian*
C. *The Postman*
D. *3000 Miles to Graceland*

1690. Married man Dan Gallagher's one-night stand comes back for revenge in *Fatal Attraction*. What does Dan do for a living?

A. Stock broker

B. Attorney

C. Ad executive

D. Sales analyst

1691. Alcoholic Brick and his dying father, Big Daddy, are reunited in *Cat on a Hot Tin Roof*. With what disease is Big Daddy afflicted?

A. Cancer

B. Parkinson's

C. Alzheimer's

D. Huntington's

1692. Monty Brewster is a minor league baseball player who inherits a large sum of money (with a few strings attached) in *Brewster's Millions*. For what minor league team does Brewster play?

A. Chattanooga Lookouts

B. Toledo Mud Hens

C. Hackensack Bulls

D. Charlotte Knights

1693. Steven Kovak is terrorized by a lonely cable installer in *The Cable Guy*. What is Steven's occupation?

A. Architect

B. Attorney

C. Car salesman

D. Grocery store manager

1694. Richard Pryor is a preacher with questionable ethics in *Car Wash*. His motto is, "The best place for money is . . . right here in my pocket." What is the name of this preacher?

A. Brother Jerome

B. Daddy Rich

C. Mr. Lindy

D. Sweets Johnson

1695. Ted Kramer is an ordinary man whose wife decides to leave him and his son one day in *Kramer vs. Kramer*. His wife later resurfaces and fights for custody. What is the name of Ted and Joanna Kramer's son?

A. Josh

B. Justin

C. Max

D. Billy

1696. Charlie Sheen plays a pitcher known affectionately as "Wild Thing" by Cleveland Indians fans in *Major League*. What is Wild Thing's real name?

A. Roger Dorn

B. Rick Vaughn

C. Jake Taylor

D. Pedro Cerrano

1697. Super spy James Bond is married in *On Her Majesty's Secret Service*. What is the name of the woman he marries?

A. Diana

B. Ruby

C. Lydia

D. Tracy

698. Henry Rowengartner is a young boy given the chance to play baseball for the Chicago Cubs in *Rookie of the Year*. What position does Henry play?

A. Pitcher
C. Catcher
B. Shortstop
D. First base

1699. Molly McGrath is hired to coach an inner-city school football team in *Wildcats*. What is the name of the high school where she is employed?

A. Renaissance High
C. Western International High
B. Central High
D. Stuyvesant High

1700. Daniel Day-Lewis plays a ladies' man named Tomas in *The Unbearable Lightness of Being*. What is Tomas's occupation?

A. Museum curator
C. Art dealer
B. Doctor
D. Professor

1701. Ray Peterson becomes obsessed with his mysterious new neighbors in *The 'Burbs*. What is the surname of these strange new neighbors?

A. Walston
C. Klopek
B. Weingartner
D. Straker

1702. What is the name of the character played by rapper Ice Cube in the 1995 hit comedy *Friday*?

A. Smokey
C. Craig
B. Terrance
D. Marvin

1703. A nurse named Hana attends to a burned plane-crash victim who appears to have amnesia in *The English Patient*. From what country does Hana hail?

A. France
C. England
B. United States
D. Canada

1704.

1705. Miles is a high school teacher, would-be novelist, and wine enthusiast in *Sideways*. What subject does Miles teach?

A. English
C. French
B. Mathematics
D. Literature

1706. Retired gunslinger Will Munny's life is changed dramatically after the death of his beloved wife in *Unforgiven*. What was the name of Will's wife?

A. Sally
C. Delilah
B. Claudia
D. Faith

1704.

Nicole Kidman was born in Honolulu, Hawaii, in 1967, and moved to Australia when she was four, where her father taught at the University of Technology in Sydney. Kidman took an interest in ballet and drama at a young age, making her acting debut at the age of fifteen in the Pat Wilson music video "Bop Girl." This led to roles on Australian television and in film.

In 1989, Kidman appeared in the Philip Noyce thriller *Dead Calm*. The following year she appeared alongside future hubby Tom Cruise in the Tony Scott film *Days of Thunder*, effectively jump-starting her career as a Hollywood leading lady.

Kidman, who has received two Oscar nominations and collected one statuette, has subsequently appeared in such films as *Far and Away*, *Malice*, *To Die For*, *Eyes Wide Shut*, *Moulin Rouge!*, *The Others*, *The Hours*, *Cold Mountain*, *Dogville*, and *The Interpreter*.

Do you know what film stars Kidman as a character named Joanna Eberhart?

A. *To Die For*
B. *Birth*
C. *The Hours*
D. *The Stepford Wives*

1707. Con man Johnny Hooker wants revenge after his mentor has been killed in *The Sting*. What was the name of his mentor?
- **A.** Studs
- **B.** Henry
- **C.** Eddie
- **D.** Luther

1708. Calvin Palmer risks losing the *Barbershop* his dead father established to a greedy loan shark. What is the name of the loan shark?
- **A.** Lester Wallace
- **B.** Ricky Nash
- **C.** J.D.
- **D.** Jimmy James

1709. Mobster-turned-film producer Chili Palmer wants to land a big-name actor he calls "Shorty" in the aptly titled *Get Shorty*. What is the actor's real name?
- **A.** Dick Allen
- **B.** Bo Catlett
- **C.** Leo Devoe
- **D.** Martin Weir

1710. In *Snow White and the Seven Dwarfs*, which character urges Snow White to "Run! Run away! Hide!"
- **A.** Prince Charming
- **B.** Grumpy
- **C.** The Magic Mirror
- **D.** The Huntsman

1711. After being victimized by a student, a high school teacher relocates to a different city and school in *187*. He is eventually driven mad by the violent students and their lack of respect. What is the name of the teacher?
- **A.** Dick Goodwin
- **B.** Eddie Davis
- **C.** Jimmy Duncan
- **D.** Trevor Garfield

1712. Sister Helen Prejean befriends a killer who's been sentenced to death row in *Dead Man Walking*. What is the inmate's name?
- **A.** Hilton Barber
- **B.** Earl Delacroix
- **C.** Matthew Poncelet
- **D.** Guy Gilardi

1713. Gary Grobowski and his girlfriend Brooke Meyers decide to part ways in *The Break-Up*. What Major League baseball team is Gary obsessed with?
- **A.** Boston Red Sox
- **B.** Chicago Cubs
- **C.** New York Yankees
- **D.** New York Mets

1714. At what university does mathematician John Nash work in *A Beautiful Mind*?
- **A.** Princeton
- **B.** Rutgers
- **C.** Yale
- **D.** University of Pennsylvania

1715. Bruno Anthony and Guy Haines concoct a diabolical plan involving murder and deception in *Strangers on a Train*. What is Guy Haines's occupation?
- **A.** College instructor
- **B.** Tennis player
- **C.** Novelist
- **D.** Stockbroker

1716. Paul Edgecomb and other death row guards meet a very unusual prisoner named John Coffey in *The Green Mile*. What is the name of the penitentiary where Edgecomb and the others work?

A. Slabhearst

B. Shawshank

C. Cold Mountain

D. San Quentin

1717. Don Lockwood and Lina Lamont are a well-known film duo who find their situation changing after the birth of the talking picture in *Singin' in the Rain*. For what company do Lockwood and Lamont make films?

A. Landmark Films

B. Meyer Bros. Pictures

C. Famous Pictures

D. Monumental Pictures

1718. Rob Gordon is a record shop owner lamenting over the loss of his girlfriend Laura in *High Fidelity*. What is the name of Rob's record shop?

A. Vintage Vinyl

B. Historic Vinyl

C. World Famous Vinyl

D. Championship Vinyl

1719. Bad cop Alonzo Harris trains newbie Jake Hoyt in *Training Day*. For what city's police department do Harris and Hoyt work?

A. Los Angeles

B. New York City

C. San Francisco

D. Chicago

1720.

1721. Sonny, Duane, and Jacey all live in a small Texas town in *The Last Picture Show*. What is the name of their hometown?

A. Archer City

B. Anarene

C. Daleville

D. Comstock

1722. In *Ace Ventura: Pet Detective*, Ace is on the hunt for a missing football team mascot. What kind of animal is this?

A. Dolphin

B. Tiger

C. Jaguar

D. Shark

1723. Drug kingpin Frank White returns home from prison and immediately fights to regain control of the city in *King of New York*. Where was White incarcerated?

A. Riker's Island

B. Sing Sing

C. Kingston

D. Leavenworth

1724. Actor Johnny Depp has played pirates, undercover cops, and even drug lords. In which of these films does he play a character named Raoul Duke?

A. *The Man Who Cried*

B. *Nick of Time*

C. *Benny & Joon*

D. *Fear and Loathing in Las Vegas*

1720.

Howard Hawks' *Bringing Up Baby* is frequently cited as the quintessential screwball comedy. The film, which stars Katharine Hepburn and Cary Grant, follows a paleontologist named David Huxley. David meets free-spirited Susan Vance, who is baby-sitting a leopard named Baby. Mistaking David for a zoologist rather than a paleontologist, Susan persuades him to assist her with the leopard. Things become complicated when Susan's dog steals a rare brontosaurus bone from David and buries it. Further complicating matters, the leopard escapes. Adding to all of this, Susan falls in love with David and tries to stop him from getting married.

Bringing Up Baby is a case of a film growing in stature in the years after its release. Critics and audiences alike greeted the film with universal disdain in 1938. Today, however, it's widely considered a classic. It was listed at number ninety-seven on the American Film Institute's list of the one hundred greatest American films.

What is the name of Susan's dog?

A. Eddie

B. Jimbo

C. George

D. Whitey

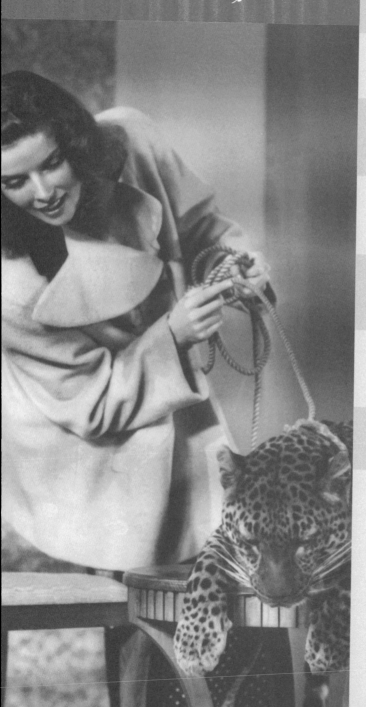

1725. Jack Nicholson plays Freddy Gale, a man obsessed with avenging the death of his daughter, in *The Crossing Guard*. What is Freddy's occupation?

A. Crossing Guard

B. Jeweler

C. Bounty Hunter

D. Banker

1726. Clara helps a young boy named David put his life back together after his parents are divorced in *Clara's Heart*. What is Clara's occupation?

A. Cab driver

B. Chef

C. Housekeeper

D. Day care operator

1727. A little girl named Pita, the daughter of a wealthy industrialist, is kidnapped in *Man on Fire*. Pita owns a much-loved stuffed teddy bear. What is the name of this bear?

A. Ted

B. Jiminy

C. Bilbo

D. Creasy Bear

1728. Hilary O'Neil goes to work as a private nurse for a dying man named Victor in *Dying Young*. She soon falls in love with him, but she knows their relationship is doomed. From what affliction is Victor dying?

A. Cardiomyopathy

B. Cystic fibrosis

C. Crohn's disease

D. Leukemia

1729. In *The Dark Half*, author Thad Beaumont decides he will retire his long-used pseudonym. However, he soon finds that his alter ego isn't ready to die. What is this pseudonym?

A. George Stark

B. Richard Bachman

C. Reggie Delesseps

D. None of these

1730. High school cheerleader Buffy Summers learns that she is destined to battle vampires in *Buffy the Vampire Slayer*. What is the name of the high school Buffy attends?

A. Lincoln High

B. Wordsworth High

C. Hemery High

D. Central High

1731. Frank Wyatt and his friends take a wrong turn, get lost, and witness a homicide in *Judgment Night*. In what city do these friends reside?

A. New York

B. Miami

C. Chicago

D. Atlanta

1732. Steve Martin plays a meteorologist trying to make sense of things in *L.A. Story*. What is the name of this character?

A. Harris K. Telemacher

B. Errol K. Richards

C. Frank K. Greenbaum

D. Mike K. Nellefex

1733. A vampire named Louis shares his story with an interviewer in the appropriately titled *Interview with the Vampire: The Vampire Chronicles*. Where does Louis say he was bitten and transformed into a vampire by Lestat?

A. Atlanta

B. Charlotte

C. New Orleans

D. Savannah

1734. *G.I. Jane* tells the heroic story of a tough female Navy SEALS trainee. What is her name?

A. Jane Harper

B. Theresa Foley

C. Karen Sisco

D. Jordan O'Neil

1735. Al Pacino plays the mayor of New York in Harold Becker's 1996 film *City Hall*. What is the mayor's name?

A. John Pappas

B. Frank Anselmo

C. Walter Stern

D. Kevin Calhoun

1736. Guy Patterson joins a band called the Oneders in *That Thing You Do!* The Oneders later change their name. What do they change it to?

A. The Cruisers

B. The Wonders

C. The Wallflowers

D. The Heardsmen

1737. Sadistic junior executives Chad and Howard play a cruel joke on a deaf secretary in *In the Company of Men*. What is the secretary's name?

A. Christine

B. Charlotte

C. Terri

D. Julie

1738. Saul Benjamin is a psychiatrist who falls in love with one of his patients in the comedy *Lovesick*. Saul believes he is visited and advised by a famous deceased person. Who is this?

A. Humphrey Bogart

B. Albert Camus

C. Benny Goodman

D. Sigmund Freud

1739. Peter Sellers played many offbeat characters. In several films, he even played multiple characters. In which of his films did he appear as a character named Sidney Wang?

A. *Soft Beds, Hard Battles*

B. *What's New, Pussycat*

C. *Murder by Death*

D. *Being There*

1740. George and Winifred Banks hire an unusual nanny to come and watch their children in *Mary Poppins*. What is George Banks's occupation?

A. Banker

B. Industrialist

C. Insurance agent

D. Jeweler

1747.

Ingrid Bergman enrolled in the Royal Dramatic Theater in Stockhom, Sweden, at the age of seventeen. That same year she appeared as an extra in the film *Landskamp*. Three years later, Bergman landed a speaking role in the film *Munkbrogreven*, and the following year she appeared in a breakthrough role in *Intermezzo*. On the strength of her performance in that film, producer David O. Selznick brought her to Hollywood.

In 1939, she reprised her role as Anita Hoffman in the American remake of *Intermezzo*, establishing herself as a Hollywood star. In 1942, she appeared in the role that she's most frequently associated with—Ilsa Lund in Michael Curtiz's *Casablanca*.

Other notable entries on Bergman's filmography include *For Whom the Bell Tolls*, *Gaslight*, *Notorious*, *Spellbound*, *The Bells of St. Mary's*, *Joan of Arc*, *Stromboli*, and *Anastasia*.

In what film does Bergman play a character named Alicia Huberman?

A. *The Bells of St. Mary's*
B. *Dr. Jekyll and Mr. Hyde*
C. *Notorious*
D. *Gaslight*

1741. Lesra Martin helps imprisoned boxer Rubin Carter get a retrial after reading his autobiography in *The Hurricane*. In what city does Lesra reside?
A. Minneapolis
C. Toronto
B. Bangor
D. Cambridge

1742. Naïve business grad Norville Barnes goes to the city, gets a job, and makes good (then bad) in *The Hudsucker Proxy*. Where did Barnes come from?
A. Parsons, Kansas
C. Addieville, Illinois
B. Muncie, Indiana
D. Mortons Gap, Kentucky

1743. Malik, Kristen, and Remy are all fresh students who experience a new world at college in *Higher Learning*. What is the name of the college they attend?
A. Freeman University
C. Rockefeller University
B. Benjamin Franklin University
D. Columbus University

1744. Denzel Washington has played a Civil War soldier, a dirty cop, and the late Malcolm X. In what film did he play a character named Easy Rawlins?
A. *Devil in a Blue Dress*
C. *Virtuosity*
B. *Fallen*
D. *John Q*

1745. Max Schumacher, Diana Christensen, and Howard Beale are employees of a television network in the film *Network*. What is the name of this network?
A. LBS
C. DBS
B. UBS
D. IBS

1746. The lead character of *Videodrome* is the president of a UHF television station. What is his name?
A. Max Harrigan
C. Max Renn
B. Tobias Evanwood
D. Ari Jamison

1747.

1748. What is the name of the church where Rose Sayer's brother, Reverend Samuel Sayer, ministers in *The African Queen*?
A. First Methodist Church Kung Du
C. Our Mother Mary Chapel Kung Du
B. First Baptist Church of Kung Du
D. First Assembly of the Lord Jesus Christ Kung Du

1749. Walter Burns is an editor for what newspaper in *His Girl Friday*?
A. *Boston Daily Globe*
C. *Hackensack Daily Gazette*
B. *Chicago Morning Post*
D. *New York Times*

1750. Vincent and Jules are partners in *Pulp Fiction*. What is Jules's surname?
A. Winstead
C. Windom
B. Winnfield
D. Winfrey

CHAPTER EIGHT:
GUILTY PLEASURES

1751. Who performed the song "A Fifth of Beethoven" for the soundtrack of the 1977 John Travolta dance flick *Saturday Night Fever*?

A. The Bee Gees

B. Walter Murphy

C. David Shire

D. Edward Montague

1752. Which one of these performers does *not* appear in the cheesy 1980 flick *Foxes*?

A. Randy Quaid

B. Jodie Foster

C. Willie Aames

D. Scott Baio

1753. Gym teacher Freddy Shoop finds out at the last minute that he has to teach *Summer School*. What subject does he have to teach?

A. Gym

B. Math

C. History

D. English

1754. What is the name of Ben Affleck's character in the disastrous 2003 Martin Brest film *Gigli*?

A. Frank Gigli

B. Larry Gigli

C. Jerry Gigli

D. Jackie Gigli

1755. Frank Davies and his wife have a baby who kills people in Larry Cohen's 1974 romp *It's Alive*. What is Mrs. Davies' name?

A. Ellen

B. Wendy

C. Lenore

D. Evelyn

1756. In *The Adventures of Buckaroo Banzai Across the Eighth Dimension*, what are the aliens that Buckaroo must defeat called?

A. Red Lectroids

B. Red Mastidions

C. Red Karponians

D. Red Herring

1757. Which character is shot in the eye while peering through a peephole in *Saw II*?

A. Xavier

B. Kerry

C. Matthew

D. Gus

OPPOSITE Will Ferrell in *Old School*, 2003

1758. What is the name of the song Kevin Costner sings with Amy Grant in the closing credits of Costner's apocalyptic dud *The Postman*?

A. "You Didn't Have to Be So Nice"   **C.** "Tell Me the Way"

B. "The Nicest One"   **D.** "I'm Sorry (We Made This Movie)"

1759. John Wayne's Genghis Khan fights for the love of a Tartar princess in *The Conqueror*. What is the princess's name?

A. Kumlek   **C.** Bortai

B. Jamuga   **D.** Chepei

1760. What object functions as a "Continuum Transfunctioner" in *Dude, Where's My Car?*

A. Rubik's Cube   **C.** Flashlight

B. Atari 2600 video game system   **D.** AM/FM radio

1761. Which of these actors does *not* appear in the silly Steven Spielberg World War II bomb *1941*?

A. John Belushi   **C.** Kevin Kline

B. Robert Stack   **D.** Treat Williams

1762. In what year was the Abrahams and Zucker comedy *Top Secret!* released?

A. 1982   **C.** 1984

B. 1983   **D.** 1985

1763.

1764. Do you know which of these is *not* the title of a film from Herschell Gordon Lewis's "Blood Trilogy"?

A. *Blood Feast*   **C.** *Two Thousand Maniacs!*

B. *The Gore Gore Girls*   **D.** *Color Me Blood Red*

1765. One of these cast members died before the release of the musical western *Cat Ballou*. Which one?

A. Nat King Cole   **C.** Michael Callan

B. Lee Marvin   **D.** Dwayne Hickman

1763.

Molly Ringwald started acting in 1974 at the tender age of five in a stage production of *Alice in Wonderland*. The following year the driven tot released a record album, *I Wanna Be Loved By You, Molly Sings*. In 1979, she landed the role of Molly Parker on the television series *Diff'rent Strokes*, which led to several appearances on the series' spin-off, *The Facts of Life*.

The film industry beckoned in 1982, and Ringwald appeared in three entirely forgettable films. This changed in 1984, however, when Ringwald appeared in her breakout film, *Sixteen Candles*. Along with peers Judd Nelson, Ally Sheedy, Emilio Estevez, Rob Lowe, Demi Moore, Andrew McCarthy, and Anthony Michael Hall, Ringwald became known as one of the "Brat Pack." Members of this unofficial collective then appeared in a string of "guilty pleasure" films, such as *The Breakfast Club* and *Pretty in Pink*.

In which of her films does Ringwald play a character named Frannie Goldsmith?

A. *P.K. and the Kid*

B. *Requiem for Murder*

C. *The Stand*

D. *Pretty in Pink*

1766. In *Never Been Kissed*, Josie Geller is a reporter who goes undercover at a high school to get a story. What newspaper does Josie write for?

A. *Picayune Post*

B. *Kansas City Times*

C. *Boston Globe*

D. *Chicago Sun-Times*

1767. What is the real name of the character Poison Ivy in Joel Schumacher's 1997 *Batman & Robin*?

A. Colby Shandler

B. Julie Madison

C. Pamela Isley

D. Karen Bixler

1768. Which of the following Prince songs does *not* appear in the 1984 movie *Purple Rain*?

A. "Pop Life"

B. "Let's Go Crazy"

C. "Purple Rain"

D. "When Doves Cry"

1769. Which member of the rap group Onyx appears as Malakai in the movie *Save the Last Dance*?

A. Sticky Fingaz

B. Fredro Starr

C. Big DS

D. Sonee Seeza

1770. By what nickname is Sylvester Stallone's character known in the disastrous 1991 film *Oscar*?

A. Bing

B. Lucky

C. Snaps

D. Bruno

1771. What is the name of the diner hangout from *Porky's* where Wendy is employed?

A. Porky's

B. Deadbeats

C. The Snack Bar

D. Ralph's

1772. A 1982 single became the basis for the campy comedy *Valley Girl*. Who sang the song?

A. Moon Unit Zappa

B. Adam Ant

C. Thomas Dolby

D. Robert Plant

1773. What is the name of Jane Hudson's abusive sister in *Whatever Happened to Baby Jane*?

A. Ann

B. Blanche

C. Camille

D. Beverly

1774. A café plays quite prominently in the movie *Fried Green Tomatoes*. What is the name of this café?

A. The Whistle Stop Café

B. The Buckeye Café

C. The Two Doors Down Café

D. The Dinner Bell Café

1775.

1776. What actor appears as Fred's little buddy Barney Rubble in *The Flintstones in Viva Rock Vegas*?

A. Alec Baldwin

B. Stephen Baldwin

C. Daniel Baldwin

D. William Baldwin

1777. Phil, Rita, and Larry are dispatched from a big-city television station to film the proceedings in *Groundhog Day*. Where is the television station located?

A. Phoenix

B. Santa Monica

C. Detroit

D. Pittsburgh

1778. On what planet does the 1982 fantasy *The Dark Crystal* take place?

A. Murrs

B. Canck

C. Thra

D. Bashe

1779. What is the name of the villainous leader of Bartertown in the apocalyptic yarn *Mad Max: Beyond Thunderdome*?

A. Aunty Carnage

B. Aunty Entity

C. Aunty Evil

D. Aunty Doria

1780. Dusty Bottoms is a character in the 1986 John Landis comedy *Three Amigos*. What actor appears in this role?

A. Steve Martin

B. Martin Short

C. Chevy Chase

D. Jon Lovitz

1781. An ambulance driver takes an interest in Laurie Strode in *Halloween II*. What is his name?

A. Eric Bowers

B. Tommy Watson

C. Eric Powers

D. Jimmy Lloyd

1782. Do you know Deuce's occupation at the beginning of the silly 1999 comedy *Deuce Bigalow: Male Gigolo*?

A. Air conditioner repairman

B. Garbageman

C. Fishtank repairman

D. Auto mechanic

1775.

The cult comedy *BASEketball* was directed by David Zucker (director of the first two *The Naked Gun* movies) and stars Trey Parker and Matt Stone, co-creators of the Emmy Award–winning television series, *South Park*. Although *South Park* was relatively unknown at the time of the film's release in 1998, it quickly became a national phenomenon and spawned its own guilty-pleasure film, *South Park: Bigger, Longer & Uncut*.

BASEketball's story begins with the two main characters, Joe Cooper (Parker) and Doug Remer (Stone), making up the slacker driveway game BASEketball, a combination of basketball and baseball, after they are challenged by jocks at a college party. Eventually the National BASEketball League is created. The film follows Cooper and Remer as they comically deal with their rising stardom.

Zucker actually created the game BASEketball well before directing the film, eventually forming his own league. Some original league players make an appearance in the film.

Which of these real-life athletes does *not* have a cameo in *BASEketball*?

A. Ken Griffey, Jr.

B. Dale Earnhardt

C. Reggie Jackson

D. Kareem Abdul-Jabbar

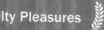

1783. Arnold Schwarzenegger plays a retired special forces soldier named John Matrix who must go to war with renegade baddies in *Commando*. What was Matrix's rank?

A. Colonel

B. Lieutenant

C. Commander

D. Captain

1784. What is the name of the professor played by Vincent Price in the 1953 chiller *House of Wax*?

A. Edward Mordred

B. Vincent Berrymore

C. Henry Jarrod

D. Thomas Wills

1785. A Righteous Brothers tune was the overplayed theme song for the 1990 schmaltz-fest *Ghost*. Can you name it?

A. "Just Once in My Life"

B. "You've Lost That Lovin' Feeling"

C. "Ebb Tide"

D. "Unchained Melody"

1786. What is the name of Chuck Norris' "good cop having a bad day" in the 1985 action film *Code of Silence*?

A. John Shepherd

B. Eddie Cusack

C. Matt Hunter

D. J.J. McQuade

1787. Whose "law" is quoted throughout the Tom Cruise vehicle *Cocktail*?

A. Conlon's

B. Cochran's

C. Conklin's

D. Coughlin's

1788. Paul Carlson is killed after staying at Dracula's home in *Scars of Dracula*. Paul's brother later shows up looking for him. What is the name of the brother?

A. Jimmy

B. Jacob

C. Simon

D. Henry

1789. Gore Vidal's Roman-history screenplay for *Caligula* was rewritten by committee as the budget soared. Vidal quit, and producer Bob Guccione (editor of *Penthouse*) integrated pornographic scenes with different actors. Which critic called *Caligula* "sickening, utterly worthless, shameful trash"?

A. Roger Ebert

B. Pauline Kael

C. Gene Shalit

D. Richard Schickel

1790. *Days of Thunder* is a 1990 racing movie starring Tom Cruise. What legendary screenwriter was responsible for writing the film?

A. Robert Towne
B. John Milius
C. Steven Zaillian
D. William Goldman

1791.

1792. Michael J. Fox plays Scott Howard, a high school student who transforms into a werewolf, in the comedy *Teen Wolf*. Scott has a crush on a blonde bombshell played by Lorie Griffin. What is her name?.

A. Darian
B. Rachel
C. Candy
D. Pamela

1793. Professional arm wrestler Lincoln Hawk gets to know his estranged son better in the film *Over the Top*. What is the name of his son?

A. Ricky
B. Michael
C. Tony
D. James

1794. What actor plays psychokinetic air traffic controller Max Fielder in the 1981 comedy *Modern Problems*?

A. Bill Murray
B. John Candy
C. Chevy Chase
D. Steve Martin

1795. According to the tagline for *Four Rooms*, how many "outrageous guests" are featured in the film?

A. Ten
B. Seven
C. Fifteen
D. Twelve

1796. What actor plays the doctor who discovers Joe Banks's inoperable brain cloud in *Joe Versus the Volcano*?

A. Don Ameche
B. Lloyd Bridges
C. Robert Stack
D. Leslie Nielsen

1797. What is the name of the Rancho Carne High School cheerleading squad in *Bring It On*?

A. The Toros
B. The Vistas
C. The Warriors
D. The Clovers

1791.

His characters are impervious to everything and seemingly have no weaknesses. He's a martial arts master, vegetarian, and a Buddhist with a side career as a country/pop/blues singer. His current movies often go straight to video. His action movies often try to push a deeper message. He directed the most questionable of his theatrically released films (*On Deadly Ground*) himself. So why do we keep watching?

For whatever reason, there can be little doubt that the films of action star Steven Seagal are guilty pleasures indeed. We love his movies, but we don't dare tell anyone.

In which of his films does Seagal quickly recover from a coma and immediately seek revenge?

A. *Marked for Death*
B. *The Patriot*
C. *Hard to Kill*
D. *Above the Law*

1798. What is the name of the magazine Andie Anderson writes for in *How to Lose a Guy in 10 Days*?

A. *Chic*

B. *Glamour*

C. *Classy*

D. *Composure*

1799. The ironically corny *Children of the Corn* takes place in the fictional town o[f] Gatlin. In what state is Gatlin located?

A. Illinois

B. Maine

C. Nebraska

D. Tennessee

1800. The 1984 Kevin Bacon movie *Footloose* is often remembered in association with its successful soundtrack. The film's love ballad, "Almost Paradise . . .", was performed by Mike Reno and Ann Wilson. Do you know what band Mike Reno was a member of?

A. Heart

B. Loverboy

C. Mike and the Mechanics

D. Journey

1801. Douglas Quaid has memories of a vacation implanted in his brain in the 1990 cheesefest *Total Recall*. What planet does he visit on his simulated vacation?

A. Mars

B. Venus

C. Tatooine

D. Jupiter

1802. Samuel L. Jackson signed on to fight off venomous attackers in *Snakes on a Plane* because of the filmmaker who was initially attached to direct it. Who was this?

A. Quentin Tarantino

B. John Woo

C. Rob Cohen

D. Ronnie Yu

1803. The 1979 Walter Hill film *The Warriors* tells the story of a gang returning to its home territory after being framed for the assassination of a rival gang leader. What is Swan's job title within the gang?

A. Warchief

B. Scout

C. Writer

D. Warlord

1804. Whose short story served as the basis for the 1985 Stuart Gordon horror favorite *Re-Animator*?

A. Shirley Jackson

B. H.P. Lovecraft

C. Ambrose Bierce

D. Edgar Allan Poe

1805. *The Time Machine* is a 1960 adaptation of the H.G. Wells novel of the same title. On what holiday does the film's story begin?

A. New Year's Eve

B. Thanksgiving

C. None of these

D. Christmas Eve

1806.

1807. In the 1984 cult film *Repo Man*, whom does Otto Maddox learn that his parents have given all of their money to?

A. The government

B. UNICEF

C. A televangelist

D. A homeless man

1808. What is the name of Johnny Rico's drill sargeant in *Starship Troopers*?

A. Zim

B. Owen

C. Levy

D. Barcalow

1809. In the wacky 1981 comedy *The Cannonball Run*, what is the name of the mechanic who has a superhero alter ego named Captain Chaos?

A. J.J. McClure

B. Shakey Finch

C. Seymour Goldfarb, Jr.

D. Victor Prinzi

1810. In what city does the 1986 Marvel Comics adaptation *Howard the Duck* take place?

A. Cincinnati

B. Cleveland

C. Detroit

D. Chicago

1811. In what year was *Highlander*'s Connor MacLeod said to have been born?

A. 1318

B. 1418

C. 1618

D. 1518

1812. Three friends decide to sell marijuana to get their friend out of jail in *Half Baked*. Which of the four friends spends most of the film in jail?

A. Kenny

B. Thurgood

C. Scarface

D. Brian

1806.

Basic Instinct is a 1992 erotic whodunit written by Joe Eszterhas and directed by Paul Verhoeven. (This same duo would later collaborate on another guilty pleasure favorite, *Showgirls*.) *Basic Instinct* was quite controversial at the time of its release, drawing ire from gay rights activists for portraying a bisexual woman as a cold-blooded murderer. It was also quite titillating for its brazen sexuality and gratuitous sex scenes.

The most notable and infamous scene is undoubtedly the one in which a room full of detectives questions Sharon Stone's character. She uncrosses her legs, and crosses them again, giving the audience a brief but unmistakable glimpse of her vagina. And in that brief instant, a star was born.

What is the name of Sharon Stone's character in *Basic Instinct*?

A. Leah Tilson

B. Sarah Little

C. Alison King

D. Catherine Tramell

1813. Old women poison old men in *Arsenic and Old Lace*. The bodies are then buried in the basement. Who buries them?

A. Jonathan

B. Mortimer

C. Uncle Teddy

D. Aunt Abby

1814. What is the name of David Carradine's character in the 1975 cult classic *Death Race 2000*?

A. Nero the Hero

B. Junior Bruce

C. "Machine Gun" Joe Viterbo

D. Frankenstein

1815. What is the name of the happy utopia where everyone loves music in *Yellow Submarine*?

A. Pepperland

B. Liverpooltopia

C. Ringonia

D. Beatleland

1816. *Tremors* tells the story of Perfection, Nevada, residents who fight wormlike monsters. Who is the town drunk in Perfection?

A. Valentine McKee

B. Earl Basset

C. Old Fred

D. Edgar Deems

1817. What type of weather condition destroys landmarks like the Hollywood sign and the Capitol Records Tower in *The Day After Tomorrow*?

A. Earthquake

B. Flood

C. Tornado

D. Tsunami

1818. Who directed the cult horror comedy *Basket Case*?

A. Sam Raimi

B. Frank Henenlotter

C. Stuart Gordon

D. Brad Paulson

1819. What do Ben Healy and his father "Big Ben" sell for a living in the 1990 comedy *Problem Child*?

A. Produce

B. Automobiles

C. Life Insurance

D. Sporting goods

1820. William Hurt plays Dr. Edward Jessup in the film *Altered States*. Who plays his daughter?

A. Drew Barrymore

B. Alyssa Milano

C. Terri Hatcher

D. Brooke Shields

1821. Texas Ranger Earl McGraw is a character played by Michael Parks in *From Dusk Till Dawn*. In which of these other films does Parks *not* appear?

A. *Kill Bill: Vol. 1*

B. *Grindhouse*

C. *Kill Bill: Vol. 2*

D. *From Dusk Till Dawn 2: Texas Blood Money*

1822.

1823. Where does mild-mannered geek Melvin Junko work in the cult film *The Toxic Avenger*?

A. Tromaville Community College

B. Tromaville Police Department

C. Tromaville Health Club

D. Tromaville Sanitation Department

1824. The campy 1986 romantic comedy *My Chauffeur* was released in the Philippines with a subtitle. What was this?

A. *Licensed to Love*

B. *Highway to Romance*

C. *Every Girl's Dream*

D. None of these

1825. The title of the film *Jumanji* (as well as the game within it) is a Zulu word. What does "jumanji" mean?

A. Too many problems

B. Many special effects

C. Chaotic nature

D. Animal trouble

1826. Nicolas Cage plays a private dick named Tom Welles in the film *8mm*. What actress plays his wife?

A. Emma Thompson

B. Janeane Garofalo

C. Catherine Keener

D. Linda Fiorentino

1827. What was James T. Kirk's Starfleet rank in the 1979 film *Star Trek: The Motion Picture*?

A. Admiral

B. Captain

C. Commander

D. Lieutenant Commander

1828. What state does Senator Jay Billington Bulworth represent in Warren Beatty's 1998 political comedy *Bulworth*?

A. New York

B. California

C. New Jersey

D. Miami

1829. This actor makes an early appearance as a camp counselor in the 1980 slasher flick *Friday the 13th*. Can you name him?

A. Johnny Depp

B. Sean Penn

C. Kevin Bacon

D. Gary Oldman

1822.

The Rocky Horror Picture Show is a campy 1975 horror musical starring then-unknowns Barry Bostwick, Susan Sarandon, and Tim Curry that was based on the stage musical *The Rocky Horror Show*.

The plot follows an uptight, newly engaged couple, Brad (Bostwick) and Janet (Sarandon), who are stranded in the middle of the woods on a rainy night with a flat tire. In search of a telephone, Brad and Janet wind up at the castle of a "sweet transvestite" Frank N. Furter (Curry) and his band of kinky minions.

Although the film did poorly during its initial release, *The Rocky Horror Picture Show* has since become a cult-classic phenomenon, screening regularly around the world at midnight showings that include costumed audience members shouting out lines to accompany the film, dancing in the aisles, and acting out the story in front of the screen. The film also has the distinction of being the highest grossing movie (more than $135 million) never to have played in more than 200 theaters simultaneously.

Which of these pop singers makes an early appearance in *The Rocky Horror Picture Show*?

A. None of these

B. Michael Jackson

C. David Bowie

D. Meat Loaf

1830. *The Breakfast Club* is a 1985 film about high school life written and directed by John Hughes. In the film, what is the name of the character who is dubbed "the Princess"?

A. Molly

B. Katie

C. Allison

D. Claire

1831. The 1999 romantic comedy *10 Things I Hate About You* is based on a play written by William Shakespeare. Which one?

A. *The Taming of the Shrew*

B. *A Midsummer Night's Dream*

C. *The Tempest*

D. *The Winter's Tale*

1832. In *Cheaper By the Dozen*, Steve Martin and Bonnie Hunt's characters raise twelve children. Which is their oldest daughter, played by Piper Perabo?

A. Kim

B. Jessica

C. Sarah

D. Nora

1833. The 1985 Brat Pack movie *St. Elmo's Fire* centers around a group of friends who have just graduated from college. What college did they attend?

A. Georgetown

B. Cornell

C. The University of Kansas

D. Yale

1834. *Cliffhanger* is a 1993 action flick starring Sylvester Stallone as mountain climber Gabe Walker, who finds himself entangled with thieves during a bungled heist. The leader of the criminals is played by John Lithgow. What is his name?

A. Hal Tucker

B. Jessie Deighan

C. Eric Qualen

D. Richard Travers

1835. In *The Adventures of Ford Fairlane*, we learn that Ed O'Neill's Lieutenant Amos is a former disco musician. What was the name of his single?

A. "Jet Airplane of Love"

B. "Booty Time"

C. "Volcano on the Dance Floor"

D. "Touch Me in Bad Places"

1836. *The Cat from Outer Space* is a 1978 Disney film about a feline from the stars. What is the name of the cat?

A. Kalbot

B. Max

C. Bagdalgar

D. Jake

1837. What is the name of the only African-American member of the *Ghostbusters* squad?

A. Ray

B. Winston

C. Egon

D. Peter

838. In the 1994 collegiate comedy *PCU*, what do the initials PCU stand for?

A. Politically Correct University

B. Pacific California University

C. Pennsylvania Charter University

D. Port Charles University

839. *Planet of the Apes* is a kitschy 1968 science fiction film starring Charlton Heston. What name do the humans dub the ape-inhabited world they discover?

A. Soror

B. Cabal

C. Borar

D. Lanae

840. What actor plays the character Carne the train conductor in the 1980 horror film *Terror Train*?

A. Warren Oates

B. Hart Bochner

C. Ben Johnson

D. Harry Dean Stanton

841. Chuck Norris is a former CIA agent living in Florida who must thwart a Russian terrorist's plan in *Invasion U.S.A.* What is the agent's name?

A. J.J. McQuade

B. Frank Shatter

C. Eddie Cusack

D. Matt Hunter

842. Jim Belushi's Detective Michael Dooley is assigned to work with a canine cop in the 1989 comedy *K-9*. What is the name of the dog?

A. Mason Dixon

B. Jerry Lee

C. Sparky

D. Elvis

1843.

1844. Which of these is *not* a food product manufactured by the Soylent Corporation in the 1973 Charlton Heston vehicle *Soylent Green*?

A. Soylent Yellow

B. Soylent Green

C. Soylent Brown

D. Soylent Red

1845. Sylvester Stallone plays a street judge in the future in the 1995 action film *Judge Dredd*. What is Dredd's first name?

A. Matt

B. Joe

C. Frank

D. John

1846. Ryan O'Neal's Oliver Barrett IV is a student at an Ivy League university who falls in love with a girl attending Radcliffe in *Love Story*. What university does he attend?

A. Harvard

B. Princeton

C. Yale

D. Dartmouth

1843.

Before becoming the thirty-eighth governor of the state of California, Arnold Schwarzenegger was simply known as an Austrian bodybuilder who became a stiff actor with heavily-accented English. Due in large part to these attributes, much of Schwarzenegger's work now falls into the "guilty pleasure" category.

Schwarzenegger's career as an actor began in the title role of the forgettable 1970 film *Hercules in New York*. He then appeared in Robert Altman's *The Long Goodbye* and the film *Stay Hungry*, but didn't begin making his true guilty pleasures until after the release of the 1977 bodybuilding documentary *Pumping Iron*. His turn as Robert E. Howard's legendary hero in 1982's *Conan the Barbarian* made Schwarzenegger a star. After that, there was no stopping him.

His best-known films include *Conan the Destroyer*, *The Terminator* and its two sequels, *Commando*, *Predator*, *The Running Man*, *Twins*, *Total Recall*, *Last Action Hero*, *True Lies*, and *Batman & Robin*.

In which of his films does Schwarzenegger play a character named Jericho Cane?

A. *Last Action Hero*

B. *End of Days*

C. *Eraser*

D. *Raw Deal*

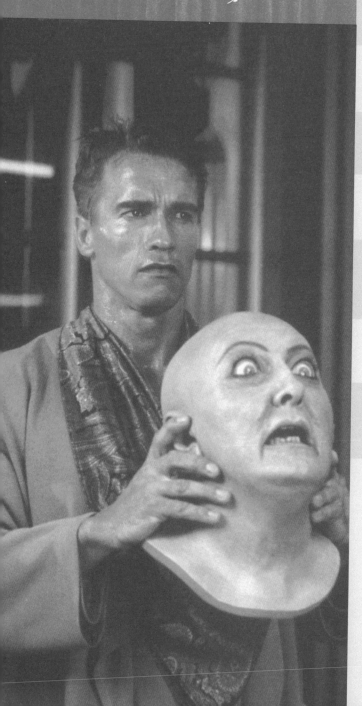

1847. What actor plays the white college student who transforms himself into a black man in the 1986 comedy *Soul Man*?

A. Kevin Bacon

B. Judd Nelson

C. C. Thomas Howell

D. Ralph Macchio

1848. What is the name of the unscrupulous real estate developer living next to the Brady family in 1995's revisionist *The Brady Bunch Movie*?

A. Mr. Schwartz

B. Mr. Ditmeyer

C. Mr. Cole

D. Mr. Barnmeyer

1849. Kurt Russell plays truck driver Jack Burton in John Carpenter's cult classic action film *Big Trouble in Little China*. What is the name of Burton's rig?

A. Big Trouble

B. Hell On Wheels

C. 18 Wheels of Destruction

D. The Pork Chop Express

1850. Richard and Larry pretend their dead boss Bernie is still alive in the comedy *Weekend at Bernie's*. From what did Bernie die?

A. He choked to death

B. Food poisoning

C. Heart attack

D. He was murdered

1851. Maggie Carpenter is a woman with the terrible habit of running out on her grooms on their wedding day in *Runaway Bride*. How many men has she run out on at the start of the film?

A. Four

B. Three

C. Five

D. None of these

1852. Chevy Chase plays reporter Irwin M. Fletcher in the 1985 Gregory McDonald adaptation *Fletch*. What does the "M" in Fletch's name stand for?

A. Maurice

B. Nothing

C. Marvin

D. Morris

1853. Former football star Bubba Smith plays the intimidating Moses Hightower in the cop comedy *Police Academy*. What does Hightower say was his career before becoming a cop?

A. Defensive end

B. Chiropractor

C. Janitor

D. Florist

1854. By what name is Frances Houseman known in the 1987 romance film *Dirty Dancing*?

A. Princess

B. Baby

C. Fran

D. June

1855. Which of these performers made their screen debut in the schlock favorite *Santa Claus Conquers the Martians*?

A. Pia Zadora

B. Stacy Keach

C. Ann-Margret

D. John Rhys-Davies

1856. In the 1976 sci-fi romp *Logan's Run*, people are killed when they reach their "Last Day." At what age do they reach this?

A. Twenty-one

B. Twenty-five

C. Forty

D. Thirty

1857. In the comedy-drama *Turner & Hooch*, Tom Hanks's canine partner sires puppies with the veterinarian's dog. With what breed of dog does Hooch have these babies?

A. Beagle

B. Poodle

C. Collie

D. Australian shepherd

1858.

1859. What song do Cheech and Chong sing to win the Battle of the Bands at the conclusion of *Up in Smoke*?

A. "Sister Mary Elephant"

B. "Up in Smoke"

C. "Basketball Jones"

D. "Earache My Eye"

1860. Keanu Reeves is a former collegiate football star turned FBI agent named Johnny Utah in *Point Break*. What position did Utah play in college?

A. Quarterback

B. Kicker

C. Defensive end

D. Center

1861. What do the lawmen led by Billy the Kid in the 1988 movie *Young Guns* call themselves?

A. Tunstall's Boys

B. Riders

C. The Regulators

D. The Badges

1862. What is the name of the warlord who destroys young Conan's village at the beginning of *Conan the Barbarian*?

A. Dagoth

B. Thulsa Doom

C. Toth-Amon

D. King Kull

1858.

Smokey and the Bandit, a light-hearted chase movie starring Burt Reynolds, Sally Field, and Jackie Gleason, was the second-highest grossing film in 1977 after *Star Wars*.

The film's story centers on Bo "Bandit" Darville (Reynolds), a moonshine runner lured out of retirement when he's offered $80,000 to transport a semi filled with Coors beer to Texarkana, Texas. (Texarkana is located in a "dry" county.) With his partner Cledus "Snowman" Snow (played by singer Jerry Reed) at the wheel of a big rig, Bandit and his black Trans-Am accept the job. On the way, Bandit picks up a runaway bride (Field) and finds a nemesis in Sheriff Buford T. Justice (Gleason), resulting in a non-stop succession of car chases, crashes, auto pile-ups, and one-liners.

Cledus is accompanied by his pet basset hound. What is the dog's name?

A. Charlie

B. Fred

C. Bear

D. Gator

1863. Can you name the actor who appears in the role of Sergeant Ray Duquette in the steamy 1998 thriller *Wild Things*?

A. Bill Murray

B. Matt Dillon

C. Robert Wagner

D. Kevin Bacon

1864. *Strange Brew*, the silly 1983 comedy starring Dave Thomas and Rick Moranis, was loosely based upon a play by William Shakespeare. Which one?

A. *Twelfth Night*

B. *Othello*

C. *Hamlet*

D. *Macbeth*

1865. This respected film critic cowrote the 1970 X-rated (since reclassified as NC-17) Russ Meyer film *Beyond the Valley of the Dolls*.

A. Richard Schickel

B. Gene Siskel

C. Gene Shalit

D. Roger Ebert

1866. The title character of *Zoolander* retires from modeling after his friends are killed in a "freak gasoline fight accident." What occupation does Zoolander then attempt?

A. Miner

B. Veterinarian

C. Secret Service agent

D. Sanitation worker

1867. Which of the following performers does *not* appear in the 1988 sequel *Poltergeist III*?

A. Heather O'Rourke

B. Craig T. Nelson

C. Lara Flynn Boyle

D. Tom Skerritt

1868. *Back to School* is a 1986 comedy in which middle-aged Rodney Dangerfield returns to college. Can you name the popular novelist who makes a cameo appearance as himself in the film?

A. Kurt Vonnegut

B. Norman Mailer

C. John Irving

D. Joseph Heller

1869. In the campy 1988 horror flick *Child's Play*, a deceased serial killer named Charles Lee Ray possesses a children's toy. What was murderer Ray's nickname?

A. The Hillside Strangler

B. The Lakeshore Strangler

C. The Marietta Mangler

D. None of these

1870. *A Knight's Tale* is a 2000 film known for its anachronistic use of modern rock songs. Which of these songs appears in the film?

A. "Start Me Up" by the Rolling Stones

B. "Another One Bites the Dust" by Queen

C. "Rock & Roll Part 2" by Gary Glitter

D. "You Shook Me All Night Long" by AC/DC

1871. Which *Saturday Night Live* alum cowrote Tim Burton's 1985 cult comedy *Pee-Wee's Big Adventure*?

A. Jan Hooks

B. Phil Hartman

C. Kevin Nealon

D. Michael McKean

1872. Samantha Caine (a.k.a. Charlie Baltimore) has her daughter kidnapped by terrorists in *The Long Kiss Goodnight*. What is her daughter's name?

A. Jaiden

B. Caitlin

C. Kayley

D. Rebecca

1873.

1874. *Camelot* is a musical film starring Richard Harris, Vanessa Redgrave, and Franco Nero. In what year was this film released?

A. 1960

B. 1963

C. 1971

D. 1967

1875. In which of these nominated categories did the 1981 film *Mommie Dearest* not win a Razzie Award?

A. Worst Director

B. Worst Picture

C. Worst Actress

D. Worst Screenplay

1876. In the 1996 Tim Burton "B" movie parody *Mars Attacks!* the aliens are killed whenever the song "Indian Love Call" is played. Who sings this song?

A. Tom Jones

B. Boxcar Willie

C. Slim Whitman

D. Wayne Newton

1877. Arnold Schwarzenegger's Dutch Schaefer leads a team of commandos in *Predator*. How many commandos make up this team?

A. Six

B. Seven

C. Eight

D. Nine

1878. U.S. Army Ranger Cameron Poe is imprisoned for murdering a man to save his pregnant wife in *Con Air*. For how many years is he imprisoned?

A. Five

B. Nine

C. Seven

D. None of these

1873.

The Godfather Part III has the dubious distinction of being the only installment of the *Godfather* trilogy that is not considered a "classic," having—unlike the first two films—not won an Oscar for Best Picture. In fairness, it's likely that *Part III* would not have seemed to fall so short if it had not been preceded by a film frequently cited as the greatest sequel ever made.

Making matters worse, screenwriter/director Francis Ford Coppola substantiated fans' claims that the third installment was unnecessary, conceding that he'd already fully told the story he'd intended to tell and admitting that the film was made only because he was experiencing financial trouble at the time.

Add the questionable casting of Coppola's daughter, Sofia, and the absence of Robert Duvall, and you've got problems.

What excuse is given for the absence of Duvall's character, Tom Hagen?

A. He's away on business

B. He's in the witness protection program

C. He's in prison

D. He's dead

1879. George Henderson unwittingly lets a sasquatch loose in the city in the comedy *Harry and the Hendersons*. What city is this?

A. Minneapolis   C. Kansas City

B. Seattle   D. San Diego

1880. What actor was first cast in the role of Rick in the 1984 comedy *Bachelor Party*, but was later replaced by Tom Hanks?

A. Scott Baio   C. Eric Stoltz

B. Michael J. Fox   D. Paul Reiser

1881. *The Ice Pirates* is a 1984 science fiction comedy that takes place in the future. In the film, what is the most valuable commodity in the world?

A. Coca-Cola   C. Gold

B. Water   D. Soil

1882. What is the name of the daughter played by Jodie Foster in the 1976 Disney film *Freaky Friday*?

A. Virginia   C. Annabel

B. Ellen   D. Tara

1883. Charlie Bucket is accompanied by his grandfather when he visits candy man Willy Wonka's top secret factory in *Willy Wonka & the Chocolate Factory*. What is his grandfather's name?

A. John   C. Frank

B. Joe   D. Buck

1884. Ferris, Sloane, and Cameron go to a major league baseball game during their hiatus in *Ferris Bueller's Day Off*. At what stadium do they watch the game?

A. Fenway Park   C. Wrigley Field

B. Candlestick Park   D. Riverfront Stadium

1885. What legendary musician makes a cameo as a pawnbroker in the Eddie Murphy-Dan Aykroyd team-up *Trading Places*?

A. James Brown   C. Chuck Berry

B. Little Richard   D. Bo Diddley

1886. Which of these films does *not* feature actor Michael Dudikoff?

A. *American Ninja 3: Blood Hunt*   C. *American Ninja*

B. *American Ninja 2: The Confrontation*   D. *American Ninja 4: The Annhiliation*

1887. What comedian makes an appearance as a bouncer in John Hughes's 1986 Brat Pack flick *Pretty in Pink*?

A. Denis Leary

B. Steven Wright

C. Andrew Dice Clay

D. Sam Kinison

1888. In *Space Truckers*, the truckers believe their cargo is a load of blow-up dolls. What are they actually carrying?

A. Plutonium

B. Cyborgs

C. Corpses

D. Laser cannons

1889.

1890. In the comedy *Superstar*, what is the name of the new friend Mary Katherine Gallagher makes in special education class?

A. Helen Lewengrub

B. Helen Corrigan

C. Helen Lowenbaum

D. Helen Cabowski

1891. In John Carpenter's *The Fog*, it is revealed that the residents of Antonio Bay sank a ship owned by a rich leper. What was the name of the ship?

A. The *Elizabeth Johansson*

B. The *Elizabeth Blake*

C. The *Elizabeth Dane*

D. The *Elizabeth Carlyle*

1892. Kirk Douglas plays the character Cactus Jack in the 1979 western *The Villain*. What is Cactus Jack's last name?

A. Johnson

B. Slade

C. Deville

D. Kincaid

1893. In the movie *Willard*, the title character's only friends in the world are his two pet rats. One of them is named Ben. What is the name of the second rat?

A. Plato

B. Socrates

C. Aristotle

D. Prodicus

1894. What is the name of the girl next door that John Travolta's character in *The Boy in the Plastic Bubble* falls in love with?

A. Karen

B. Amy

C. Gina

D. Ellen

1889.

Whoopi Goldberg is a talented actress when given the opportunity to actually act, but many of her films (*The Color Purple*, *The Player*, and *Girl, Interrupted* being notable exceptions) fall distinctly into the guilty pleasure category.

Goldberg started as a stand-up comic, working up to Broadway where she appeared in a one-woman show produced by Mike Nichols. In 1985, Steven Spielberg cast Goldberg as the lead in *The Color Purple*, earning her an Academy Award nomination for Best Actress.

Following her 1985 Oscar nomination, Goldberg has appeared in such films as *Jumpin' Jack Flash*, *Burglar*, *Ghost*, *Clara's Heart*, *Soapdish*, *Sister Act*, *Sarafina!*, *Loaded Weapon 1*, *Made in America*, *Sister Act 2: Back in the Habit*, *Star Trek: Generations*, *Boys on the Side*, *Moonlight and Valentino*, *Eddie*, *Bogus*, *The Associate*, and *Rat Race*, among others.

Which of these animated films does *not* feature the voice of Whoopi Goldberg?

A. *Racing Stripes*

B. *Finding Nemo*

C. *The Rugrats Movie*

D. *Doogal*

1895. What subliminal message does Nada discover printed on all of the money in the 1988 sci-fi film *They Live*?

A. "I am your God."

B. "Without me you are nothing."

C. "Die for me."

D. "Obey."

1896. What is Eddie Hawkins' expertise in the 1991 Bruce Willis vehicle *Hudson Hawk*?

A. Hacking computers

B. Armed robbery

C. Killing

D. Safecracking

1897. What song plays on the soundtrack when Laney steps down the stairs and unveils her transformation in the romantic comedy *She's All That*?

A. "Sugar" by Stretch Princess

B. "Kiss Me" by Sixpence None the Richer

C. "Prophecy" by Remy Zero

D. "Baby Got Going" by Liz Phair

1898. *Love Potion #9* is a 1992 romantic comedy starring Sandra Bullock. The film was inspired by the popular doo-wop song of the same title. This song also appears in the film. Who sings it?

A. The Edsels

B. The Five Satins

C. The Clovers

D. Jerry Butler & the Impressions

1899. The golf comedy *Caddyshack* was ranked at number 71 on the American Film Institute's list of the 100 funniest American films. At what number is the film listed on Bravo's "100 Funniest Movies" list?

A. It is not ranked on its list at all

B. Ninth

C. Sixty-third

D. Second

1900. *Drop Dead Gorgeous* is a 1999 mockumentary about a small town beauty pageant in Minnesota. Kirsten Dunst plays contestant Amber Atkins. Who is Amber's hero?

A. Judge Judy

B. Diane Sawyer

C. Hillary Clinton

D. Oprah Winfrey

1901. What does Doris Day's character share with Rock Hudson's character in the romantic comedy *Pillow Talk*?

A. Her house

B. A swimming pool

C. A telephone line

D. An inheritance

1902. What does Anton Phibes inject into his body at the end of the camp classic *The Abominable Dr. Phibes*?

A. Bleach

B. Rat poison

C. Cyanide

D. Embalming fluid

1903. *Real Genius* is a 1985 comedy starring Val Kilmer that takes place on the campus of a fictitious college. What is the name of this college?

- **A.** Carver Tech
- **B.** Pacific Tech
- **C.** Universal Tech
- **D.** Madison Tech

1904. Who appears as Marty and Jane's alcoholic uncle in the 1985 horror flick *Silver Bullet*?

- **A.** Gary Busey
- **B.** Tom Skerritt
- **C.** Michael Gross
- **D.** William Smith

1905. In the 1995 thriller *Copycat*, the lyrics of a song titled "Murder By Numbers" are quoted prominently. What band recorded this song?

- **A.** The Beatles
- **B.** Aerosmith
- **C.** The Rolling Stones
- **D.** The Police

1906.

1907. *Ishtar*, the 1987 comedy starring Warren Beatty and Dustin Hoffman, was one of the biggest box office flops in history. What is the name of the lounge singer character played by Beatty?

- **A.** Chuck Clarke
- **B.** Mark Gardner
- **C.** Lyle Rogers
- **D.** Ryan Robertson

1908. Tom Selleck plays a novelist named Phil Blackwood in *Her Alibi*. In what genre does Blackwood write?

- **A.** Romance
- **B.** Science fiction
- **C.** Mystery
- **D.** Horror

1909. Edward D. Wood, Jr.'s *Plan 9 from Outer Space* is often cited as being the worst film ever made. One of the film's actors, Tor Johnson, was known for something else. What was this?

- **A.** He was a network weatherman
- **B.** He was a professional boxer
- **C.** He was a popular novelist
- **D.** He was a professional wrestler

1910. Which character in Stephen King's *It* is a novelist and is the author of *The Glowing*?

- **A.** Mike Hanlon
- **B.** Bill Denbrough
- **C.** Ben Hanscom
- **D.** Richie Tozier

1911. What is the name of the boxer Rocky Balboa trains in *Rocky IV*?

- **A.** Ivan Drago
- **B.** Apollo Creed
- **C.** Billy Gunn
- **D.** Marion Cobretti

1906.

Showgirls is a 1995 sexploitation film starring former *Saved by the Bell* star Elizabeth Berkley and Gina Gershon. The film's story line focuses on a down-on-her-luck hottie named Nomi Malone (Berkley), who goes to work as a stripper in Las Vegas. From there the "story" touches on virtually every naughty theme imaginable, from bisexuality to rape.

Today it seems laughably inconceivable that United Artists films and director Paul Verhoeven expected *Showgirls* to be a massive box-office success prior to its release, but it's true. The movie was surrounded by controversy due to its nudity and "erotic sexuality," and became the first movie with an NC-17 rating to receive a wide theatrical release.

Showgirls was quickly labeled one of the worst films ever made. The film received a record thirteen Razzie Award nominations, "winning" seven.

What is the name of the Vegas ensemble production in which Nomi is hired to dance?

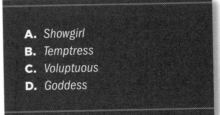

- **A.** *Showgirl*
- **B.** *Temptress*
- **C.** *Voluptuous*
- **D.** *Goddess*

1912. What band got its name from a character in the cheesy 1968 science fiction romp *Barbarella*?

A. Duran Duran

B. Stone Temple Pilots

C. Devo

D. Pet Shop Boys

1913. In what year does the noir horror film *Angel Heart* take place?

A. 1935

B. 1945

C. 1955

D. 1965

1914. Rusty Wells and his band go on their yearly trip to a vacation spot in the Elvis Presley vehicle *Girl Happy*. What is this vacation spot?

A. Ft. Lauderdale

B. Virginia Beach

C. Galveston

D. Palm Springs

1915. Which of these actors does *not* appear in the 1996 action film *The Rock*?

A. David Morse

B. John Spencer

C. William Forsythe

D. Paul Giamatti

1916. Do you know which of these titles is *not* an actual movie featuring comedians Bud Abbott and Lou Costello?

A. *Abbott and Costello in the Foreign Legion*

B. *Abbott and Costello Meet Bela Lugosi*

C. *Abbott and Costello Meet the Keystone Kops*

D. *Abbott and Costello Meet Captain Kidd*

1917. Jim Carrey plays the character Lloyd in *Dumb and Dumber*. What is Lloyd's last name?

A. Christmas

B. Jupiter

C. Macintosh

D. Klondike

1918. How many people are invited to stay in the haunted house in the 1959 fright flick *House on Haunted Hill*?

A. Zero

B. Five

C. Six

D. Four

1919. Three women terrorize a young couple in the desert in the Russ Meyer trash classic *Faster, Pussycat! Kill! Kill!* What is the shared occupation of the three women?

A. Model

B. Waitress

C. Stripper

D. None of these

1920. What band performed the theme song "Flash" for the campy 1980 sci-fi yarn *Flash Gordon*?

A. Queen

B. Bread

C. Men at Work

D. Iron Maiden

1921. What is the name of the music mogul who produced the cheesy action film *The Last Dragon*?

A. Quincy Jones

B. Berry Gordy

C. Phil Spector

D. Clive Davis

1922.

1923. *The Last Action Hero* is a silly action satire that finds a young boy catapulted into an action movie. What is the name of this fictional movie?

A. *Jack Slater II*

B. *Jack Slater III*

C. *Jack Slater IV*

D. *Jack Slater V*

1924. What performer plays the title character in the Luc Besson science fiction film *The Fifth Element*?

A. Chris Tucker

B. Ian Holm

C. Bruce Willis

D. Milla Jovovich

1925. *RoboCop* is a campy action film set in the future. In what city does the film take place?

A. Detroit

B. Chicago

C. San Diego

D. Phoenix

1926. Can you name the acclaimed screenwriter who performed an uncredited rewrite on the 1997 horror film *Mimic*?

A. Robert Towne

B. John Milius

C. Steven Zaillian

D. John Sayles

1927. *Better Off Dead* is a 1985 black comedy starring John Cusack. In what fictional city does the film's story take place?

A. Dumont

B. Derry

C. Greendale

D. West Harbor

1928. *Crazy/Beautiful* is a romance film about a rich girl, Nicole, and a kid from the wrong side of the tracks, Carlos. What is the occupation of Nicole's father?

A. Bank president

B. Congressman

C. Art curator

D. Stock broker

1922.

Rambo: First Blood Part II, the sequel to 1982's *First Blood*, is a true guilty pleasure. In the film, Sylvester Stallone's John Rambo returns to Vietnam and single-handedly accomplishes what the entire U.S. military could not: he beats the Viet Cong. Despite having only fifty-nine confirmed kills during the entire Vietnam conflict, Rambo kills more than a hundred people in just ninety-four minutes. (We actually see him kill sixty-one people on screen, but he also destroys an entire village and a prison camp, killing many more.)

The screenplay was first written by James Cameron, but then rewritten by Stallone himself. (Stallone's version makes his character more heroic, even eliminating a sidekick character.)

Rambo received seven Razzie nominations, winning four. These included prizes for Worst Picture, Worst Screenplay, and Worst Actor.

In which of the following categories did *Rambo* win its fourth Razzie Award?

A. Worst Original Song

B. Worst Supporting Actress

C. Worst Director

D. Worst New Star

1929. Which experimental filmmaker appears in a cameo in Matt Stone and Trey Parker's film *Cannibal! The Musical*?

A. Stan Brakhage

B. Shirley Clarke

C. Kenneth Anger

D. Willard Maas

1930. In *The Goonies*, a group of children go searching for the buried treasure of a legendary pirate. What is the name of this pirate?

A. Barnacle Bill

B. Captain Blood

C. Davey Jones

D. One-Eyed Willie

1931. What is the name of the real-life dictator who is holding Dexter captive in *Hot Shots! Part Deux*?

A. Ayatollah Khomeini

B. Saddam Hussein

C. Idi Amin Dada

D. Fidel Castro

1932. *Young Sherlock Holmes* finds Holmes and Watson meeting as youngsters in a boarding school. What is the name of Holmes's girlfriend?

A. Emily

B. Marion

C. Elizabeth

D. Helen

1933. Which of the following actresses from the comedy *Nine to Five* went on to reprise her character in the television series of the same title?

A. Dolly Parton

B. Lily Tomlin

C. Jane Fonda

D. None of these

1934. *UHF* is a 1989 comedy starring "Weird Al" Yankovic. Which of the following actors does *not* appear in *UHF*?

A. Michael Richards

B. Andrew Dice Clay

C. Fran Drescher

D. Kevin McCarthy

1935. What is the title of the first film to feature Tom Laughlin's idealistic character Billy Jack?

A. *Billy Jack*

B. *The Trial of Billy Jack*

C. *The Born Losers*

D. *When He Comes Around*

1936. *Legally Blonde* is a 2001 comedy in which Reese Witherspoon's not-so-ditzy character attends law school. What school does she attend?

A. Harvard

B. Stanford

C. Yale

D. Columbia

1937. David Bowie plays the goblin king in Jim Henson's fantasy *Labyrinth*. What is his name?

A. Borak

B. Jareth

C. Hoggle

D. Abrosius

1938. Joel Goodson sinks his father's car into Lake Michigan in *Risky Business*. What type of car was this?

A. Porsche 550 Spyder

B. Porsche 944

C. Porsche 928

D. Porsche Carrera GT

1939.

1940. Two nations invade the United States in the 1984 John Milius action film *Red Dawn*. One of these is the Soviet Union. What is the other?

A. Iran

B. Germany

C. Libya

D. Cuba

1941. On what television series did Sharon Stone appear in 1995 as a character named Trailer Park Resident?

A. *Homicide: Life on the Street*

B. *Roseanne*

C. *Frasier*

D. *Malcolm in the Middle*

1942. Which of these performers does *not* appear in the 1984 crime spoof *Johnny Dangerously*?

A. Rodney Dangerfield

B. Dom DeLuise

C. Danny DeVito

D. Joe Piscopo

1943. Clu Gulager plays the warehouse owner in *The Return of the Living Dead*. What is his name?

A. Frank

B. Burt

C. Freddy

D. Ernie

1944. Which of the following statements is not a part of the three-sentence tagline for the Michael Bay action flick *Armageddon*?

A. "For Love"

B. "For Honor"

C. "For Mankind"

D. "For Hope"

1939.

Director John Waters's entire career could be called a guilty pleasure. From feeling like you might actually go to hell for watching *Pink Flamingos* to the sweet temptation of singing along to *Hairspray*, Waters celebrates the trashy side of life. This focus has made him a cult figure, and has brought him mainstream acclaim as well: the Ricki Lake vehicle *Hairspray* was made into a hit musical, and remade as a film starring John Travolta, Queen Latifah, and Christopher Walken.

Waters's 1990 musical *Cry-Baby*, set in 1950s Baltimore, stars Johnny Depp as a rock 'n' roller from the wrong side of the tracks. Depp's talent for letting a solitary tear roll down his cheek gets him any girl he wants—even "square" beauty Allison. But will the other squares hold her back? Not if Depp and crew can help it—and with the supporting cast of Ricki Lake, Iggy Pop, Traci Lords, and Patty Hearst in his corner, he's sure to get the girl.

What is the last name of Depp's character in *Cry-Baby*?

A. Johnson

B. Barrett

C. Nance

D. Walker

1945. Pee-Wee Herman actor Paul Reubens plays a waiter in the musical comedy *The Blues Brothers*. What is the name of the upscale restaurant where he works?

A. Chez Chesterfield   **C.** Chez Paul

B. Chez Bernardo   **D.** Chez François

1946. Whose novel was the 1970 cult film *Myra Breckinridge* adapted from?

A. Norman Mailer   **C.** Jacqueline Susann

B. Gore Vidal   **D.** Sidney Sheldon

1947. A character played by Samantha Mathis helps Christian Slater's pilot Hale thwart the evil plans of John Travolta's Deakins in *Broken Arrow*. What is the occupation of Mathis's character?

A. Pilot   **C.** DEA agent

B. Meteorologist   **D.** Park ranger

1948. In the nuclear ants movie *Them!*, what actor played the role of FBI agent Robert Graham?

A. Leonard Nimoy   **C.** James Arness

B. Fess Parker   **D.** James Whitmore

1949. There is a bomb on a bus in the action movie *Speed*. If the bus dips below a certain speed, the bomb will detonate. How many miles per hour must the bus travel in order to keep from exploding?

A. 20   **C.** 50

B. 30   **D.** 40

1950. For which of his films did action actor Jean-Claude Van Damme win a Razzie Award for Worst New Star?

A. *Kickboxer*   **C.** *Hard Target*

B. *Bloodsport*   **D.** *Double Impact*

1951. The DVD for the science fiction parody *Galaxy Quest* features an alternate audio track in which all dialogue is spoken in an alien language from the film. What is the name of this language?

A. Durtopian   **C.** Quellbit

B. Gobellisque   **D.** Thermian

1952 C. Thomas Howell plays Jim, the protagonist, in the horror film *The Hitcher*. What is Jim's last name?

A. Nash

C. Starr

B. Halsey

D. Esteridge

1953. Griffin Dunne plays a character named Louden Trott in the 1987 Madonna vehicle *Who's That Girl*. What is Trott's occupation?

A. Chef

C. Lawyer

B. Accountant

D. Investment banker

1954.

1955. What was the original title of the horror film *Dead Alive* when it was released in its homeland of New Zealand?

A. *Braindead*

C. *Bad Taste*

B. *Dead and Buried*

D. *Guts and All*

1956. What actor plays the character Arnold Rothstein in the 1991 crime film *Mobsters*?

A. Patrick Dempsey

C. Chris Penn

B. Anthony Quinn

D. F. Murray Abraham

1957. Reese Witherspoon's *Cruel Intentions* chraracter Annette Hargrove has just moved to Long Island. From where did she move?

A. Kansas City

C. Green Bay

B. Iowa Falls

D. Jersey City

1958. Who is the comedian who plays the mystical character Rufus in *Bill & Ted's Excellent Adventure*?

A. Chevy Chase

C. George Carlin

B. Steven Wright

D. Bill Murray

1959. James and Mollie have a baby together in *Look Who's Talking*. James is a cabbie. What is Mollie's occupation?

A. Teacher

C. News anchor

B. Accountant

D. Lawyer

1954.

Charlton Heston was born in St. Helen, Michigan, on October 4, 1924. He was raised in Chicago, and his passion for acting began on stage as a student at New Trier Township High School. His hard work and apparent talent led to his receiving a drama scholarship to Northwestern University. Heston then enlisted, serving two years as a radio operator and gunner in the U.S. Army Air Corps, returning to the stage in 1948 and ultimately landing a role in the Broadway production *Antony and Cleopatra*.

In 1950, Heston appeared in his first feature, *Dark City*. His breakthrough, however, came with his turn in *The Greatest Show on Earth*. His films include *The Ten Commandments, Touch of Evil*, and *Ben-Hur*.

Despite his considerable talents and largely respectable film credits, Heston is also known for such iconic guilty pleasure films as *Planet of the Apes, The Omega Man*, and, of course, *Soylent Green*. ("*Soylent Green is people!*")

The Heston vehicle *The Omega Man* was a remake of a film starring Vincent Price. Do you know the name of that original film?

A. *More Dead Than Alive*

B. *The Last Man on Earth*

C. *The Story of Mankind*

D. *Diary of a Madman*

1960. Do you know which of these legendary rock stars appears in the 1982 comedy *National Lampoon's Class Reunion*?

A. Carl Perkins   **C.** Little Richard

B. Jerry Lee Lewis   **D.** Chuck Berry

1961. What actress appears as the character Mercedes Lane in the 1988 Corey Feldman/Corey Haim collaboration *License to Drive*?

A. Courteney Cox   **C.** Heather Graham

B. Demi Moore   **D.** Alyssa Milano

1962. What is the name of the geeky character played by Alan Cumming who grew up to be independently wealthy in *Romy and Michele's High School Reunion*?

A. Patrick Sayde   **C.** Daniel Orgelbrand

B. Sandy Frink   **D.** Eugene Hockenfuss

1963. Which of these actors makes a cameo in the revenge flick *Paparazzi* playing himself as Bo Laramie's costar?

A. Vince Vaughn   **C.** Matthew McConaughey

B. Chris Rock   **D.** Mel Gibson

1964. The nerds in *Revenge of the Nerds* are persecuted by a fraternity of popular jocks. What is the name of this enemy fraternity?

A. Pi Beta Phi   **C.** Gamma Phi Beta

B. Kappa Alpha Theta   **D.** Alpha Beta

1965. One of these actors is *not* a member of the band featured in the 1994 comedy *Airheads*. Which one?

A. Adam Sandler   **C.** Ben Stiller

B. Brendan Fraser   **D.** Steve Buscemi

1966. Every character in the beauty queen comedy *Miss Congeniality* has the same room number. What is this?

A. 301   **C.** 102

B. 103   **D.** 201

1967. According to the tagline for *Die Hard*, how many "stories of sheer adventure!" does the movie offer?

A. Forty   **C.** Twenty

B. Thirty   **D.** Ten

1968. Only one of these films did not land Pauly Shore a Razzie nomination for either Worst Actor or Worst New Star. Which one?

- **A.** *Encino Man*
- **B.** *Bio-Dome*
- **C.** *Jury Duty*
- **D.** *In the Army Now*

1969. *Spice World* is a comedy film starring the short-lived pop music group the Spice Girls. In the film, which of the band members is known as "Sporty Spice"?

- **A.** Geri Halliwell
- **B.** Emma Bunton
- **C.** Melanie Chisholm
- **D.** Victoria Adams

1970. What kind of car does Brian O'Conner lose to Dominic Toretto in their pink slips race in *The Fast and the Furious*?

- **A.** Toyota Supra
- **B.** Mitsubishi Eclipse
- **C.** Chevrolet Chevelle
- **D.** Mazda RX-7

1971.

1972. In the 1993 sci-fi action film *Demolition Man*, it is said that as a result of the "restaurant wars," there is only one restaurant in the future. What is this restaurant?

- **A.** Taco Bell
- **B.** McDonald's
- **C.** Jack in the Box
- **D.** Burger King

1973. Detective John Kimble goes undercover as a kindergarten teacher in the comedy *Kindergarten Cop*. In what Oregon city does he do this?

- **A.** Portland
- **B.** Oregon City
- **C.** Astoria
- **D.** Hillsboro

1974. The piece of music "Rhapsody on a Theme of Paganini" plays throughout the time travel romance movie *Somewhere in Time*. What composer is responsible for this piece?

- **A.** Sergei Rachmaninoff
- **B.** Igor Stravinsky
- **C.** Richard Strauss
- **D.** Franz Liszt

1975. Michael J. Fox plays time traveler Marty McFly in the 1985 comedy *Back to the Future*. What is McFly's age in the film?

- **A.** Sixteen
- **B.** We are never told
- **C.** Eighteen
- **D.** Seventeen

1971.

The mere mention of actor Patrick Swayze's name instantly brings to mind a number of iconic images and quotable lines from a handful of guilty pleasure films. And this isn't meant as a knock against Mr. Swayze! To the contrary, it's a compliment: there are a number of his movies that we've all watched a half dozen times or more. Maybe he's no Laurence Olivier, but credit the man for having the ability to select projects that connect with audiences and—as much as we may hate to admit it—show staying power.

Who over the age of twenty isn't familiar with that scene where Swayze and Demi Moore mold pottery together as the Righteous Brothers sing "Unchained Melody" in the 1990 schmaltz-fest *Ghost*? Of course there are several scenes between Swayze and the pre-nose job Jennifer Grey from *Dirty Dancing* that are equally memorable ("Nobody puts Baby in a corner!").

Other Swayze guilty pleasures include *The Outsiders, Red Dawn, Road House, Next of Kin, Point Break, To Wong Foo, Thanks for Everything! Julie Newmar,* and *Dirty Dancing: Havana Nights,* among others.

Swayze plays a character named Jack in three of these films. In which film does he *not* play "Jack"?

- **A.** *Father Hood*
- **B.** *Three Wishes*
- **C.** *Black Dog*
- **D.** *Youngblood*

1976. What is the name of the Jasper, Missouri *Road House* where Patrick Swayze's character is employed?

A. The Next Round

B. Sharky's

C. Double Deuce

D. Wade's Place

1977. What is the name of the dummy who comes to life and falls in love with Andrew McCarthy in the 1987 comedy *Mannequin*?

A. Flora

B. Emmy

C. Gail

D. Trisha

1978. The character Michael is a foreign exchange student in the derivative 1982 sequel *Grease 2*. What country is Michael from?

A. New Zealand

B. None of these

C. Australia

D. England

1979. What restaurant do the title characters find has replaced the New Brunswick White Castle in *Harold & Kumar Go to White Castle*?

A. Burger World

B. Burgers-2-Go

C. Burger Shack

D. Burgers-N-Stuff

1980. Which of these is not one of Melanie's last names in the 2002 romantic comedy *Sweet Home Alabama*?

A. Hennings

B. Carmichael

C. Smooter

D. Perry

1981. What actor appears as Guitar Store Dude in the rock-and-roll comedy *Tenacious D: The Pick of Destiny*?

A. Meat Loaf

B. Ben Stiller

C. Owen Wilson

D. Luke Wilson

1982. What are the last words spoken in the 1985 western *Silverado*?

A. "That was close."

B. "That ain't right."

C. "That wasn't so bad, now was it?"

D. "We'll be back."

1983. Writer-director Mel Brooks plays five roles in the comedy *History of the World: Part I*. Which of these is *not* one of them?

A. Comicus

B. Moses

C. Count de Monet

D. Louis XVI

1984. Can you name the rap artist who makes an appearance in *Teenage Mutant Ninja Turtles II: The Secret of the Ooze?*

A. Tone Loc

B. Young MC

C. MC Hammer

D. Vanilla Ice

1985. What actress gave voice to Jessica Rabbit in the cult favorite *Who Framed Roger Rabbit?*

A. Kathleen Turner

B. Meg Tilly

C. Sigourney Weaver

D. Melanie Griffith

1986. *The Wedding Singer's* Robbie Hart meets a famous singer while flying in first class. Who is this?

A. David Lee Roth

B. Adam Ant

C. Billy Idol

D. Sammy Hagar

1987.

1988. Daniel "Rudy" Ruettiger gets the unlikely opportunity to play college football in the film *Rudy*. What university does he play for?

A. Alabama State University

B. Auburn University

C. University of Notre Dame

D. Michigan State University

1989. Kate ultimately falls for Frenchman Luc Teyssier in the romantic comedy *French Kiss*. What is Teyssier's occupation?

A. Bartender

B. Police officer

C. Assassin

D. Thief

1990. *Staying Alive* is the title of the 1983 *Saturday Night Fever* sequel. Who directed this film, sometimes referred to as the worst sequel ever made?

A. John Travolta

B. Sylvester Stallone

C. John Badham

D. John G. Avildsen

1991. Which Monty Python member plays a character who is repeatedly injured throughout *National Lampoon's European Vacation?*

A. Eric Idle

B. John Cleese

C. Terry Jones

D. Michael Palin

1992. Winona Ryder's character is the only person who can see the ghosts of the Maitlands in *Beetlejuice*. What is her name?

A. Lydia

B. Lindy

C. Lizzie

D. Lilith

1987.

The 1990 Brian De Palma film *The Bonfire of the Vanities* was adapted from the bestselling novel by Tom Wolfe, but has little in common with its original source material.

The studio first decided to overhaul the story completely. They believed the "problem" with Wolfe's original story was that the protagonist, Sherman McCoy, wasn't likeable enough. Then it was decided that a minor Jewish character from the novel, Judge Leonard White, should be given his own separate story line and be played by an African-American. (They believed this would make the racial issues at the core of the film easier for audiences to digest.) It was then decided that the now black White should be given a melodramatic monologue essentially explaining that racism is bad.

Then the studio decided to cast "bankable" actors in roles they weren't suited for.

The end result? A colossal stinker.

Which of these actors was previously cast to play Judge White?

A. Robert Duvall

B. Alan Arkin

C. Ed Harris

D. Bruce Dern

1993. Nicolas Cage plays a yuppie literary agent named Peter Loew in the 1989 black comedy *Vampire's Kiss*. There is a picture of an existentialist writer on the wall at Loew's office. Who is this?

A. Albert Camus

B. Jean-Paul Sartre

C. Friedrich Nietzsche

D. Franz Kafka

1994. Geena Davis is journalist Veronica Quaife in the 1986 movie *The Fly*. What is the name of the magazine for which she writes?

A. *Fly Paper*

B. *Specifics*

C. *Particle*

D. *In Focus*

1995. What is the name of the designer drug the title characters of the action movie *Harley Davidson and the Marlboro Man* accidentally steal?

A. Crystal Blue Persuasion

B. Crystal Dream

C. Crystal Heaven

D. Crystal Climax

1996. High school student David Lightman hacks into the school computer and changes his grade from an "F" to something better in *WarGames*. To what does he change it?

A. "D"

B. "B"

C. "C"

D. "A"

1997. What is the name of the Jefferson Airplane tune *The Cable Guy* Chip Douglas belts out during the karaoke scene?

A. "We Can Be Together"

B. "White Rabbit"

C. "Somebody to Love"

D. "Good Shepherd"

1998. On what planet does Princess Vespa reside in the *Star Wars* parody *Spaceballs*?

A. Druidia

B. Eragonia

C. Skroob

D. Dinkinia

1999. Which of these films marks the acting debut of pop princess Britney Spears?

A. *Crossroads*

B. *Austin Powers in Goldmember*

C. *Longshot*

D. *Drive Me Crazy*

2000. Which of these schlock-fests features a young Leonardo DiCaprio?

A. *Pumpkinhead II: Blood Wings*

B. *Candyman: Farewell to the Flesh*

C. *Critters 3*

D. *Leprechaun 2*

CHAPTER NINE:

CONTEMPORARY FILMS 1970-PRESENT

2001. What is the name of Andy Robinson's sniper serial killer in Don Siegel's *Dirty Harry*?
- **A.** Capricorn
- **B.** Virgo
- **C.** Scorpio
- **D.** Gemini

2002. What is the name of the news editor at Union Broadcasting System in the satire *Network*?
- **A.** Howard Beale
- **B.** Max Schumacher
- **C.** Diana Christensen
- **D.** Frank Hackett

2003. What director was fired from the production of the 1970 Pearl Harbor epic *Tora! Tora! Tora!*?
- **A.** Richard Fleischer
- **B.** Akira Kurosawa
- **C.** Steven Spielberg
- **D.** John Huston

2004. Singer John Denver plays protagonist Jerry Landers in the comedy film *Oh, God!* What is Jerry's occupation?
- **A.** Restaurant manager
- **B.** Radio DJ
- **C.** Photographer
- **D.** Supermarket manager

2005. What is the name of Sue Snell's boyfriend in the 1976 Stephen King adaptation *Carrie*?
- **A.** Tommy
- **B.** Chris
- **C.** Gage
- **D.** Billy

2006. Where does Tommy shoot Spider the first time in the 1990 Martin Scorsese film *Goodfellas*?
- **A.** Arm
- **B.** Foot
- **C.** Hand
- **D.** Ear

2007. What is the name of Lenny Bruce's stripper wife in the 1974 Bob Fosse biopic *Lenny*?
- **A.** Sugar
- **B.** Trixie
- **C.** Honey
- **D.** Bambi

OPPOSITE John Turturro in *The Big Lebowski*, 1998

2008. What singer plays Annie's Hollywood executive boyfriend in Woody Allen's seminal romantic comedy *Annie Hall*?

A. Kris Kristofferson
C. Neil Young
B. Paul Simon
D. Art Garfunkel

2009. What actor appears as Ginger's ex-boyfriend Lester Diamond in the 1995 Martin Scorsese film *Casino*?

A. Kevin Pollak
C. Alan King
B. Joe Pesci
D. James Woods

2010.

2011. In Warren Beatty's 1981 film *Reds*, the actor/director plays lead character John Reed. What is Reed's occupation in the film?

A. Artist
C. Teacher
B. Journalist
D. Smuggler

2012. Gene Hackman is the coach of a small-town basketball team in the inspiring 1986 drama *Hoosiers*. What is the name of the school where he coaches?

A. Whitmore High School
C. Hickory High School
B. Jefferson High School
D. Johnson County High School

2013. *Norma Rae* is the 1979 Martin Ritt film about a small-town woman who becomes involved with a labor union at the factory where she is employed. What do they manufacture at this factory?

A. Automobiles
C. Rebar
B. Textiles
D. Radios

2014. Dustin Hoffman plays autistic savant Raymond Babbitt in the 1988 Barry Levinson film *Rain Man*. When Raymond's father dies, he leaves him an inheritance. How much is this?

A. $2 million
C. $3 million
B. $7 million
D. $10 million

2015. In *The Big Chill*, a group of college friends reunite after many years for the death of a friend. What is the name of the deceased friend (played by an unseen Kevin Costner, whose scenes were cut out)?

A. Alex
C. Adam
B. Mikey
D. Josh

2016. A young woman is killed by a shark at the beginning of *Jaws*. The greedy mayor, however, lies about the cause of her death. What does he say this was?

A. Murder
C. Drowning
B. Boat propeller
D. Boating collision

2010.

The Exorcist is a 1973 horror film directed by William Friedkin and adapted from the novel by William Peter Blatty. The frightening film is notable because of its usage of subliminal images and messages. (The film was so scary that people began passing out and injuring themselves at screenings, entangling Warner Bros. in litigations that were, incidentally, all settled out of court.)

The film's story centers on a young girl named Regan McNeil, who is possessed by a demon after playing with a Ouija board. Regan starts to transform, becoming strangely inappropriate and dangerous. Regan's mother calls upon the church for help, and two priests are dispatched to perform the exorcism.

In 1974, *The Exorcist* did something few horror films have ever done before or since: it received ten Academy Award nominations (including Best Picture, Best Director, and Best Adapted Screenplay) and won two.

Today the film is widely considered the single greatest horror film ever made.

How does Father Damien Karras die in the film?

A. He is impaled
B. He catches fire
C. He throws himself through a window
D. Regan smashes his head into the wall

2017. Tom Hagen's occupation within the Mafia family in *The Godfather* is *consigliere*. What does this mean?

A. Hit man

B. Counselor

C. Enforcer

D. Shylock

2018. Billy Hayes is sentenced to four years in a Turkish prison after being caught attempting to transport hash in *Midnight Express*. This sentence is changed after an appeal, however. How much time is he then sentenced to serve?

A. Ten years

B. Thirty years

C. Twenty years

D. Forty years

2019. *McCabe & Mrs. Miller* tells the story of a gambler named John McCabe who goes to a frontier town to establish a brothel. What is the town's name?

A. Haysville

B. Presbyterian Church

C. Lynchburg

D. Hanging Tree

2020. Sandy Olsson is from another country in the 1978 musical *Grease*. What country is this?

A. Sweden

B. Denmark

C. Australia

D. Greenland

2021. Warren Beatty portrays the famous gangster "Bugsy" Siegel in the 1991 film *Bugsy*. What was Bugsy's real first name?

A. Peter

B. Charlie

C. Ben

D. Joel

2022. What magazine does *Bull Durham*'s Annie want to inform about Crash's dubious record?

A. *Baseball Weekly*

B. *Sports Illustrated*

C. *The Sporting News*

D. *The Hardball Gazette*

2023. The Welton Academy is said to be based upon four principles in the 1989 drama *Dead Poets Society*. Which of these is *not* one of them?

A. Tradition

B. Honor

C. Morality

D. Discipline

2024. In *Kramer vs. Kramer*, Ted's wife Joanna walks out on him and his son Billy. What is Ted's occupation?

A. Author

B. Advertising executive

C. Professor

D. Architect

2025. What does one-night stand Alex Forrest tell Dan Gallagher she will not do in the 1987 thriller *Fatal Attraction*?

A. Shut her mouth

B. Play nice

C. Be ignored

D. Go silently into the night

2026. *Gandhi* is a 1982 biopic about the life of Mohandas Karamchand Gandhi, who led the nonviolent resistance movement against British rule in India. With what event does the film begin?

A. Gandhi's birth

B. Gandhi's death

C. Gandhi's most famous speech

D. Gandhi's hunger strike

2027. Youngster Josh Baskin makes a wish, it comes true, and he's transformed into an adult man in the comedy *Big*. How old is Josh?

A. Eleven years old

B. Thirteen years old

C. Ten years old

D. Twelve years old

2028. The 1987 comedy *Good Morning, Vietnam* stars Robin Williams as Armed Forces Radio disc jockey Adrian Cronauer. Cronauer tells his listeners, "This is not a test." What does he say it is?

A. War

B. Rock and roll

C. Vietnam

D. Mass confusion

2029.

2030. Norman and Ethel Thayer are a retired couple who return to their summer home in *On Golden Pond*. What was Norman's occupation prior to his retirement?

A. Sports writer

B. Professor

C. Banker

D. Lawyer

2031. What actor appeared uncredited as Michael Dorsey's roommate in the 1982 Sydney Pollack comedy *Tootsie*?

A. Chevy Chase

B. Dan Aykroyd

C. Bill Murray

D. Brian Doyle-Murray

2032. Jeffrey Beaumont finds something odd while walking through the park in the David Lynch drama *Blue Velvet*. What does he find?

A. A hand

B. A toe

C. An ear

D. A leg

2033. In the mockumentary *Zelig*, what celebrated writer first discovers Leonard Zelig's unique, chameleon-like abilities?

A. John Steinbeck

B. Ernest Hemingway

C. J.D. Salinger

D. F. Scott Fitzgerald

2029.

All the President's Men, a 1976 adaptation of the best-selling book by Pulitzer Prize–winning *Washington Post* investigative reporters Bob Woodward and Carl Bernstein, depicts the Watergate scandal investigation. Despite the film's two high-priced leads (Robert Redford and Dustin Hoffman), an argument could be made that the film's magnificent screenplay (adapted by the legendary William Goldman) is as much the star of this film as anyone.

The film, which also features Jack Warden, Hal Holbrook, and Jason Robards, was a box office success, grossing more than $70 million in the U.S. alone. *All the President's Men* received eight Academy Award nominations, including Best Picture, Best Director, and Best Adapted Screenplay, winning four.

Which of these future stars does *not* appear in *All the President's Men*?

A. F. Murray Abraham

B. Dominic Chianese

C. Stephen Collins

D. Michael Gross

2034. *Analyze This* is a 1999 comedy about a gangster and a psychiatrist. What is the name of the gangster played by Robert De Niro?

- **A.** Ace Rothstein
- **B.** Paul Vitti
- **C.** Lorenzo Anello
- **D.** Des Spellacy

2035. In the 2006 drama *The Da Vinci Code*, Paul Bettany plays a killer monk named Silas. By what name does Silas refer to his boss?

- **A.** Father
- **B.** Teacher
- **C.** Master
- **D.** Lord

2036. *Tin Cup* is a comedy about a pro golfer played by Kevin Costner. Which of the following real-life pro golfers does *not* make an appearance in the film?

- **A.** Fred Couples
- **B.** Chi Chi Rodriguez
- **C.** Phil Mickelson
- **D.** Corey Pavin

2037. *Erin Brockovich* is a Steven Soderbergh biopic about one woman's fight against a giant energy company. How many children does Brockovich have in the film?

- **A.** One
- **B.** Three
- **C.** Four
- **D.** Two

2038. Peg Boggs meets the title character in *Edward Scissorhands* while selling something door to door. What is this?

- **A.** Insurance
- **B.** Avon products
- **C.** Greeting cards
- **D.** Magazine subscriptions

2039. Why doesn't Arthur Bach want to marry Susan Johnson, whom he's prearranged to marry, in the 1981 Dudley Moore vehicle *Arthur*?

- **A.** He's homosexual
- **B.** He doesn't love her
- **C.** Her nose is too large
- **D.** Her voice annoys him

2040. The 1983 film *Silkwood* tells the story of Karen Silkwood, a woman who disappeared while investigating wrongdoing at the Kerr-McGee plutonium plant. Who was Karen going to meet with when she disappeared?

- **A.** A reporter
- **B.** A government agent
- **C.** A former employee
- **D.** A lawyer

2041. Richard Gere's *Days of Heaven* character Bill travels from Chicago to a small Texas town because he's wanted for a crime. What is it?

- **A.** Arson
- **B.** Murder
- **C.** Embezzlement
- **D.** Robbery

2042. What publication does James Woods' *Salvador* journalist Richard Boyle write for?

A. *Newsweek*

B. He's a freelance journalist

C. *Time*

D. *The New York Times*

2043. Which astronaut in *The Right Stuff* nearly drowns (and later burned to death in real life for the same reason) because the hatch to his spacecraft malfunctions?

A. Chuck Yeager

B. Gus Grissom

C. Alan Shepard

D. Gordon Cooper

2044.

2045. In the Ridley Scott science fiction film *Blade Runner*, how many years is the lifespan of a Nexus-6 replicant?

A. Five years

B. Four years

C. Six years

D. Seven years

2046. Who does Mrs. Mulwray hire Jake Gittes to spy on in Roman Polanski's 1974 thriller *Chinatown*?

A. Her business partner

B. Her father

C. Her sister

D. Her husband

2047. What is the name of the high school where Pedro Sanchez runs for class president in the film *Napoleon Dynamite*?

A. Fillmore High School

B. Toluca Lake High School

C. Preston High School

D. Andover High School

2048. Jose was shot trying to rescue Cole from the middle of World War I in *12 Monkeys*. What explanation do the French doctors have for Jose's ability to speak English?

A. Insanity

B. Shell shock

C. Aberration

D. He is possessed

2049. *Crash* is a 2004 film that follows the lives of several characters in Los Angeles, California, for a certain period of time. How much time?

A. Twelve hours

B. Twenty-four hours

C. Thirty-six hours

D. Forty-eight hours

2050. Paul Giamatti plays a character named Miles in *Sideways*. Miles is an unpublished author, wine enthusiast, and teacher. What grade does he teach?

A. Second grade

B. Fifth grade

C. Eighth grade

D. Tenth grade

2044.

Apocalypse Now, a 1979 film about one soldier's mission during the Vietnam conflict, was loosely adapted from Joseph Conrad's classic novella *Heart of Darkness* by John Milius and directed by Francis Ford Coppola.

The film's story line centers on U.S. Army Captain Benjamin Willard (Martin Sheen), who is sent on a top-secret mission to travel into the Cambodian jungle and terminate an American colonel (Marlon Brando) who has gone insane. Willard meets a number of interesting people along the way, and by the time he reaches the colonel's camp, we see that even the "sane" soldiers have been made crazy by the war.

The film was released to mixed reviews, but some, like *Chicago Sun-Times* critic Roger Ebert, quickly hailed the film as the masterpiece it is recognized as today. The film received eight Academy Award nominations, winning two awards for its cinematography and sound.

How old was actor Laurence Fishburne during filming of this movie?

A. 17

B. 14

C. 13

D. 11

2051. *Cold Mountain* is a 2003 Anthony Minghella Civil War romance. In what state is Cold Mountain located?

A. North Carolina

B. Alabama

C. Mississippi

D. Georgia

2052. Which of these musicians does *not* appear in the 2001 thriller *Training Day*?

A. Dr. Dre

B. Snoop Dogg

C. Ludacris

D. Macy Gray

2053. One of the bullies who prey on guys like Peter Parker in *Spider-Man* is named Eugene Thompson. Eugene is known by a nickname. What is this?

A. Spec

B. Flash

C. Harry

D. Speedy

2054. Robert De Niro's Max Cady comes home from a lengthy stay in prison to get revenge against Sam Bowden in the 1991 version of *Cape Fear*. For how many years has he been in prison?

A. Twelve years

B. Ten years

C. Fourteen years

D. Twenty years

2055. With what country does the United States engage in a fabricated war in order to distract the media from the president's sex scandal in *Wag the Dog*?

A. Czechoslovakia

B. Turkey

C. Albania

D. Kazakhstan

2056. Oliver Stone's 1991 conspiracy theory drama *JFK* opens with a presidential address. Who is the United States President giving this address?

A. John Kennedy

B. Ricnard Nixon

C. Dwight Eisenhower

D. Ronald Reagan

2057. Leonard tells the story of a man named Sammy who killed his wife in the film *Memento*. How did Sammy kill his wife?

A. Gunshot

B. Stabbing

C. Insulin overdose

D. Poisoning

2058. What is the location for the first scene in Quentin Tarantino's classic crime film *Pulp Fiction*?

A. Hallway of apartment building

B. Lance's apartment

C. Paul's bar

D. Diner

2059. *Anchorman: The Legend of Ron Burgundy* relates the exploits of a Southern California news team. What channel do Ron and his pals work for?

A. Six

B. Five

C. Four

D. Seven

2060. "Peter Pan" author J.M. Barrie befriends a young woman and her sons in *Finding Neverland*. How many sons does she have?

A. Two
B. Three
C. Five
D. Four

2061.

2062. Joseph Fiennes plays a struggling young William Shakespeare in the 1998 romantic comedy *Shakespeare in Love*. What is the name of the "pirate's daughter" in the title of the play Shakespeare is working on in the film?

A. Melinda
B. Ethel
C. Marion
D. Constance

2063. *Kinsey* is Bill Condon's 2004 biopic of sexology pioneer Alfred Kinsey. By what nickname is the professor known to his graduate students?

A. Skinsey
B. Professor Gall Wasp
C. Prok
D. R.K.

2064. Melvin Udall befriends his neighbor, Simon Bishop, in the 1997 comedy *As Good as It Gets*. What is Simon's occupation?

A. Author
B. Artist
C. Poet
D. Sculptor

2065. After building a baseball diamond in his cornfield, Ray Kinsella takes author Terence Mann to a major league baseball game in *Field of Dreams*. What team do they watch?

A. Milwaukee Brewers
B. San Diego Padres
C. Boston Red Sox
D. Baltimore Orioles

2066. The 1993 drama *Philadelphia* tells the story of an ambitious young lawyer named Andrew Beckett who is fired from his job when it is discovered that he has AIDS. How old is Andrew?

A. Twenty-seven
B. Twenty-five
C. Twenty-nine
D. Thirty-one

2067. *Thelma & Louise* is a 1991 road movie that follows two housewives on an unexpected cross-country crime spree. What do Thelma and Louise drive?

A. 1966 Buick Riviera
B. 1966 Thunderbird
C. 1966 Mustang
D. 1966 Pontiac Grand Prix

2068. What is the name of Richard Gere's United States Naval Aviation officer candidate in the drama *An Officer and a Gentleman*?

A. Dan Rausch
B. Zack Mayo
C. Sid Worley
D. Emil Foley

2061.

Amadeus is the 1984 Milos Forman film adaptation of the Peter Shaffer play, which is loosely based upon Aleksandr Pushkin's *Mozart and Salieri*, a tragic examination of envy and revenge.

The story is centered around Antonio Salieri (F. Murray Abraham), a Viennese court composer to Holy Roman Emperor Joseph II, whose accomplishments are obscured in the massive shadow of his hero Mozart (Tom Hulce). When Salieri finally meets Mozart, he is appalled to find an arrogant, immature man whom he deems unworthy of the talents bestowed upon him. As his own mediocrity becomes more apparent in contrast to Mozart's seemingly endless talents, Salieri becomes embittered and so blinded with hatred and envy that he begins to plot Mozart's death.

Amadeus received eleven Academy Award nominations, winning eight statuettes, including Best Picture, Best Adapted Screenplay, Best Director, and Best Actor (Abraham).

To whom does Salieri tell the story?

A. His biographer
B. A priest
C. Mozart's widow
D. A detective

2069. The film *Chariots of Fire* documents the real-life competition between two runners in the 1924 Summer Olympics. One of the runners is Eric Liddell. What is his nickname?

A. Feet of the Gods

B. Flying Scotsman

C. The Wellington Wonder

D. White Lightning

2070. *Raiders of the Lost Ark* is a 1981 action film about archaeologist Indiana Jones. What is the name of the ancient Egyptian city where the Ark is kept that the Nazis locate in the film?

A. Hamunaptra

B. Qantir

C. Tanis

D. Toht

2071. Sally Bowles is an American singer working at a Berlin nightclub in the 1972 musical *Cabaret*. What is the name of the club where she is employed?

A. La Cage

B. Kit Kat Club

C. Mudia Art

D. Blue Moon

2072. The David Lean film *Ryan's Daughter* tells the story of an Irish girl who falls in love with a British soldier during World War I. What is the girl's name?

A. Kate

B. Maureen

C. Rosy

D. Marie

2073. Name the singer who plays Jack Nicholson's roommate in the 1971 Mike Nichols drama *Carnal Knowledge*.

A. Jackson Browne

B. Bob Dylan

C. Art Garfunkel

D. James Taylor

2074. *Sounder* is a 1972 film that tells the story of an African-American family's struggles in the south in 1933. What state do they live in?

A. Georgia

B. Mississippi

C. Louisiana

D. Kentucky

2075. In one of the more memorable scenes from *The Goodbye Girl*, Elliot Garfield performs in a gay production of a William Shakespeare play. Dost thou know which one?

A. *Romeo & Juliet*

B. *Richard III*

C. *The Taming of the Shrew*

D. *Hamlet*

2076. Can you name the actor who played Fire Chief Michael O'Hallorhan in the 1974 disaster thriller *The Towering Inferno*?

A. Richard Chamberlain

B. Paul Newman

C. William Holden

D. Steve McQueen

2077. A cowboy slashes a prostitute's face at the beginning of *Unforgiven*. What is the name of the saloon and hotel where this incident occurs?

- **A.** Greely's
- **B.** The Gem
- **C.** Callahan's
- **D.** Skinny's

2078. Before going to work for Miss Daisy, *Driving Miss Daisy's* Hoke Colburn had chauffeured a judge. What happened to that job?

- **A.** Hoke was accused of stealing
- **B.** The judge died
- **C.** Hoke was accused of sleeping with the judge's wife
- **D.** Hoke quit

2079. What is Karl eating when Vaughan confides in him about his life as a gay man in the film *Sling Blade*?

- **A.** Mashed potatoes
- **B.** A hamburger
- **C.** Ice cream
- **D.** French fries

2080. PFC Downey and Lance Corporal Dawson are accused of murdering a fellow marine in the 1992 drama *A Few Good Men*. What was the dead marine's name?

- **A.** Jessep
- **B.** Santiago
- **C.** Kaffee
- **D.** Bavel

2081.

2082. How old was Rose when she boarded the doomed ocean liner in James Cameron's epic film *Titanic*?

- **A.** Eighteen
- **B.** Seventeen
- **C.** Nineteen
- **D.** Twenty

2083. Name the mutant character who transforms and becomes a powerful figure known as the Phoenix in *X-Men: The Last Stand*.

- **A.** Wolverine
- **B.** Storm
- **C.** Jean Grey
- **D.** Cyclops

2084. What was the name of the Israeli covert operation depicted in the Steven Spielberg film *Munich*, in which the people responsible for the 1972 Munich massacre were tracked down and killed?

- **A.** Operation Hand of God
- **B.** Operation Will of God
- **C.** Operation Wrath of God
- **D.** Operation Fury of God

2085. Who makes an uncredited cameo appearance in the Elmore Leonard adaptation *Get Shorty* as the widow of Harry Zimm's former partner?

- **A.** Bette Midler
- **B.** Susan Sarandon
- **C.** Jane Fonda
- **D.** Lily Tomlin

2081.

The Last Temptation of Christ is Martin Scorsese's 1988 adaptation of Nikos Kazantzakis' controversial and oft-banned 1951 novel about the life of Jesus Christ. Predictably, Scorsese's film was equally controversial, focusing on Christ's subjection to human temptations. In a dream sequence, Satan tempts the dying Christ with the gift of life if he will turn his back on his heavenly mission, denounce God, and live a human life. Christ momentarily imagines this life, but is then shown the light, rebukes Satan, and returns to the cross.

All ideological issues aside, *The Last Temptation of Christ* is one of the finest and most underappreciated films by one of the greatest filmmakers ever to work in the medium. It earned Scorsese his second Academy Award nomination for Best Director, although it would take another six nominations for him to take home a statuette.

In Christ's dream, which of the disciples convinces him to return to the cross and carry out his duty?

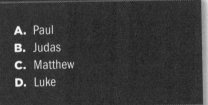

- **A.** Paul
- **B.** Judas
- **C.** Matthew
- **D.** Luke

2086. For what crime was High Priest Imhotep mummified alive with flesh-eating scarabs in the Brendan Fraser vehicle *The Mummy*?

A. Robbing the pharaoh

B. Sleeping with the pharaoh's mistress

C. Removing the tag from his mattress

D. Murdering the pharoah

2087. Al Pacino's *The Insider* character Lowell Bergman is a news producer for a television news show. What is the title of this show?

A. *Hard Copy*

B. *Dateline*

C. *60 Minutes*

D. *20/20*

2088. The character of astronaut Garrett Breedlove (played by Jack Nicholson) in the film *Terms of Endearment* was originally written for a different actor. Can you name this actor?

A. Richard Crenna

B. Burt Reynolds

C. Robert Duvall

D. William Hurt

2089. Oliver Stone's *Wall Street* tells the story of an up-and-coming stockbroker named Bud Fox, who partners up with corporate raider Gordon Gekko. What is the name of the interior decorator Bud falls for?

A. Elizabeth

B. Darien

C. Linnea

D. Heidi

2090. . . . *And Justice for All* tells the story of a lawyer who is blackmailed into defending a rapist judge. In what city does this film take place?

A. New York

B. Baltimore

C. San Francisco

D. Washington, DC

2091. Name the Nazi portrayed by Gregory Peck in the Ira Levin adaptation *The Boys from Brazil*.

A. Josef Mengele

B. Adolf Hitler

C. Irwin Rommel

D. Hermann Goering

2092. *The Deer Hunter* is a 1978 film about three friends who go to war in Vietnam. Which of the friends shoots himself in the head playing Russian roulette?

A. Mike

B. Nick

C. Stanley

D. Steven

2093. Steve is dating Curt's sister in the 1973 George Lucas film *American Graffiti*. What is her name?

A. Laurie

B. Carol

C. Wendy

D. Debbie

2094. What is the name of Rocky's villainous opponent in the Sylvester Stallone vehicle *Rocky III*?

A. Apollo Creed
B. Clubber Lang
C. Ivan Drago
D. Tommy Gunn

2095. The film *Bang the Drum Slowly* tells the story of a major league baseball season, and of a catcher who learns he is dying. What is the name of the team depicted in the film?

A. New York Yankees
B. New York Mammoths
C. New York Yorkies
D. New York Mets

2096.

2097. In *The Apostle*, Pentecostal minister Sonny attacks a man after learning that he is sleeping with his wife. With what weapon does he attack the man?

A. Baseball bat
B. Crowbar
C. Knife
D. Gun

2098. In *Born on the Fourth of July*, Ron Kovic's world changes when he accidentally shoots one of his comrades. What is the name of this soldier?

A. Thompson
B. Jones
C. Wilson
D. Stone

2099. *Altered States* tells the story of a scientist played by William Hurt who makes a scientific breakthrough by experimenting on himself. Into what does he transform?

A. A child
B. Monster
C. Ape
D. Nothing

2100. *Good Will Hunting* centers around an incredibly intelligent young man who works as a college custodian. He ultimately befriends a community college psychologist. What is this man's name?

A. Sean Maguire
B. Gerald Lambeau
C. Brent Bates
D. Dick Enright

2101. The practice of crashing weddings in the comedy film *The Wedding Crashers* was started by Chaz Reinhold. What actor plays Reinhold?

A. Will Ferrell
B. Owen Wilson
C. Vince Vaughn
D. Ben Stiller

2102. What happens to Secret Service Agent Frank Horrigan at the end of the Wolfgang Petersen action film *In the Line of Fire*?

A. He dies
B. He is promoted
C. He retires
D. He is shot three times, but lives

2096.

Borat: Cultural Learnings of America for Make Benefit Glorious Nation of Kazakhstan is a 2006 mockumentary starring comedian Sacha Baron Cohen and directed by Larry Charles.

The film's premise is that character Borat Sagdiyev (Cohen) is commissioned by the Kazakh government to travel to the United States to film a documentary about American culture. As in Cohen's television series, *Da Ali G Show*, much of Borat's travels are unscripted and focus on putting unsuspecting people in humorous situations. In the film, Borat encounters a wide array of Americans, as he travels to such locales as gun shops, rodeos, and etiquette classes. Interestingly, the film, which at first seems to poke fun at the naive Kazakh character, ultimately exposes ignorance, racism, sexism, homophobia, arrogance, warmongering, and cultural intolerance in the unscripted words and actions of the Americans Borat encounters.

Borat becomes obsessed with an American actress. Who is this?

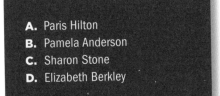

A. Paris Hilton
B. Pamela Anderson
C. Sharon Stone
D. Elizabeth Berkley

2103. Can you name the astronaut portrayed by Tom Hanks in the 1995 Ron Howard film *Apollo 13*?

A. Neil Armstrong

B. Dick Scobee

C. Jim Lovell

D. John Glenn

2104. James Caan plays novelist Paul Sheldon in *Misery*. What is the name of the novel in which Sheldon's most famous heroine, Misery Chastain, dies?

A. *Misery's End*

B. *Sweet Misery*

C. *Misery's Lover*

D. *Misery's Child*

2105. What actor appears in the film *Mississippi Burning* as Mayor Tilman?

A. Brad Dourif

B. Michael Rooker

C. Tobin Bell

D. R. Lee Ermey

2106. Joe Gideon frequently talks with a character named Angelique in the movie *All That Jazz*. Who is Angelique?

A. His ex-wife

B. Joe's vision of God

C. The angel of death

D. His psychiatrist

2107. Gene Hackman plays surveillance expert Harry Caul in Francis Ford Coppola's film *The Conversation*. What piece of clothing does Caul wear all the time?

A. Orange suspenders

B. Raincoat

C. Fedora

D. Slippers

2108. Joe Pendleton returns to earth in the body of millionaire Leo Farnsworth in *Heaven Can Wait*. Leo's wife, Julia, is having an affair with someone. What is his name?

A. Max

B. Bentley

C. Everett

D. Tony

2109. Michael Caine plays a famous playwright named Sidney Bruhl in *Death-trap*. What is the name of Bruhl's most famous play?

A. *Sleuth*

B. *The Murder Game*

C. *Case in Point*

D. *Murder Most Foul*

2110. Al Pacino portrays the famous whistleblower cop Frank Serpico in the film *Serpico*. What happens in the film's first scene?

A. Serpico talks with his bosses about corruption.

B. Serpico is raced to the hospital, bleeding.

C. Serpico is shown graduating from the police academy.

D. Serpico reports to his first day of duty at the NYPD.

2111. Richard Dreyfuss plays UFO-obsessed Roy Neary in *Close Encounters of the Third Kind*. Roy and many others travel to the Devil's Tower to meet with benign aliens. Where is the Devil's Tower located?

A. Arizona
C. Montana
B. Wyoming
D. New Mexico

2112.

2113. A Green Beret war veteran defends a hippie school in the film *Billy Jack*. What is the name of the school?

A. Peace School
C. Freedom School
B. Love School
D. Tranquility School

2114. The cops in the 1997 James Ellroy adaptation *L.A. Confidential* uncover corruption while investigating a homicide that occurs at a coffee shop. What is the name of this coffee shop?

A. Manny's
C. The Nite Owl
B. Coffee Palace
D. The Dirty Spoon

2115. A young man named Harold and an elderly woman named Maude become unlikely friends in the aptly titled film *Harold and Maude*. Harold has an obsession. What is this?

A. Circuses
C. Death
B. War
D. Movies

2116. Hubbell is an author in *The Way We Were*. He does something his girlfriend, Katie, considers a colossal waste of his talents. What is this?

A. Writes movie quiz books
C. Writes nonfiction
B. Works as a screenwriter
D. Retires from writing

2117. Which of the four men in *Deliverance* plays "Dueling Banjos" with the dim hillbilly boy?

A. Lewis
C. Drew
B. Ed
D. Bobby

2118. *The Sting* is a 1973 movie about con men. At the film's beginning, grifter Luther Coleman says he is retiring. In what city does he plan to "go straight"?

A. Denver
C. Tulsa
B. Little Rock
D. Kansas City

2119. Armand and Albert are lovers and housemates in the film *The Birdcage*. Their housekeeper's name is Agador. What does Agador hardly ever wear?

A. Pants
C. Shoes
B. Shirt
D. Underwear

2112.

Quiz Show is a 1994 Robert Redford film about the infamous *Twenty-One* quiz show scandal of 1958. The film, adapted from Richard Goodwin's book *Remembering America* by Paul Attanasio, stars Ralph Fiennes, John Turturro, and Rob Morrow.

The film follows three men on their individual paths to success. Dick Goodwin (Morrow) is an idealistic lawyer working for a Congressional subcommittee investigating corruption in television game shows, Charles Van Doren (Fiennes) is a college professor who was born into one of the nation's premier literary families, and Herbie Stempel (Turturro) is a former *Twenty-One* champion who gladly accepted the answers to the questions in advance, but then became angry when he was asked to take a dive and incorrectly answer a simple question that he knew the answer to.

The film was critically acclaimed, and received four Academy Award nominations, including Best Picture, Best Director, and Best Adapted Screenplay. Unfortunately, however, these nominations failed to yield a single statuette.

What noted filmmaker appears in a cameo as the show's sponsor, Martin Rittenhome?

A. Robert Redford
B. John Sayles
C. Martin Scorsese
D. Roger Corman

2120. *Mother* is a 1996 comedy written and directed by Albert Brooks. In the film, what actress plays Brooks' mother?

A. Doris Day
C. Debbie Reynolds
B. Elizabeth Taylor
D. Nancy Reagan

2121. Frank Slade takes Charlie to a swanky restaurant called the Oak Room in *Scent of a Woman*. How much do hamburgers cost at this restaurant?

A. $16
C. $24
B. $32
D. $53

2122. *Awakenings* tells the true story of a doctor who saw remarkable (but limited) results in his long-term catatonic patients with the aid of a new drug. What is the name of this drug?

A. Enalapril
C. Psilocybin
B. L-Dopa
D. Flintstones Chewable Multi-Vitamins

2123. Elliott and Gertie are siblings who befriend a benign alien in *E.T.: The Extra-Terrestrial*. Elliott and Gertie have a pet dog. What is the name of their dog?

A. Ernie
C. Harvey
B. Freddie
D. Petey

2124. In *Children of a Lesser God*, what does Sarah say she could always do as well as anyone with hearing?

A. Math
C. Sing
B. Sex
D. Love

2125. The 1986 Woody Allen film *Hannah and Her Sisters* follows the lives and loves of three sisters. The film ends with the three women coming together at a family dinner. What is the cause for this dinner?

A. Thanksgiving
C. A wedding
B. Death of a relative
D. Christmas

2126. Mr. Huph requests the services of Mr. Incredible when a dangerous robot wreaks havoc in the animated film *The Incredibles*. What is the name of the robot?

A. Deathbot 6XG
C. Argobot 56X-9
B. Omnidroid 9000
D. Invincibot 999.9

2127. *The Aviator* is Martin Scorsese's 2004 biopic of aviator and industrialist Howard Hughes. The film depicts the creation of the aircraft H-4 Hercules. By what nickname is this plane referred by its detractors?

A. Hughes' Blues
C. Spruce Goose
B. Hughes' Folly
D. Flying Junkyard

2128. William Miller is a music journalist following the band Stillwater on tour in Cameron Crowe's *Almost Famous*. For what publication does Miller write?

A. *Spin*

B. *Rolling Stone*

C. *Billboard*

D. *Esquire*

2129. *American History X* follows a reformed ex-skinhead named Derek Vinyard, who just got released from prison for murder. For how many murders was Derek incarcerated?

A. One

B. Two

C. Three

D. Four

2130. Ben Kingsley plays an immigrant fighting for a house he just purchased in *House of Sand and Fog*. What country does his character hail from?

A. Iraq

B. Saudi Arabia

C. Iran

D. Afghanistan

2131. *Natural Born Killers* is an over-the-top hyperviolent crime film directed by Oliver Stone. In what location does the film begin?

A. Mallory's house

B. Prison

C. Diner

D. Television production studio

2132. In the film *Ordinary People*, Conrad Jarrett is involved in a sailing accident in which his brother Buck is killed. Wracked with grief, Conrad attempts to commit suicide. How?

A. Overdose

B. Cutting his wrists

C. Hanging

D. Gunshot

2133. The 1985 drama *Mask* tells the story of Roy L. Dennis, a young man suffering from craniodiaphyseal dysplasia. What is the nickname Roy goes by?

A. Junior

B. Rocky

C. Shorty

D. Robbie

2134. *Coal Miner's Daughter* is a 1980 biopic about country music legend Loretta Lynn. How old is Loretta when she marries "Moonie" Lynn?

A. Sixteen years old

B. Fourteen years old

C. Fifteen years old

D. Thirteen years old

2135. William Hurt is a hotshot young news reporter in the film *Broadcast News*. What is the name of his character?

A. Aaron Altman

B. Martin Klein

C. Bill Rorich

D. Tom Grunnick

2139.

The Usual Suspects is a 1995 crime thriller written by Christopher McQuarrie and directed by Bryan Singer. The film, shot on an economical budget of $4 million, stars Kevin Spacey, Gabriel Byrne, Chazz Palminteri, Benicio Del Toro, Stephen Baldwin, and Kevin Pollak.

The film centers on the interrogation by Agent Kujan (Palminteri) of a small-time hood named "Verbal" Kint (Spacey). Kujan has been investigating a suspicious fire on a Turkish merchant ship, and the name "Keyser Soze" keeps popping up. Soze, Verbal informs him, is a mysterious crime figure of mythic proportions whom no one ever sees, but who controls everything in the crime world. In the course of the interrogation, Kujan begins to suspect that one of Verbal's associates may well be Soze himself.

The film did very little box office business and received lukewarm critical reception—although it did receive two Academy Awards for McQuarrie's screenplay and Spacey's bravura performance—but has since become a bona fide cult favorite.

When the "usual suspects" are first rounded up at the beginning of the film, they are accused of hijacking a truck. What was in the truck?

A. Computer equipment
B. Gun parts
C. Expensive men's suits
D. Cigarettes

2136. Bull "The Great Santini" Meechum is a marine who moves from post to post with his unhappy family in the film *The Great Santini*. How many children does he have?

A. Two   **C.** Four
B. Three   **D.** Five

2137. Richard Kimble is a successful Chicago doctor who is found guilty of murder in *The Fugitive*. In one scene, Kimble escapes into a parade when being pursued. What is the occasion of the parade?

A. Kwanzaa   **C.** Christmas
B. Saint Patrick's Day   **D.** Easter

2138. Eliott Ness and *The Untouchables* make a gaffe when trying to stop a shipment of Canadian whiskey. What do the crates actually contain?

A. Ketchup bottles   **C.** Umbrellas
B. Teddy bears   **D.** Lamps

2139.

2140. Oskar Schindler saves many Jews from impending death in the Holocaust film *Schindler's List*. How many Jews does he ultimately save?

A. 650   **C.** 2,300
B. 3,050   **D.** 1,100

2141. Wide receiver Ron Tidwell is the sports agent title character's top client in *Jerry Maguire*. What team does Tidwell play for?

A. New England Patriots   **C.** St. Louis Rams
B. Arizona Cardinals   **D.** Dallas Cowboys

2142. What is the name of the mentally handicapped man in *Do the Right Thing* who sells photographs of Malcolm X and Martin Luther King, Jr.?

A. Smiley   **C.** Junebug
B. Mookie   **D.** Red

2143. Jerry Lundegaard has his wife kidnapped so he can ransom his father-in-law in *Fargo*. How much money does he request as ransom?

A. $50,000   C. $500,000
B. $1 million   **D.** $2 million

2144. *Talladega Nights: The Ballad of Ricky Bobby* is a 2006 comedy starring Will Ferrell. What was Ricky Bobby said to have been born to do?

A. "Go fast"   **C.** "Speed . . . a lot"
B. "Win"   **D.** "Be the best"

2145. An old woman makes her way to the prince's castle at the beginning of *Beauty and the Beast*. What does she offer him as payment?

A. A rose

B. A ring

C. Her only coin

D. Her eyeglasses

2146. *Forrest Gump* explains that he is named after a man who founded something. What is this?

A. Republican Party

B. Ku Klux Klan

C. Boy Scouts

D. The Dalton Gang

2147. The title character pig in *Babe* befriends a sheepdog named what?

A. Fly

B. Roy

C. Tiny

D. Bo

2148. Fergus uses a pseudonym when he goes to meet Jody's "girlfriend" in *The Crying Game*. What is the alias he uses?

A. Billy

B. Jimmy

C. Sean

D. Maguire

2149. Richard Dreyfuss' character Glenn Holland is a teacher in *Mr. Holland's Opus*. What subject does he teach?

A. Spanish

B. Art

C. Music

D. Literature

2150. Viewers of a cursed videotape are given a finite amount of time to live in the horror flick *The Ring*. How many days is this?

A. Five

B. Seven

C. Six

D. Four

2151. Terence Stamp plays Wilson, a vengeful father, in *The Limey*. Stamp later appeared quite briefly as Wilson in which other Steven Soderbergh film?

A. *Out of Sight*

B. *Bubble*

C. *Full Frontal*

D. *Eros*

2152. *Capote* depicts author Truman Capote's work on the landmark true crime book *In Cold Blood*, which chronicled the murder of a rural Kansas family. What is the name of this family?

A. Cornish

B. Carver

C. Coyle

D. Clutter

2153. Tom Mullen's son is kidnapped and held for a $2 million ransom in the aptly titled thriller *Ransom*. What is his son's name?

A. Corey

B. Sean

C. David

D. Brad

2155.

The 1984 comedy *Beverly Hills Cop* represents a better time in the career of comic Eddie Murphy. Back then, he was still making the kinds of movies we typically saw him in. In edgy, adult humor movies like *Beverly Hills Cop*, *Trading Places*, and *48 Hrs.*, the comedian played brash, funny characters that seemed very close to his stage persona. But a 1997 scandal involving Murphy's picking up a transvestite prostitute ended all of that. He underwent a career and image makeover, now appearing in mostly family-oriented films such as *Shrek* and *Dr. Dolittle* (although *Dreamgirls* is a step in the right direction). While funny, these are not the kinds of movies we originally came to know and love Murphy for.

Beverly Hills Cop tells the story of a foul-mouthed Detroit cop named Axel Foley (Murphy), who travels to Beverly Hills to investigate the murder of a childhood friend. In this humorous fish-out-of-water story, Foley gets himself into trouble in California, but ultimately tracks down the baddies responsible for his friend's premature demise.

What kind of vehicle does Axel Foley drive in *Beverly Hills Cop*?

A. Ford Torino
B. Chevy Nova
C. Volkswagen
D. Chevy Citation

2154. Ludacris plays an unlikable rap artist in *Hustle & Flow*. What is his rap moniker?

A. DJay
B. Skinny Black
C. Big Syke
D. Blue Lou

2155.

2156. Name the secret secondary occupation of Wilbur Larch in the 1999 Lasse Hallstrom film *The Cider House Rules*.

A. Assassin
B. Ku Klux Klansman
C. Abortionist
D. Warlock

2157. What is the name of the blue tang fish suffering short-term memory loss in the animated film *Finding Nemo*?

A. Deb
B. Peach
C. Dory
D. Bruce

2158. Truman Burbank's true love, Meryl, is taken away from him in *The Truman Show*. What article of clothing of Meryl's does he save?

A. Letter jacket
B. Scarf
C. Sweater
D. Shoe

2159. *Platoon* centers around Private Chris Taylor, a soldier who has just arrived in Vietnam. Who does Taylor write letters to throughout the film?

A. His grandmother
B. His best friend
C. His father
D. His girlfriend

2160. In the classic boxing film *Rocky*, what does Rocky say Thanksgiving is for him?

A. A waste of time
B. Turkey Day
C. Thursday
D. None of these

2161. A man named Sam owns the only theater in Anarene, Texas, in the film *The Last Picture Show*. What is Sam's nickname?

A. Sam the Sham
B. Sambo
C. Samuel the Great
D. Sam the Lion

2162. *Nashville* is a 1975 ensemble film directed by Robert Altman. Which of these actors does *not* appear in the film?

A. Ronnie Cox
B. Scott Glenn
C. Ned Beatty
D. Henry Gibson

2163. *Dog Day Afternoon* is a heist film starring Al Pacino. What is Pacino's character robbing the bank to finance?

- **A.** His own business
- **B.** Nose job
- **C.** Sex change
- **D.** New car

2164. *Braveheart* tells the story of Scottish hero William Wallace. The film opens with someone saying he will tell us the story of Wallace. Who is this?

- **A.** Hamish Campbell
- **B.** Longshanks
- **C.** Malcolm Wallace
- **D.** Robert the Bruce

2165. Which of these Bee Gees songs does not appear in the disco film *Saturday Night Fever*?

- **A.** "More Than a Woman"
- **B.** "Too Much Heaven"
- **C.** "You Should Be Dancing"
- **D.** "Night Fever"

2166. The *Heaven's Gate* characters of actors John Hurt and Kris Kristofferson graduate from the same college. What is this college?

- **A.** Bob Jones University
- **B.** Brigham Young University
- **C.** University of Notre Dame
- **D.** Harvard University

2167. Like its predecessor, *Funny Girl*, the Barbra Streisand vehicle *Funny Lady* is about a real-life singer and actress. Who is this?

- **A.** Judy Garland
- **B.** Anna Held
- **C.** Fanny Brice
- **D.** Alice Faye

2168. *Legends of the Fall* is an Edward Zwick movie that centers on a Montana family named the Ludlows. Which of these characters narrates the film?

- **A.** Decker
- **B.** Tristan
- **C.** Stab
- **D.** Samuel

2169.

2170. *The English Patient* tells the story of a badly burned researcher named László de Almásy. However, he is not English. What is his nationality?

- **A.** Hungarian
- **B.** American
- **C.** Israeli
- **D.** German

2171. Harold Crick discovers that he's a character in a novel in the 2006 film *Stranger Than Fiction*. What is Harold's occupation?

- **A.** Insurance adjuster
- **B.** Auditor
- **C.** Accountant
- **D.** County Treasurer

2169.

The 1971 Gordon Parks film *Shaft* is usually referred to as the second "blaxploitation" film. (The first was Melvin Van Peebles' revolutionary film *Sweet Sweetback's Baadasssss Song*.) *Shaft*, along with *Sweetback*, kicked off a cycle of African-American cinema that lasted from 1971 to roughly 1975, and included more than two hundred films.

Unlike many of the like-minded films that followed, *Shaft* didn't depict its subjects in a negative light. The film's lead character, John Shaft, exhibited the bravado and coolness that typified characters from the blaxploitation cycle, but its story isn't dependent on race; the story could have been told in the same way with a Caucasian detective at its center. In this light, *Shaft* could be said to be one of the only blaxploitation films to truly treat its actors and subjects as equals.

Shaft spawned two sequels, *Shaft's Big Score!* and *Shaft in Africa*, as well as a 2000 re-imagining starring Samuel L. Jackson.

What is the name of the black mob boss played by Moses Gunn?

- **A.** Biggie Smalls
- **B.** Bumpy Jonas
- **C.** Tommy Gibbs
- **D.** Slim

2172. Neil McCauley won't allow himself to get close to anyone he can't walk away from in a certain amount of time in the film *Heat*. How long is this?

A. Ten seconds

B. Twenty seconds

C. Thirty seconds

D. One minute

2173. Joey Cusack's brother is the head of the Philadelphia mob in the film *A History of Violence*. What is his name?

A. Tom

B. Richie

C. Carl

D. John

2174. Colin Sullivan and Billy Costigan both have feelings for the same woman in the Martin Scorsese thriller *The Departed*. What is her occupation?

A. Internal affairs officer

B. Psychiatrist

C. Pharmacist

D. Assistant district attorney

2175. Christopher Nolan's 2005 film *Batman Begins* depicts the beginning of Batman's story. What villain is discussed at the end of the film for his "taste for the theatrical" and habit of leaving cards at his crime scenes?

A. Scarecrow

B. Riddler

C. Penguin

D. Joker

2176. The 1998 Farrelly brothers' film *There's Something About Mary* tells the story of several men who are obsessed with one lovely lady. What was the name of Mary's high school prom date who has an accident with a zipper?

A. Pat Healy

B. Ted Stroehmann

C. Dom Woganowski

D. Norman Phipps

2177. *Gosford Park* is a stylish whodunit directed by Robert Altman. In the film, what is the name of the dog that eventually leaves with Elsie?

A. Pip

B. Cracker Jack

C. Fred

D. Captain Morgan

2178. Do you know which of these performers does *not* appear in the Stephen Soderbergh film *Traffic*?

A. Amy Irving

B. Freddy Rodriguez

C. Topher Grace

D. Benjamin Bratt

2179. What actor was first cast to voice the animated character *Shrek* before being replaced by Mike Myers?

A. Eddie Murphy

B. Chris Farley

C. Dana Carvey

D. Dennis Quaid

2180. *The Royal Tenenbaums* is an offbeat comedy that follows the lives of three prodigy siblings who find difficulty in adulthood. A member of the Tenenbaum family has sued patriarch Royal Tenenbaum twice. Who is this?

A. Etheline
B. Chas
C. Margot
D. Richie

2181. In *The Sixth Sense*, Dr. Malcolm Crowe is shot in the opening moments of the film. In what part of his body is he shot?

A. Arm
B. Chest
C. Stomach
D. Throat

2182. *Gladiator* tells the story of farmer-turned-general-turned-slave Maximus Decimus Meridius. What actor plays the doomed Emperor Marcus Aurelius?

A. Peter O'Toole
B. Michael Caine
C. Richard Harris
D. Oliver Reed

2183. A package keeps Tom Hanks' character company (as does a volleyball) in the film *Cast Away*. There is a custom logo on the package. What is this?

A. Smiley face
B. Yorkshire terrier
C. Angel wings
D. Sports car

2184. Widower Hank Grotowski must come to grips with the suicide of his son in the dark drama *Monster's Ball*. What is Hank's occupation?

A. Sheriff
B. Security guard
C. Police officer
D. Prison guard

2185.

2186. All but one of these characters appear to John Nash in *A Beautiful Mind* and urge him to murder his wife Alicia—which does not?

A. Charles
B. Marcee
C. Sol
D. Parcher

2187. *Catch Me If You Can* tells the story of real-life teenage con artist Frank Abagnale, Jr. In his six years as a hustler, how much money did Abagnale steal?

A. $1 million
B. $2 million
C. $3 million
D. $4 million

2188. Jamie Foxx portrays the late great musician Ray Charles in the biopic *Ray*. The musician was banned from a state for not supporting Jim Crow racism. What state was this?

A. Alabama
B. Georgia
C. Louisiana
D. Mississippi

2185.

Spike Lee's 1992 film *Malcolm X* is an epic biopic about the life and times of activist and Nation of Islam minster Malcolm X, adapted by Lee from *The Autobiography of Malcolm X* by Alex Haley and Malcolm X. The film is Lee's greatest achievement.

The story begins with Malcolm's early years as a small-time hustler. He is eventually sent to prison, where he is introduced to the Islamic teachings of the Honorable Elijah Muhammad. Malcolm serves his time, is freed, and goes to work for Elijah Muhammad, becoming one of the Nation of Islam's most recognizable representatives. Malcolm ultimately has a falling out with Elijah Muhammad and separates from the Nation of Islam. He soon has a revelation that blacks and whites are equal in the eyes of Allah, leading him to denounce the separatist doctrine of the Nation of Islam. All of this leads to his tragic assassination.

What was Malcolm's last name before changing it to "X"?

2189. Which of his Apostles does Jesus Christ not find sleeping against a tree at the opening of the Mel Gibson-helmed *The Passion of the Christ*?

A. James

B. Peter

C. Judas

D. John

2190. In the David Fincher film *Se7en*, serial killer John Doe punishes or acts out six of the seven deadly sins. He manipulates Detective David Mills into embodying the seventh. Which sin is this?

A. Greed

B. Sloth

C. Wrath

D. Envy

2191. *The Natural* is a 1984 film about a baseballer named Roy Hobbs. Roy burns a word into his wooden baseball bat. What is this?

A. Natural

B. Wonderboy

C. Molly

D. Nelly

2192. What is the name of Pol Pot's ethnic cleansing program depicted in *The Killing Fields* that caused the death of more than two million Cambodians?

A. Project Cambodia

B. Khmer Rouge Peace Program

C. Year Zero

D. Sunday Bloody Sunday

2193. Adelaide plans to leave her entire fortune to her feline pets in the Disney animated film *The Aristocats*. What is the name of the greedy butler who plans to kill the cats?

A. Harry

B. Laurence

C. Edgar

D. Chester

2194. Randle Patrick McMurphy, a petty criminal pretending to be crazy, is labotomized in *One Flew Over the Cuckoo's Nest*. Which of McMurphy's friends subsequently puts him out of his misery by killing him?

A. Taber

B. Martini

C. Chief Bromden

D. Harding

2195. Ennis and Jack discover they have feelings for one another while working a shepherding job on *Brokeback Mountain*. Where is this mountain located?

A. North Carolina

B. Wyoming

C. Utah

D. Arizona

2196. *Flags of Our Fathers* recounts the true story of five marines and a naval corpsman who were credited with raising the American flag atop Mt. Suribachi on the island of Iwo Jima. One of the marines, an American Indian, has been immoratalized in a popular song. What is his name?

A. Ira Hayes

B. John "Doc" Bradley

C. Rene Gagnon

D. Keyes Beech

2197. What is the name of the miner played by Charlize Theron who heads up a class action sexual harassment suit against her employer in the film *North Country*?

A. Cathy Kirkendall

B. Josey Aimes

C. Gwen Sunday

D. Sara Deever

2198. *Walk the Line* is a 2005 biopic about the life and times of country music singer Johnny Cash. What song does Johnny write while in the military and later perform for Sun Records impresario Sam Phillips?

A. "I Walk the Line"

B. "Ring of Fire"

C. "A Boy Named Sue"

D. "Folsom County Blues"

2199. *Good Night, and Good Luck.* depicts the conflict between television journalist Edward R. Murrow and Senator Joseph McCarthy. What is the title of the CBS show Murrow hosts?

A. *Meet the Press*

B. *See It Now*

C. *There You Have It*

D. *60 Minutes*

2200. *The Green Mile* is a Stephen King adaptation about death row in a Louisiana prison. By what name do the guards refer to the electric chair?

A. The Toaster

B. The Shocker

C. Old Sparky

D. Seat-O-Lightning

2201. Paul Rusesabagina attempts to save the lives of others during the Rwandan genocide in the film *Hotel Rwanda*. Is Paul a Hutu or a Tutsi?

A. We are never told

B. Tutsi

C. Hutu

D. He is neither

2202. *The Thin Red Line* follows a company of soldiers during the World War II battle of Guadalcanal. What is this company?

A. A Company

B. C Company

C. B Company

D. D Company

2203.

2204. Name the actor who plays racing analyst and commentator Tick Tock McGlaughlin in the 2003 horseracing film *Seabiscuit*.

A. David McCullough

B. Jeff Bridges

C. William H. Macy

D. Chris Cooper

2205. Jude Law plays hit man Harlen Maguire in *Road to Perdition*. What is Maguire's side job?

A. Auto mechanic

B. Police officer

C. Photographer

D. Cabbie

2203.

M*A*S*H is a 1970 Robert Altman dark comedy about a field hospital in the Korean War. (Altman intended audiences to compare the setting with Vietnam.)

The film centers around two rebellious and anti-authoritarian surgeons, Hawkeye Pierce (Donald Sutherland) and Trapper John (Elliott Gould), who clash with the hardheaded Major Frank Burns (Robert Duvall) and his by-the-book love interest, Major Margaret O'Houlihan (Sally Kellerman). As you can imagine, sparks fly and hilarity ensues.

M*A*S*H won the Grand Prix Award at the 1970 Cannes Film Festival. The film received five Academy Award nominations, winning a single Oscar for Best Adapted Screenplay. In addition, the American Film Institute ranked it as the fifty-sixth greatest American film on their 1998 "100 Years . . . 100 Movies" list, and has appeared on both Bravo and AFI's lists of the one hundred funniest films of all time.

What nickname do Hawkeye and Trapper John give Major O'Houlihan?

A. Tight End

B. Sweet Dreams

C. Major Hula Hoop

D. Hot Lips

2206. George Clooney plays Danny Ocean in the 2001 remake *Ocean's Eleven*. What is the name of Ocean's wife?

A. Devin

B. Leah

C. Tess

D. Alicia

2207. Supes's son is revealed in *Superman Returns*. What is his son's name?

A. Charles

B. Mike

C. Josh

D. Jason

2208. Bill Murray's Bob Harris is an aging actor whose career is on the downward spiral in *Lost in Translation*. He is in Japan to appear in a commercial. What type of product is he hawking?

A. Soft drink

B. Gin

C. Scotch

D. Energy drink

2209. Baroness Blixen lives on a farm in Kenya in the film *Out of Africa*. What is the primary crop grown on this farm?

A. Beans

B. Coffee

C. Sugarcane

D. Rice

2210. In *Witness*, Harrison Ford and Kelly McGillis dance in the barn during the film's most iconic scene. What classic tune do they dance to?

A. "A Change Is Gonna Come"

B. "You Send Me"

C. "(What a) Wonderful World"

D. "Somewhere There's a Girl"

2211. Mr. Miyagi teaches Daniel La Russo the art of karate in the film *The Karate Kid*. What is Mr. Miyagi's occupation?

A. Mechanic

B. Handyman

C. Karate instructor

D. Television repairman

2212. Gene Wilder plays an alcoholic gunslinger known as the "Waco Kid" in the Mel Brooks comedy *Blazing Saddles*. The gunslinger says he has likely killed more men than a famous filmmaker. Who is this?

A. Howard Hawks

B. John Ford

C. Cecil B. DeMille

D. Alfred Hitchcock

2213. Which of these actors made his debut as James Bond in *Casino Royale*?

A. Pierce Brosnan

B. Daniel Craig

C. Roger Moore

D. Timothy Dalton

2214. Tony Scott's *Crimson Tide* is a submarine thriller starring Denzel Washington and Gene Hackman. What is the name of the sub on which the story is set?

A. USS *Ohio*

B. USS *Alabama*

C. USS *Georgia*

D. USS *Tennessee*

2215. In the comedy film *The 40-Year-Old Virgin*, which of the four friends is the virgin referred to in the film's title?

A. David
B. Jay
C. Andy
D. Cal

2216. The tagline for *The Color Purple* says the film is about three things. Which of these things is not one of them?

A. Life
B. Love
C. Us
D. Learning

2217. Martin Scorsese's *Gangs of New York* centers on the native and immigrant gangs in the Five Points district. What is the name of the Irish immigrant gang?

A. Dead Rabbits
B. 19th Street Gang
C. Westies
D. Grady Gang

2218. *Mystic River* tells the lifelong story of three friends. One of them is kidnapped and sexually abused as a child. Which one?

A. Sean
B. Dave
C. Tommy
D. Jimmy

2219. Morgan Freeman plays an ex-boxer named Eddie Dupris in *Million Dollar Baby*. In his boxing days, Eddie had a nickname. What was this?

A. Brown Bomber
B. Scrap Iron
C. Dynamite Kid
D. Quick Silver

2220. *Adaptation* depicts screenwriter Charlie Kaufman attempting to adapt a book by Susan Orlean. Which Susan Orlean book was this?

A. *The Orchid Thief*
B. *Throw Me a Bone*
C. *Red Sox and Blue Fish*
D. *My Kind of Place*

2221.

2222. What is the name of the ship in *Pirates of the Caribbean: The Curse of the Black Pearl* that carries Governor Swann and his daughter Elizabeth?

A. HMS *Courageous*
B. HMS *Courteous*
C. HMS *Dauntless*
D. HMS *Fearless*

2223. Muhammad Ali's life is chronicled in *Ali*, starring Will Smith. Which actor portrays activist Malcolm X in the film?

A. Denzel Washington
B. Mario Van Peebles
C. Jamie Foxx
D. Jeffrey Wright

2224. How many years after the original *Alien* does the sequel *Aliens* take place?

A. Twenty-seven
B. Thirty-seven
C. Fifty-seven
D. Forty-seven

2221.

The 1976 film *Taxi Driver*, director Martin Scorsese's first masterpiece (with *Raging Bull* and *Goodfellas* yet to come), is widely considered one of the greatest films ever produced. The film has also made stars out of actors Robert De Niro and Jodie Foster.

The story line focuses on a lonely, alienated Vietnam veteran named Travis Bickle (De Niro). Suffering from insomnia, Travis goes to work as a cabbie working the midnight shift in New York City's most dangerous neighborhoods. In doing this, he soon becomes obsessed with the notion of cleansing the decaying city. Travis contemplates assassinating Senator Charles Palantine, then reconsiders and shifts his focus to an adolescent prostitute named Iris (Foster). He becomes hell-bent on saving her (even though she doesn't want to be "saved"), and ultimately attacks her pimp (Harvey Keitel).

The film won numerous awards, allegedly inspired would-be assassin John Hinckley, Jr. to shoot President Reagan, and has since been ranked at number twenty-two on the American Film Institute's list of the one hundred greatest American films.

How old is Iris?

A. Fifteen
B. Fourteen
C. Twelve
D. Thirteen

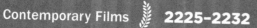

2225. The 1982 film *Sophie's Choice* tells the story of a Polish immigrant and her lover. What is the name of the character who narrates the film?

A. Sophie

C. Yetta

B. Nathan

D. Stingo

2226. What, according to the tagline for the 1994 masterpiece *The Shawshank Redemption*, "can set you free"?

A. Hope

C. Courage

B. Determination

D. Belief

2227. In the original John Grisham novel *The Firm*, Mitch McDeere swindles $10 million from the law firm before disappearing into the sunset. How much does he steal from the firm in the film?

A. $3 million

C. $12.3 million

B. $6 million

D. Nothing

2228. Do you know which of these performers does *not* appear in the Michel Gondry film *Eternal Sunshine of the Spotless Mind*?

A. Tom Wilkinson

C. Mark Ruffalo

B. Elijah Wood

D. Jude Law

2229. *Black Hawk Down* chronicles a 1993 U.S. Army Rangers mission into a city in Somalia. What is this city?

A. Merca

C. Beledweyne

B. Mogadishu

D. Galcaio

2230. *The Pianist* is a 2002 Roman Polanski film about a Polish piano player who manages to survive the German deportation of Jews to concentration camps. What, according to the film's tagline, "was his masterpiece"?

A. Freedom

C. Survival

B. Life

D. Escaping

2231. *Reservoir Dogs* tells the story of a botched jewel heist. As the thieves prepare for the heist, they discuss and analyze a Madonna song. What is this song?

A. "Like a Virgin"

C. "Justify My Love"

B. "Papa Don't Preach"

D. "Material Girl"

2232. The Alexander Payne film *About Schmidt* tells the story of a man's life after the passing of his wife. Schmidt narrates the film to an African child. What is the child's name?

A. Sabiha

C. Gimbya

B. Ndugu

D. Basha

2233. Jessica Rabbit is Roger's voluptuous wife in the film *Who Framed Roger Rabbit*. What is the name of the club where Jessica works?

A. Toon Saloon
B. The Ink and Paint Club
C. Anna Mae's
D. Art House

2234. Eddie Murphy plays a character named Prince Akeem in *Coming to America*. What is the name of the fictitious country he is from?

A. Neruda
B. Zamunda
C. Kayobi
D. Jareshua

2235. *The Omen* is a 1976 horror film about a child who is the spawn of Satan. In the film, how is Robert Thorn killed?

A. Hanging
B. Falling down stairs
C. Shooting
D. Fire

2236. Ahmad Abdul Rahim is the Muslim right fielder for the original *Bad News Bears*. What pro baseball player is he a huge fan of?

A. Willie McCovey
B. Joe Morgan
C. Hank Aaron
D. Frank White

2237. *Crocodile Dundee* is a 1986 comedy about an Australian man who comes to the United States. What is "Crocodile" Dundee's first name?

A. Rodney
B. Steve
C. Michael
D. Thomas

2238. *The Little Mermaid* tells the story of a beautiful young mermaid named Ariel. One of her best friends is named Scuttle. What kind of creature is Scuttle?

A. Seahorse
B. Fish
C. Octopus
D. Seagull

2239.

2240. Murtaugh's daughter Rianne appears in a commercial in *Lethal Weapon 2*. What type of product is the commercial selling?

A. Tampons
B. Pregnancy tests
C. Condoms
D. Oral contraception

2241. David and Diana Murphy are newlyweds who travel to Las Vegas in *Indecent Proposal*. Things become complicated when they meet a billionaire interested in Diana. What is his name?

A. Mike Clark
B. Don Winters
C. John Gage
D. Jim Lansdown

2239.

American Beauty is a 1999 drama directed by Sam Mendes and written by Alan Ball. The film examines the elusive nature of happiness and the imperfect world that lies just behind the façade of a seemingly perfect picturesque suburban neighborhood.

The film focuses primarily on the three members of the Burnham household: forty-two-year-old patriarch Lester (Kevin Spacey), who has just lost his job and is experiencing a midlife crisis; his wife Carolyn (Annette Bening), the ambitious career-obsessed realtor who ignores her family and is having an affair with an ultra-successful realtor; their daughter Jane (Thora Birch), who resents them both, is embarrassed by her father's blatant desire for her high school cheerleader best friend, and is becoming romantically involved with their pot-dealing neighbor.

This beautiful, poetically written film was nominated for eight Academy Awards, yielding five Oscars, including Best Picture, Best Director, and Best Actor.

Ricky's father is a retired marine. What is his rank?

A. Sergeant First Class
B. Lieutenant
C. Colonel
D. Major

2242. What actor plays the President of the United States in the disaster fantasy *Deep Impact*?

A. Jon Favreau

B. Maximilian Schell

C. Morgan Freeman

D. Robert Duvall

2243. Angry neo-nationalists take the president hostage while in flight in the film *Air Force One*. What country are these neo-nationalists from?

A. Iraq

B. Zaire

C. Kazakhstan

D. Afghanistan

2244. Which of these is the first film by director and activist Michael Moore?

A. *Fahrenheit 9/11*

B. *Roger & Me*

C. *Bowling for Columbine*

D. *The Big One*

2245. *American Dreamz* is a 2006 film parodying American politics and popular culture. What is the name of the character who hosts the TV show depicted in the film?

A. Joseph Staton

B. Martin Tweed

C. Sally Kendoo

D. William Williams

2246. This 1999 film's tagline is: "Things fall down. People look up. And when it rains it pours." What film is this?

A. *Falling Down*

B. *Magnolia*

C. *Bruce Almighty*

D. *Spanglish*

2247. Carol Anne is lost in the television set in the 1982 horror flick *Poltergeist*. What is Carol Anne told to stay away from?

A. Strangers

B. The voices

C. The light

D. Demons

2248. What is Private James Ryan's middle name in Steven Spielberg's epic World War II film *Saving Private Ryan*?

A. Joseph

B. Edward

C. Michael

D. Francis

2249. What is the name of Edward Norton's character in *Fight Club*, David Fincher's 1999 adaptation of Chuck Palahniuk's novel?

A. His name is never given

B. Rob

C. Jones

D. Hanson

2250. Where are the alien cocoons kept to restore their life force in the 1985 sci-fi favorite *Cocoon*?

A. Underground

B. Swimming pool

C. Greenhouse

D. Freezer

CHAPTER TEN:
ANYTHING GOES

2251. The Lumière Brothers were among the earliest and most important filmmakers in history. One of the brothers' name was Louis. What was the name of the second brother?
- **A.** Auguste
- **B.** Augustus
- **C.** Alfredo
- **D.** Alfred

2252. What is the name of the film company that eccentric tycoon Howard Hughes took over in 1948?
- **A.** RKO
- **B.** Paramount
- **C.** Warner Bros.
- **D.** United Artists

2253. In 1998, what publication published a survey revealing that more U.S. teenagers knew who Leonardo DiCaprio was than Vice President Al Gore?
- **A.** *Time*
- **B.** *The Nation*
- **C.** *USA Today*
- **D.** *The New York Times*

2254. What actor played the character Nick Charles in the popular *Thin Man* films of the '30s and '40s?
- **A.** William Powell
- **B.** Gary Cooper
- **C.** Fredric March
- **D.** Don Ameche

2255. Jackie Gleason's nephew is a well-known actor. Who is this?
- **A.** Kevin Bacon
- **B.** Jason Patric
- **C.** Aaron Eckhart
- **D.** Tony Shalhoub

2256. The twelve-minute 1903 film *The Great Train Robbery* is often credited as the first narrative movie of length. Do you know who directed it?
- **A.** Thomas Edison
- **B.** Edwin S. Porter
- **C.** Georges Méliès
- **D.** D.W. Griffith

2257. John Carpenter directed the 1979 Elvis Presley biopic *Elvis*. Coincidentally, Presley once played a character named John Carpenter. In what film was this?
- **A.** *Clambake*
- **B.** *Charro!*
- **C.** *Harum Scarum*
- **D.** *Change of Habit*

OPPOSITE *E.T.: The Extra-Terrestrial*, 1982

2258. The James Bond action film *Never Say Never Again* is a remake of another Bond film. What is this film?

A. *Thunderball*

B. *Dr. No*

C. *Moonraker*

D. *Goldfinger*

2259. Talk show host and columnist Larry King frequently pops up in film cameos. Which of these films does *not* feature a cameo by Larry King?

A. *Enemy of the State*

B. *Armageddon*

C. *The Contender*

D. *The Stepford Wives*

2260.

2261. This 2001 film's tagline is: "Open your eyes." What is the name of this film?

A. *Vanilla Sky*

B. *Look Who's Talking*

C. *American Beauty*

D. *They Live*

2262. Which of the following Tom Clancy adaptations stars Ben Affleck as CIA agent Jack Ryan?

A. *Patriot Games*

B. *The Sum of All Fears*

C. *The Hunt for Red October*

D. *Clear and Present Danger*

2263. In *The Princess Bride*, what kind of poison does Westley put in the wine during his battle of wits with Vizzini?

A. Cyanide

B. Iocane

C. Ipecac

D. Hemlock

2264. This actor wrote an inspirational book about the stories of famous successful people like Jimmy Carter, Bill Clinton, and Cal Ripken. Its title is *A Hand to Guide Me*. Who is this?

A. Bill Cosby

B. Tom Hanks

C. Michael Douglas

D. Denzel Washington

2265. A real-life inventor is a character played by David Bowie in the 2006 movie *The Prestige*. Who is this?

A. Nikolas Tesla

B. Thomas Edison

C. Lars Magnus Ericsson

D. Eli Whitney

2260.

The 1998 classic *Saving Private Ryan* is one of a handful of masterpieces in the Steven Spielberg canon of films, and is the measuring stick by which all war movies have since been judged. The epic World War II film, which stars Tom Hanks, has been lauded for its ultra-realistic depiction of the June 6, 1944, Omaha beachhead assault. In fact, the film was so intensely realistic that it reportedly sent a few veterans into shock.

The story line centers on the search for a single soldier, Private Ryan, after it is learned that each of his three brothers have been killed in the line of duty. (The War Department's thinking is that perhaps they can cushion the blow for the matriarchal Mrs. Ryan by sending her one remaining son to be by her side after she receives this terrible news.) Captain John Miller (Hanks) leads a motley band of soldiers on this search for the proverbial needle in a haystack.

Saving Private Ryan received an impressive eleven Academy Award nominations, winning five, including Best Director and Best Cinematography.

What is the peacetime occupation of Captain Miller?

A. Banker

B. Accountant

C. Journalist

D. Teacher

2266. Cheeta, the chimpanzee made famous by his appearances in the Johnny Weissmuller Tarzan films, holds a record in the *Guinness Book of World Records*. What is this?

A. Oldest chimpanzee

B. Most fish eaten by a chimp in a single sitting

C. Tallest chimpanzee

D. Farthest dung throwing by a chimp

2267. Many old television shows have been updated into Hollywood films. Which of these television series has not yet been adapted into a Hollywood feature film?

A. *Maverick*

B. *Sgt. Bilko*

C. *Father Knows Best*

D. *Leave It to Beaver*

2268. Which of these Martin Scorsese–directed films does *not* feature the Rolling Stones song "Gimme Shelter"?

A. *Mean Streets*

B. *Goodfellas*

C. *Casino*

D. *The Departed*

2269. *Everyone's Hero* is an animated film about a boy trying to get a baseball bat to his favorite pro player. Who is this?

A. Mickey Mantle

B. Ted Williams

C. Mel Ott

D. Babe Ruth

2270. Jeff Goldblum's character attempts to teleport a baboon in the 1986 film *The Fly*. What happens to the baboon?

A. Mutates

B. Grows to twice its size

C. Starts on fire

D. Turns inside out

2271. What villain did the Caped Crusader battle in the 1992 action film *Batman Returns*?

A. Joker

B. Scarecrow

C. Two-Face

D. Penguin

2272. What well-known actor made his film debut in the 1955 *Creature from the Black Lagoon* sequel *Revenge of the Creature*?

A. Warren Beatty

B. Clint Eastwood

C. Jack Nicholson

D. Bruce Dern

2273. How does Robin Williams' *What Dreams May Come* character, Chris Nielsen, die?

A. Plane crash

B. Automobile accident

C. Fire

D. Train crash

2274. Westerns *Hondo*, *The Quick and the Dead*, and *Crossfire Trail* were all adapted from novels by the same author. Who is this?

A. Louis L'Amour
C. Zane Grey
B. Larry McMurtry
D. Elmore Leonard

2275. What is the subtitle of the third installment in the *Lord of the Rings* trilogy?

A. The *Lord of the Rings: The Hobbit*
C. The *Lord of the Rings: The Two Towers*
B. The *Lord of the Rings: The Return of the King*
D. The *Lord of the Rings: The Fellowship of the Ring*

2276.

2277. Steven Spielberg directed all but one of these films—which is the odd one out?

A. *Memoirs of a Geisha*
C. *Munich*
B. *Jurassic Park*
D. *Always*

2278. With what device does Peter Stormare's character dispose of the body of Steve Buscemi's character in the 1996 film *Fargo*?

A. Paper shredder
C. Woodchipper
B. Chainsaw
D. Power drill

2279. Legendary actors Omar Sharif and Peter O'Toole appear together in five films. Which of these is *not* one of them?

A. *Doctor Zhivago*
C. *The Night of the Generals*
B. *One Night with the King*
D. *The Rainbow Thief*

2280. Robert Louis Stevenson's classic novel got a reworking for the 1996 film *Muppet Treasure Island*. In the film, what type of creature sits atop Long John Silver's shoulder?

A. Parrot
C. Lobster
B. Mouse
D. Monkey

2281. *Laura* is a classic 1944 mystery directed by Otto Preminger. What actress appeared in the title role?

A. Gene Tierney
C. Tallulah Bankhead
B. Jeanne Crain
D. Joan Bennett

2276.

After hearing the criticism regarding his sluggish fourth film, *Jackie Brown*, and repeated questions about his inability to match previous efforts *Reservoir Dogs* and *Pulp Fiction*, Quentin Tarantino made the stylish tour de force *Kill Bill*. An homage to the gritty grindhouse revenge flicks of the 1970s and Shaw Brothers chop-socky pictures, it was originally intended to be a single film. However, due to its four-hour running time, it was ultimately released in two parts.

Kill Bill tells the story of a former assassin who loses everything in her life at the hands of her former boss, an assassin named Bill. After a lengthy coma, the woman (billed only as "The Bride") tracks down each member of her former assassination squad to exact her bloody revenge.

The film developed an immediate following, and is widely considered one of the greatest revenge films ever produced.

Which of these actors does *not* appear in *Kill Bill*?

A. Sonny Chiba
B. Sammo Hung
C. Michael Parks
D. Gordon Liu

2282. Every successful horror film breeds a sequel or ten these days. Do you know which of these horror flicks has spawned the most sequels?

A. *Jaws*

B. *Scream*

C. *The Howling*

D. *The Omen*

2283. The mystery films *And Then There Were None*, *Murder on the Orient Express*, and *The Mirror Crack'd* are all based on the novels of the same author. Who is it?

A. Arthur Conan Doyle

B. Robert R. McCammon

C. Dashiell Hammett

D. Agatha Christie

2284. *Mr. Deeds Goes to Town* is a classic 1936 film directed by Frank Capra. What actor plays Mr. Deeds in the film?

A. Henry Fonda

B. James Stewart

C. Gregory Peck

D. Gary Cooper

2285. *Ben-Hur* is a classic 1959 film directed by William Wyler. What is Ben-Hur's full name?

A. Quintus Ben-Hur

B. Balthasar Ben-Hur

C. Judah Ben-Hur

D. Marcello Ben-Hur

2286. Three of these films have a plot that deals with time travel. Which one does *not*?

A. *12 Monkeys*

B. *Frankenstein Reborn*

C. *The Bone Collector*

D. *Déjà Vu*

2287. James Stewart's character works as a clown in the 1952 circus film *The Greatest Show on Earth*. What is his clown name?

A. Binky

B. Buttons

C. Bobo

D. Baggy

2288. The horrific events in the film *Pet Sematary* begin after Louis and Jud bury the Creed family's dead cat in the Indian burial ground. What is the name of the cat?

A. Gage

B. Paxcow

C. Church

D. Gato

2289. Three of these films have spawned television series—which one has *not*?

A. *Private Benjamin*

B. *Dirty Dancing*

C. *Weird Science*

D. *Homeward Bound*

2290. It's a Wonderful Life is an inspirational 1946 film about a small-town man who learns the importance of his life. What is the name of the town in which the film takes place?

A. Ruby Falls   C. Bedford Falls

B. Sioux Falls   D. Blackwater Falls

2291. A Playboy Playmate and actress from the film They All Laughed was murdered by her husband in 1980. Who was this?

A. Patti Hansen   C. Linda MacEwen

B. Dorothy Stratten   D. Sharon Tate

2292. Wall Street is an Oliver Stone film starring Michael Douglas and Charlie Sheen. What year was this film released?

A. 1986   C. 1987

B. 1988   D. 1985

2293. What film's tagline is "Collide with destiny"?

A. Sliding Doors   C. Deep Impact

B. Titanic   D. Armageddon

2294. Three of these movies were adapted from books by novelist Nick Hornby. Which of them was not?

A. High Fidelity   C. Fever Pitch

B. Bridget Jones's Diary   D. About a Boy

2295.

2296. San Francisco, California, serves as the backdrop for all of these films but one. Which one?

A. The Towering Inferno   C. Ladder 49

B. Vertigo   D. The Fan

2297. Jeff Bridges plays a character known as "the Dude" in the 1998 Coen Brothers' comedy The Big Lebowski. What is the name of the Dude's landlord?

A. Marty   C. Marvin

B. Harold   D. Dwight

2298. Three of these legendary actors have portrayed President Abraham Lincoln in a movie. One of them has not. Which one?

A. James Stewart   C. Raymond Massey

B. Walter Huston   D. Henry Fonda

2295.

Joanne Woodward's cinematic career began with the 1955 oater Count Three and Pray, in which she appeared alongside Van Heflin and Raymond Burr. She worked extensively in television and theater before giving a star-making performance in The Three Faces of Eve, for which she was awarded an Oscar (her first of four nominations). In 1958, Woodward married actor Paul Newman, with whom she has subsequently appeared in ten films. Other impressive entries on Woodward's filmography include The Long, Hot Summer, Sybil, Mr. & Mrs. Bridge, Philadelphia, and The Age of Innocence.

Joanne Woodward has appeared in five films directed by hubby Paul Newman. Which of these films was not directed by Newman?

A. Mr. & Mrs. Bridge

B. Rachel, Rachel

C. Harry & Son

D. The Glass Menagerie

2299. What actress was born with the name Anna Maria Louisa Italiano?

A. Maria Bello

B. Anne Bancroft

C. Patty Duke

D. Rose Marie

2300. What is the name of the actor who physically plays Darth Vader in *Star Wars*?

A. James Earl Jones

B. Peter Mayhew

C. Mark Gardner

D. David Prowse

2301. Who is famous for designing the monstrous extraterrestrial baddie in Ridley Scott's *Alien*?

A. H.R. Giger

B. Carlo Rambaldi

C. Nancy St. John

D. Ray Harryhausen

2302. *Signs* is a 2002 science fiction film about an attack on the earth by aliens. What substance kills the aliens?

A. Salt

B. Water

C. Oxygen

D. Sugar

2303. Mia and Vincent compete and win the Jack Rabbit Slim's dance contest in the film *Pulp Fiction*. What prize do they win for their effort?

A. Trophy

B. New car

C. $100 cash prize

D. Jack Rabbit Slim's jackets

2304. Actor Richard Kiel is known for playing James Bond villain Jaws. In which of these films does he appear?

A. *The Spy Who Loved Me*

B. *The Man with the Golden Gun*

C. *Live and Let Die*

D. *Moonraker*

2305. Which *Cheers* actor makes brief appearances in the films *Superman*, *Superman II*, and *The Empire Strikes Back*?

A. George Wendt

B. John Ratzenberger

C. Nicholas Colasanto

D. Ted Danson

2306. *Taps* is a 1981 drama directed by Harold Becker. Which of these cast members made his feature film debut with this film?

A. Tom Cruise

B. Giancarlo Esposito

C. Timothy Hutton

D. Sean Penn

2307. The *Treasure of the Sierra Madre* character known as Gold Hat famously says, "We don't need no stinkin' badges." Who was this actor?

A. Diego Gonzales

B. Alfonso Bedoya

C. Raul Macias

D. Ricky Martin

2308. The late great comedic actor Dudley Moore was also an accomplished jazz musician. What instrument did he play?

A. Piano

B. Clarinet

C. Guitar

D. Saxophone

2309.

2310. What does Charles Chaplin's Tramp character accidentally swallow in the 1931 masterpiece *City Lights*?

A. Pocket watch

B. Nickel

C. Whistle

D. Penny

2311. Three of these films are remakes of films by Japanese director Akira Kurosawa. One of them is not. Which one?

A. *Last Man Standing*

B. *Duel in the Sun*

C. *The Outrage*

D. *A Fistful of Dollars*

2312. Marilyn Monroe plays the sexy character Sugar Kane in the classic film *Some Like It Hot*. What was her character's real last name?

A. Kowalczyk

B. Baker

C. Arden

D. Carlisle

2313. Which of these 1958 science fiction films features Moe Howard of *The Three Stooges*?

A. *Conquest of Space*

B. *This Island Earth*

C. *Space Master X-7*

D. *Destination Moon*

2309.

Man on Fire is a 2004 Tony Scott film adapted from a novel by A.J. Quinnell. (The novel had been adapted previously in a much less noteworthy 1987 version starring Scott Glenn.)

The film tells the story of an alcoholic burned-out military man named John Creasy (Denzel Washington) who is hired by a wealthy Mexico City businessman to protect his nine-year-old daughter, Pita (Dakota Fanning). Pita continually tries to make a friend out of her new bodyguard, but Creasy doesn't want to get emotionally involved with his job. In fact, all Creasy really wants to do is die, but he fails in his attempt to commit suicide. He eventually warms to young Pita, the two become friends, and the young girl inadvertently gives his life meaning. But when Pita is kidnapped and held for ransom, the payment goes wrong and all signs point to Pita's being dead. Creasy goes on the offensive and begins hunting her kidnappers down one by one, using creative methods by which to torture and kill them.

Pita is leaving an appointment when she is kidnapped. What kind of appointment is this?

A. Piano lessons

B. Dentist

C. Therapist

D. Vocal coach

2314. Actors Karl Malden and Marlon Brando appear in three films together. Which of these films is not one of them?

A. *The Young Lions*
B. *One-Eyed Jacks*
C. *A Streetcar Named Desire*
D. *On the Waterfront*

2315. Bruce Willis plays a famous film cowboy in the 1988 Blake Edwards comedy *Sunset*. Who is this?

A. Lash Larue
B. Tom Mix
C. Buck Jones
D. Hopalong Cassidy

2316. When the story lines are viewed in chronological order, which of these Indiana Jones adventures takes place first?

A. *Raiders of the Lost Ark*
B. *Indiana Jones and the Last Crusade*
C. *Indiana Jones and the Temple of Doom*
D. We are not told the years in which these films take place

2317. Which of these Blake Edwards–helmed *Pink Panther* comedies was released first?

A. *Inspector Clouseau*
B. *The Pink Panther*
C. *A Shot in the Dark*
D. *Trail of the Pink Panther*

2318. Three of these films are disaster films. Which of them is not?

A. *The Hurricane*
B. *Earthquake*
C. *Volcano*
D. *Dante's Peak*

2319. Three of these *Saturday Night Live* alums have directed at least one feature film. Which one has not?

A. Eddie Murphy
B. Chevy Chase
C. Bill Murray
D. Billy Crystal

2320. Tom Hanks' *Big* character gets a job at a toy company. What is the name of this company?

A. FAO Schwartz
B. Tick Tock Toys
C. Mainway Toys
D. MacMillan Toy Company

2321. What film marks comedian-turned-actor Denis Leary's feature film debut?

A. *Being Bill Hicks*
B. *Strictly Business*
C. *Lethal Weapon*
D. *The Sandlot*

2322. A character played by Julia Roberts says, "Bite my ass, Krispy Kreme!" Name this film.

- **A.** *Full Frontal*
- **B.** *Erin Brockovich*
- **C.** *Pretty Woman*
- **D.** *Mona Lisa Smile*

2323.

2324. Name the film in which Robert Redford plays a former rodeo star named Sonny Steele, who now hawks breakfast cereal onstage in Las Vegas.

- **A.** *The Horse Whisperer*
- **B.** *Rhinestone Cowboy*
- **C.** *Urban Cowboy*
- **D.** *The Electric Horseman*

2325. Benjamin takes Elaine on the worst date of her life in *The Graduate*. After ignoring her all evening, he takes her someplace she does not want to be. Where is this?

- **A.** Strip club
- **B.** Biker bar
- **C.** Porn theater
- **D.** Brothel

2326. Cecil B. DeMille's office repeatedly calls Norma Desmond's home in *Sunset Boulevard*. What do they want?

- **A.** To film Norma's movie
- **B.** To use Norma's car in a movie
- **C.** To cast Norma in a movie
- **D.** To use Norma's chimp in a movie

2327. Taylor's friend Private Gardner is killed by a grenade thrown by one of his own comrades in *Platoon*. Who threw the grenade?

- **A.** Sergeant Red O'Neil
- **B.** Staff Sergeant Barnes
- **C.** Private Chris Taylor
- **D.** Junior

2328. All but one of these films star California Governor Arnold Schwarzenegger. Which one?

- **A.** *Raw Deal*
- **B.** *Predator*
- **C.** *Red Scorpion*
- **D.** *Red Heat*

2329. Sean Connery was the first of (so far) six actors to play James Bond. Which of these Bond films stars Connery?

- **A.** *Never Say Never Again*
- **B.** *On Her Majesty's Secret Service*
- **C.** *The Spy Who Loved Me*
- **D.** *The Living Daylights*

2330. D.W. Griffith directed more than one hundred films in his prolific career. Which of these Griffith films is a 1915 film that is a technical masterpiece, but offensively depicts Ku Klux Klansmen as heroes?

- **A.** *Broken Blossoms*
- **B.** *Intolerance*
- **C.** *The Birth of a Nation*
- **D.** *Judith of Bethulia*

2323.

Rob Reiner's 1989 film *When Harry Met Sally . . .*, written by Nora Ephron, is widely recognized as one of the finest comedies ever made. In addition, it is credited with popularizing the term "high-maintenance" as a label for people who require a lot of attention.

The movie tells the story of Harry (Billy Crystal) and Sally (Meg Ryan), who begin the film as unlikely traveling partners who disagree on almost everything. During the trip Harry observes that men and women cannot be friends in the traditional sense of the word because men always want to sleep with women. The two of them argue this point, and the question of whether or not men and women can ever be simply friends becomes the film's theme. They leave on bad terms.

The story line picks up ten years later when they bump into one another in a bookstore. Both have changed, and they become friends. At first they are nothing more than friends, but in time, they develop feelings for one another.

The woman in the famous deli scene who follows Sally's impromptu fake orgasm with the classic one liner, "I'll have what she's having," is the mother of someone involved with the film. Who?

- **A.** Rob Reiner
- **B.** Billy Crystal
- **C.** Meg Ryan
- **D.** Nora Ephron

2331. Michael Caine and Christopher Reeve share a kiss in a film directed by Sidney Lumet. What is this film?

A. *Switching Channels*

B. *Deathtrap*

C. *Noises Off . . .*

D. *So That's Why Superman Wears Tights!*

2332. Three of these films feature both Burt Reynolds and Dom DeLuise. One of them does not. Which one is this?

A. *Smokey and the Bandit II*

B. *Hooper*

C. *Silent Movie*

D. *All Dogs Go to Heaven*

2333. James Caan plays a character named Freebie in the 1974 comedy *Freebie and the Bean*. What actor appears as Bean?

A. Bruce Dern

B. Bill Cosby

C. Alan Arkin

D. George Segal

2334. Barbra Streisand was affectionately given a new nickname by her fellow cast members on the set of the film *Meet the Fockers*. What was this?

A. Silly Focker

B. Dottie

C. Boob

D. Chi-Chi

2335. A famous filmmaker was attached to direct the film *One-Eyed Jacks*, but ultimately backed out. Producer/lead Marlon Brando then directed the film himself. Who was the original director?

A. Elia Kazan

B. William Wyler

C. Stanley Kubrick

D. Joseph L. Mankiewicz

2336. Luke Skywalker learns that his nemesis Darth Vader is his true father. In which film does this revelation occur?

A. *Star Wars*

B. *Return of the Jedi*

C. *The Empire Strikes Back*

D. *Attack of the Clones*

2337. Which of these future movie stars did *not* appear on the TV series *The Many Loves of Dobie Gillis* at the beginning of their career?

A. Ryan O'Neal

B. Burt Reynolds

C. Warren Beatty

D. Tuesday Weld

2338. The film *Indiana Jones and the Last Crusade* contains flashbacks of Indy's youth. What actor appears in those scenes as the younger incarnation of Indiana Jones?

A. Fred Savage

B. Brian Austin Green

C. River Phoenix

D. Neil Patrick Harris

2339. *The X-Men* are a band of superheroes who have joined forces to battle evil. Which of these is not the name of a member of the X-Men?

A. Cyclops

B. Rogue

C. Magneto

D. Wolverine

2340. In what film do characters played by Matt Damon and Ben Affleck reflect upon a wager they once had about whether *Krush Groove* would be bigger than *E.T.*?

A. *Good Will Hunting*

B. *Dogma*

C. *Glory Daze*

D. *School Ties*

2341. Which *Star Trek* cast member has recorded multiple albums as a singer, appeared on *T.J. Hooker*, and directed *Star Trek III: The Search for Spock*?

A. DeForest Kelley

B. Leonard Nimoy

C. William Shatner

D. James Doohan

2342. Sacha Baron Cohen lends his voice to the lemur King in the animated film *Madagascar*. What is his name?

A. King Bobo

B. King Luther

C. King Julien

D. King Terrence

2343. In *Good Morning, Vietnam*, who does Cronauer refer to as "a man who's screaming out to be made fun of"?

A. Lieutenant Hauk

B. PFC Garlick

C. Richard Nixon

D. Spiro Agnew

2344.

2345. In 2006, a group that included documentarian Albert Maysles announced its plans to make a one-second film for charity. What is the name of this film?

A. *The Big Short Movie*

B. *Quickie*

C. *1 Second Film*

D. *Blink*

2346. Which of filmmaker Steven Spielberg's movies is based upon the short story "Super Toys Last All Summer Long" by Brian Aldiss?

A. *Always*

B. *The Sugarland Express*

C. *A.I.: Artificial Intelligence*

D. *Hook*

2344.

Mel Gibson's 2004 epic film *The Passion of the Christ* depicts the last twelve hours in the life of Jesus Christ. The powerful film was released to mixed reviews, but proved to be a monster at the box office, grossing an astounding $25 million per day in its first five days of release. The film went on to gross more than $600 million worldwide. When it was released on DVD on August 31, 2004, it reportedly sold 2.4 million copies by midday.

The film begins with Jesus (Jim Caviezel) in the Garden of Gethsemane. Jesus is engaged in an inner struggle, weighing his human desire to live with his divine mission to die. But Jesus knows that his fate was sealed before he came to earth, and he accepts this truth. After the traitorous Judas Iscariot informs the High Priest of Jesus' whereabouts, Jesus is arrested. He is then beaten to within an inch of his life in some of the most shockingly violent scenes ever committed to film. After this, he is crucified.

How many times does the Apostle Peter deny affiliation with Jesus Christ?

A. One

B. Three

C. Two

D. Four

2347. Thus far there are eleven installments in the *Friday the 13th* franchise. What is the name of the film in which Jason Voorhees is on board a spacecraft killing people?

A. *Friday the 13th Part VI: Jason Lives*

B. *Jason X*

C. *Friday the 13th: A New Beginning*

D. *Friday the 13th: The Final Chapter*

2348. Edwin S. Porter's classic 1903 western ends with a man firing directly at the screen. What is the title of this film?

A. *Ten Nights in a Barroom*

B. *The Train Wreckers*

C. *The Great Train Robbery*

D. *A Tale of the West*

2349. "Everybody wants to be Cary Grant," explained one actor. "Even I want to be Cary Grant." Who said this?

A. James Stewart

B. Clark Gable

C. Henry Fonda

D. Cary Grant

2350. One film's tagline is "This is a hell of a way to make a living." Can you name this film?

A. *The Best Little Whorehouse in Texas*

B. *Tootsie*

C. *Thank You for Smoking*

D. *Lord of War*

2351. Andy screams the name of a pop singer when he's having his chest waxed in the Judd Apatow comedy *The 40-Year-Old Virgin*. Who is this?

A. Jessica Simpson

B. Kelly Clarkson

C. Britney Spears

D. Christina Aguilera

2352. Three of the following science fiction films focus on evil robots. One of them does not. Which one is this?

A. *The Terminator*

B. *I, Robot*

C. *The Iron Giant*

D. *Sky Captain and the World of Tomorrow*

2353. *Friday* is a 1995 F. Gary Gray comedy starring Ice Cube and Chris Tucker. What is the name of its 2000 sequel?

A. *Friday After Next*

B. *Next Friday*

C. *Saturday*

D. *Friday 2*

2354. This actor dies in the films *The Last Temptation of Christ*, *Platoon*, and *Shadow of the Vampire*. Who is this?

A. Harvey Keitel

B. Willem Dafoe

C. John Malkovich

D. Tom Berenger

2355. Ingrid Bergman portrays the great title character in the 1948 film *Joan of Arc*. She later reprised her role in a film directed by her husband Roberto Rossellini. What is the title of this film?

A. *Joan of Arc at the Stake*

B. *Joan of Arc: The Last Days*

C. *The Messenger: The Story of Joan of Arc*

D. *The Legend of Joan of Arc*

2356. Three of these films were adapted from video games. One of them was not. Which one?

A. *House of the Dead*

B. *Sky Captain and the World of Tomorrow*

C. *Lara Croft: Tomb Raider*

D. *Doom*

2357. Singer Lyle Lovett appears in four films directed by Robert Altman. Which of these title is *not* one of them?

A. *Cookie's Fortune*

B. *The Player*

C. *A Prairie Home Companion*

D. *Short Cuts*

2358.

2359. This man was the first president of the Motion Picture Association of America, and is the namesake of the film censorship code known as "the Hays Code." Who is this?

A. John Hays

B. Will Hays

C. Edward Hays

D. Chester Hays

2360. What rock star appears in the 1973 film *That'll Be the Day*?

A. Chuck Berry

B. Ringo Starr

C. Keith Richards

D. Bill Haley

2361. Which of these animated films features the voice of the late great actor James Stewart as a character named Wylie Burp?

A. *All Dogs Go to Heaven*

B. *The Great Mouse Detective*

C. *An American Tail: Fievel Goes West*

D. *The Secret of NIMH*

2362. What Elliott Gould film character was played on television by Wayne Rogers?

A. Philip Marlowe

B. Theodore Rasputin Waterhouse

C. John Francis McIntyre

D. Max Devlin

2358.

Legendary writer Hunter S. Thompson covered presidential elections, sporting events, and various long strange trips for *Rolling Stone* and other magazines in the '60s and '70s, with a notorious disregard for conventional values like staying sober on the job. The iconoclastic hero of "gonzo" journalism wrote several books based on his wild, drug-fueled experiences, including his most famous work, 1971's *Fear and Loathing in Las Vegas: A Savage Journey to the Heart of the American Dream*.

The book became a movie in 1998, called simply *Fear and Loathing in Las Vegas*. Actor Johnny Depp briefly moved in with Thompson in order to play him in the film (as "Raoul Duke"). Benicio Del Toro plays his wild-haired attorney, as the two set off for Vegas in a red convertible with a suitcase full of drugs to cover a motocross race—and track down the American dream.

Actor Bill Murray portrays Thompson in an earlier film. What is this film's title?

A. *The Razor's Edge*

B. *Where the Buffalo Roam*

C. *Loose Shoes*

D. *Nothing Lasts Forever*

2363. The films *A Streetcar Named Desire*, *Cat on a Hot Tin Roof*, and *The Glass Menagerie* are all based on plays by the same writer. Name him.

A. Edward Albee

B. Tennessee Williams

C. Arthur Miller

D. Samuel Beckett

2364. Marilyn Monroe is one of the most celebrated screen icons in the history of motion pictures. How many times was she married?

A. One

B. Three

C. Two

D. Four

2365. There are currently five films based on Thomas Harris' cannibalistic character Hannibal Lecter. Which of these films was the first sequel to *The Silence of the Lambs*?

A. *Hannibal Rising*

B. *Hannibal*

C. *Manhunter*

D. *Red Dragon*

2366. *Battle Royale* is a controversial 2000 Japanese film about teenagers in a not-so-distant future who are forced to kill one another in a macabre game in order to survive. What is the title of its 2003 sequel?

A. *Battle Royale II: Blitz Royale*

B. *Battle Royale 2 the Death*

C. *Battle Royale II: Deathblow*

D. *Battle Royale II: Requiem*

2367. Producer Michael Douglas purchased the rights to *One Flew Over the Cuckoo's Nest* and got the movie made with Jack Nicholson in the lead. What actor had originated the role on stage?

A. Michael Douglas

B. Paul Newman

C. Bruce Dern

D. Kirk Douglas

2368. Vincent van Gogh was a famous Dutch painter who lived from 1853 to 1890. Which of the following films is *not* about Van Gogh's life?

A. *Vincent & Theo*

B. *Lust for Life*

C. *The Young Painter*

D. *Vincent*

2369. The animated film *Shrek 2* introduced a feisty feline character named Puss In Boots. What color is Puss In Boots primarily?

A. Black

B. White

C. Orange

D. Gray

2370. Rhett Butler and his new bride Scarlett go on a honeymoon in *Gone with the Wind*. To what city do they go?

A. Paris

B. New York

C. New Orleans

D. London

2371. Meg Ryan and Tom Hanks appear in three films together. Which of these films is *not* one of them?

A. *Joe Versus the Volcano*

C. *Sleepless in Seattle*

B. *You've Got Mail*

D. *Volunteers*

2372. What legendary 1930s screen icon was nicknamed the "King of Hollywood"?

A. Spencer Tracy

C. Clark Gable

B. James Stewart

D. Gary Cooper

2373.

2374. What war is depicted in the 1970 Robert Altman film *M*A*S*H*?

A. Vietnam

C. Korean War

B. World War II

D. The Clone Wars

2375. Hong Kong action star Bruce Lee died of cerebral edema on July 20, 1973. What film was he working on at the time of his death?

A. *Return of the Dragon*

C. *The Chinese Connection*

B. *Game of Death*

D. *Enter the Dragon*

2376. *Oldboy* won the Grand Prix and *Fahrenheit 9/11* won the Palme d'Or at the 2004 Cannes Film Festival. What filmmaker was jury president that year?

A. Martin Scorsese

C. Quentin Tarantino

B. Lars von Trier

D. Michael Radford

2377. What famous filmmaker's autobiography was originally titled *An Oily Toad*, but was later retitled to *Something Like An Autobiography*?

A. John Woo

C. Akira Kurosawa

B. Federico Fellini

D. Ingmar Bergman

2378. What film studio famously boasted of having more stars in its stable than there were stars in heaven?

A. Warner Bros

C. RKO

B. Paramount

D. United Artists

2373.

Fight Club is an adaptation of Chuck Palahniuk's novel of the same title. When the David Fincher–helmed film was initially released in 1999, it received mixed reviews and was a box office disappointment. However, it has since developed a tremendous cult following.

The film follows the path of an unhappy insomniac whose name is never given (Edward Norton). He begins attending support groups for ailments and conditions he doesn't have. The man's life finds meaning when he encounters a soap salesman named Tyler Durden (Brad Pitt), and the two of them establish a club in which men can beat each other to a pulp simply for the sake of doing so.

What is the name of the man with "man boobs" who the narrator befriends at a testicular cancer support group?

A. Bob

B. Adam

C. Tom

D. Jim

2379. The unseen creatures known as Those We Don't Speak Of in the film *The Village* are said to be angered by the sight of a color. What is this "bad color"?

A. Yellow

B. Black

C. Chartreuse

D. Red

2380. His fans want a constitutional amendment added that will make people born in foreign countries eligible for U.S. presidency. In what country was Arnold Schwarzenegger born?

A. Austria

B. Germany

C. Czechoslavakia

D. Croatia

2381. *West Side Story* is a 1961 musical update of Shakespeare's *Romeo & Juliet*. In the film, who kills the character Riff?

A. Chino

B. Action

C. Tony

D. Bernardo

2382. One of the four lovely ladies from the TV show *Sex and the City* also appears in the films *Porky's*, *Police Academy*, and *Turk 182*. Do you know which one?

A. Sarah Jessica Parker

B. Kristin Davis

C. Kim Cattrall

D. Cynthia Nixon

2383. *Moulin Rouge!* is a 2001 musical directed by Baz Luhrmann. Which character dies at the end of the film?

A. Christian

B. The Duke

C. Satine

D. Harold Zigler

2384. A famous filmmaker once observed, "All you need for a movie is a gun and a girl." Who said this?

A. Sam Peckinpah

B. Quentin Tarantino

C. Jean-Luc Godard

D. François Truffaut

2385. The title character from the *Harry Potter* films is a young wizard. What is the name of Harry's best friend?

A. Dudley Dursley

B. George Weasley

C. Ron Weasley

D. Rubeus Hagrid

2386. A character in one of Alfred Hitchcock's films says, "I wouldn't even hurt a fly." Which film features this line?

A. *Vertigo*

B. *North by Northwest*

C. *Marnie*

D. *Psycho*

2387. One film's tagline describes the movie as having "one heterosexual male" and "eighteen lesbians." What is the name of this film?

A. Bound

B. Straight from the Suburbs

C. She Hate Me

D. The Sex Monster

2388. Three of these films were directed by Woody Allen. Which one was not?

A. Interiors

B. Crimes and Misdemeanors

C. Celebrity

D. Play It Again, Sam

2389.

2390. The avant-garde collective known as Dogme 95 was established in 1995, but didn't produce its first film until 1998. The first Dogme film was directed by Thomas Vinterberg. Can you name it?

A. The Idiots

B. The Celebration

C. Breaking the Waves

D. The King Is Alive

2391. Ferris pretends to be a man named Abe Frohman in *Ferris Bueller's Day Off*. What is Abe Froman said to be the Chicago king of?

A. Used automobiles

B. Quality footwear

C. Fashion accessories

D. Sausage

2392. At the end of the horror classic *Alien*, only Ripley and her cat survive. What is the name of her cat?

A. Red

B. Tom

C. Bean

D. Jones

2393. Two students go to the institution to interview Karl in *Sling Blade*. What are they expressly warned not to do with Karl?

A. Mention his father

B. Take his picture

C. Touch him

D. Make sudden movements

2394. *The Body*, the novella the film *Stand By Me* is based upon, takes place in Maine. What state serves as the setting for the film?

A. Connecticut

B. Oregon

C. Washington

D. Maine

2389.

James Dean is one of the most legendary actors in American film history, and has become a cultural icon since his untimely death at the age of twenty-four.

Dean held smaller roles in numerous movies before landing the three big films he would become known for: *East of Eden*, *Giant*, and *Rebel Without a Cause*. He was said to take many of his cues from Marlon Brando, following both Brando's acting techniques and his rebellious lifestyle. After getting a part in *East of Eden*, a film loosely based on the John Steinbeck novel of the same name, Dean bought himself a red MG TD race car, which sparked his appetite for racing. Later, he would trade in the MG for a Porsche 550 Spyder, nicknamed "Little Bastard"—the car in which he ultimately lost his life in a head-on collision.

Dean was the first actor ever to receive a posthumous Academy Award nomination for Best Actor. He was nominated for both *East of Eden* and *Giant*, although it is his role as Jim Stark in *Rebel Without a Cause* for which he is most widely known.

James Dean died only days after completing work on a film. What is this film?

A. Somebody Up There Likes Me

B. Giant

C. Rebel Without a Cause

D. East of Eden

2395. Bruce Campbell's *Evil Dead 2* character Ash loses his hand. He then attaches something to his arm in its place. What is this?

A. Knife

B. Chainsaw

C. Power drill

D. Sword

2396. What was the first film ever to gross more than $100 million at the box office?

A. *Star Wars*

B. *Jaws*

C. *Close Encounters of the Third Kind*

D. *The Godfather*

2397. In what film does Angelina Jolie's real-life dad play her character's father?

A. *Lara Croft: Tomb Raider*

B. *Girl, Interrupted*

C. *Foxfire*

D. *Gone in 60 Seconds*

2398. The 2006 animated film *Happy Feet* is about a penguin who cannot sing, but tap dances instead. What is his name?

A. Shakes

B. Mumble

C. Wiggles

D. Barry

2399. Which of these Akira Kurosawa films does *not* feature the great Toshiro Mifune?

A. *Yojimbo*

B. *Seven Samurai*

C. *Kagemusha*

D. *Rashomon*

2400. Everyone shown watching television in the silly sequel *Creepshow 2* is watching the same show. What is this TV series?

A. *Gunsmoke*

B. *The Cisco Kid*

C. *The Lone Ranger*

D. *Bonanza*

2401. The character Morrie owes Jimmy some cash in the film *Goodfellas*. Morrie owns his own store. What does he sell?

A. Toupees

B. Women's wear

C. Shoes

D. Auto supplies

2402. LesterCorp, the company where John Cusack's character works in *Being John Malkovich*, is located on an unusual floor of its building. What floor is this?

A. 5 1/2

B. 6 1/2

C. 7 1/2

D. 8 1/2

2403. What do the title characters of the film *Harold and Maude* steal and then drive into the country to give it freedom?

A. Pigeon

B. Tree

C. Canary

D. Rosebush

2404. In *Amadeus*, Salieri says he cannot remember a time when he didn't know Mozart's name. What does he say his father called Mozart?

A. A national treasure

B. A trained monkey

C. A gift from God

D. Genius

2405.

2406. What is the only movie to feature then-husband and wife Sean Penn and Madonna?

A. *Who's That Girl*

B. *Shanghai Surprise*

C. *Vision Quest*

D. *Desperately Seeking Susan*

2407. Henry Fonda is typically remembered for the many good guys he played onscreen. In which of these films did he play a bad guy?

A. *The Rounders*

B. *The Last of the Cowboys*

C. *The Cheyenne Social Club*

D. *Once Upon a Time in the West*

2408. The film *12 Angry Men* focuses on the jury deliberations of a murder trial. With what type of weapon was the murder committed?

A. .45 caliber handgun

B. Hunting knife

C. Shotgun

D. Switchblade knife

2409. *The Trial* is a surreal 1962 Orson Welles thriller starring Anthony Perkins. It is based on a novel by an existentialist author. Who is this?

A. Albert Camus

B. Friedrich Nietzsche

C. Franz Kafka

D. Jean-Paul Sartre

2410. Nicolas Cage's character Ronny Cammareri loses his hand in an accident in the 1987 film *Moonstruck*. With what type of device does this occur?

A. Lawn mower

B. Paper shredder

C. Tiller

D. Bread slicer

2405.

The 1954 thriller *Rear Window* is widely considered one of director Alfred Hitchcock's finest films. The film, which stars James Stewart, Grace Kelly, and Raymond Burr, was adapted from Cornell Woolrich's 1942 short story "It Had to Be Murder."

The film focuses on a photographer named L.B. Jefferies (Stewart), who is momentarily confined to his apartment while recovering from an accident. As he stays home and mends, Jefferies becomes somewhat of a peeping Tom, spying on his neighbors through binoculars. This leads to his seeing some things that cause him to believe one of his neighbors has murdered his wife.

Rear Window received four Academy Award nominations, including Best Director and Best Screenplay, and is frequently listed on many all-time greatest film lists.

Which of these items is used by Jefferies as a weapon against Thorwald?

A. Coat rack

B. Camera

C. Pencil

D. Screwdriver

2411. Cary Grant plays a thief named John Robie in the film *To Catch a Thief*. By what nickname is John Robie known professionally?

A. The Leopard

B. The Cat

C. The Panther

D. The Jaguar

2412. The mask Michael Myers wears in the *Halloween* films is actually a mask depicting the face of a famous person. Do you know who this is?

A. Richard Nixon

B. William Shatner

C. Ronald Reagan

D. Howard Cosell

2413. A deceased screen icon makes a return to the screen in the film *Sky Captain and the World of Tomorrow* via some slick editing. Who is this?

A. Clark Gable

B. Carole Lombard

C. Laurence Olivier

D. John Wayne

2414. Holly Golightly has a pet in the film *Breakfast at Tiffany's*. What is its name?

A. Doc

B. Fluffy

C. Cat

D. Whiskers

2415. What is the title of the Beatles tune that serves as the theme song to *The World According to Garp*, an offbeat 1982 film starring Robin Williams?

A. "Eleanor Rigby"

B. "Lucy in the Sky with Diamonds"

C. "When I'm Sixty-Four"

D. "A Day in the Life"

2416. One legendary actor once quipped, "I'm a whore. All actors are whores. We sell our bodies to the highest bidder." Who said this?

A. Spencer Tracy

B. Clark Gable

C. Marlon Brando

D. William Holden

2417. Screenwriter William Goldman and director Rob Reiner have collaborated on two films to date. Which one of these films is one of them?

A. *Stand by Me*

B. *Misery*

C. *A Few Good Men*

D. *The Sure Thing*

2418. Quentin Tarantino wrote the fictitious Mexican sanctuary El Rey into the screenplay for *From Dusk Till Dawn* after reading about it in a novel by Jim Thompson. What is this novel?

A. *The Grifters*

B. *The Killer Inside Me*

C. *The Getaway*

D. *The Kill-Off*

2419. Director Wayne Wang made two films, *Smoke* and *Blue in the Face*, simultaneously. What year saw the release of these two films?

A. 1994

B. 1995

C. 1996

D. 1997

2420. Bill Murray's character Bob Wiley in *What About Bob?* says there are only two kinds of people: the kind who like a particular singer, and those who don't. Who is this?

A. Donna Summer

B. Barbra Streisand

C. Elton John

D. Neil Diamond

2421. Actors Freddie Prinze, Jr. and Matthew Lillard have made a number of films together. Which of these titles is *not* one of them?

A. *Scream*

B. *Summer Catch*

C. *Scooby Doo*

D. *Wing Commander*

2422.

2423. *High Noon* finds Sheriff Will Kane waiting for the imminent arrival of gunmen hoping to kill him. How many gunmen arrive?

A. Three

B. Four

C. Five

D. Six

2424. Much is made of Indio's pocket watch in the film *For a Few Dollars More*. Whose watch was it originally?

A. Colonel Mortimer

B. Colonel Mortimer's wife

C. Colonel Mortimer's daughter

D. Colonel Mortimer's son

2425. *A Christmas Story* is a 1983 film that has become a holiday favorite. In the film, what does Ralphie want for Christmas?

A. Cowboy boots

B. BB gun

C. Pocket knife

D. Chemistry set

2426. The Berlin International Film Festival was first established in 1951. What is the name of the top honor bestowed upon a film at this festival?

A. Golden Bear

B. Golden Lion

C. Golden Goose

D. Golden Eagle

2427. Rupert Everett plays William Shakepeare's rival in the film *Shakespeare in Love*. What is his name?

A. Hugh Fennyman

B. Philip Henslowe

C. Christopher Marlowe

D. Richard Burbage

2422.

Memento is a critically acclaimed psychological thriller, written and directed by Christopher Nolan and starring Guy Pearce, Carrie-Anne Moss, and Joe Pantoliano, that tells its story in reverse chronological order.

In the story, Leonard Shelby is suffering from anterograde amnesia, which allows Leonard to remember everything that happened prior to his injury (a blow to the head when he unsuccessfully attempted to save his wife's life) but unable to form new memories. Leonard is determined to seek vengence, but he must constantly remind himself of his mission and everything that has happened by leaving himself messages on the walls and even on his flesh.

The film, which received two Academy Award nominations and a Golden Globes nod, won the AFI for Best Screenplay and introduced the world to an exciting new artistic talent in writer/director Christopher Nolan.

What is the name of Natalie's drug-dealer boyfriend?

A. Dodd

B. Jimmy Grants

C. Sammy Jankis

D. John G

2428. Christopher Walken has made a career out of playing criminals. In what film does Walken play a mob boss known only as The Man With The Plan?

A. *Suicide Kings*

B. *Things to Do in Denver When You're Dead*

C. *Last Man Standing*

D. *True Romance*

2429. Quentin Tarantino's *Pulp Fiction*, *Jackie Brown*, and *Kill Bill* have all been released by the same studio. What is this studio, sometimes referred to as the "House That Quentin Built"?

A. Miramax

B. New Line

C. Warner Bros.

D. Artisan

2430. One of the characters from *The Godfather* is murdered while sitting at a toll booth. Which character is this?

A. Michael Corleone

B. Vito Corleone

C. Sonny Corleone

D. Fredo Corleone

2431. This Oscar-winning screenwriter released four films in 2006: *The Last Kiss*, *Flags of Our Fathers*, *Letters from Iwo Jima*, and *Casino Royale*. Who is this?

A. William Goldman

B. Steven Zaillian

C. Akiva Goldsman

D. Paul Haggis

2432. One legendary actor remarked in 1996, "I just wish every film I liked wasn't either foreign or made in America with such terrible difficulty. It's the worst period ever for trying to do interesting work." Who said this?

A. Peter O'Toole

B. Robert De Niro

C. Jack Nicholson

D. Warren Beatty

2433. Legendary author Harlan Ellison successfully sued the producers of *The Terminator*, saying the film stole elements of two episodes he wrote for a television series. What is this series?

A. *The Twilight Zone*

B. *Night Gallery*

C. *Alfred Hitchcock Presents*

D. *The Outer Limits*

2434. Film noir is a genre of crime film that is usually black and white and features cynical dialogue and a femme fatale. What is the literal meaning of the term "film noir"?

A. Detective film

B. Crime film

C. Gray film

D. Black film

2435. The same composer scored the films *Star Wars*, *Superman*, and *Raiders of the Lost Ark*. Who is he?

A. John Barry

B. Jerry Goldsmith

C. John Williams

D. Danny Elfman

2436. Clint Eastwood and Lee Van Cleef are generally regarded as the two biggest names to emerge from the so-called Spaghetti Western films of the 1970s. Which of these films features both actors?

A. *A Fistful of Dollars*

B. *The Magnificent Stranger*

C. *Once Upon a Time in the West*

D. *For a Few Dollars More*

2437. This actor played the title character in Charles Chaplin's *The Kid* and later played Uncle Fester on the television series *The Addams Family*. Who is this?

A. Chester Conklin

B. Jackie Coogan

C. Christopher Lloyd

D. Billy House

2438.

2439. *Point of No Return* is a 1993 remake of a Luc Besson film. What is the title of Besson's original film?

A. *Leon*

B. *The Last Combat*

C. *La Femme Nikita*

D. *The Big Blue*

2440. With which of these films did accomplished screenwriter Shane Black make his own directorial debut?

A. *The Long Kiss Goodnight*

B. *Kiss Kiss Bang Bang*

C. *The Last Boy Scout*

D. *Last Action Hero*

2441. The late Rodney Dangerfield is remembered as one of the greatest comics of all time. With what film did he make his acting debut?

A. *Caddyshack*

B. *The Projectionist*

C. *Easy Money*

D. *Moving*

2442. Both of actress Jamie Lee Curtis' parents were accomplished actors. Her father is Tony Curtis. Who is her mother?

A. Tippi Hedren

B. Janet Leigh

C. Kim Novak

D. Grace Kelly

2443. Three of these films were adapted from plays. One of them was not. Which is the odd man out?

A. *Rear Window*

B. *Key Largo*

C. *Sabrina*

D. *Dial M for Murder*

2438.

Anchorman: The Legend of Ron Burgundy is a 2004 comedy starring Will Ferrell, Christina Applegate, and Steve Carell. The film, cowritten (with Ferrell) and directed by Adam McKay, parodies 1970s American culture and the serious-as-a-heart-attack silliness of television "Action News" anchors.

The film tells the story of a pompous award-winning anchor named Ron Burgundy (Ferrell), who is the star of his San Diego news team, comprised of sex-obsessed field reporter Brian Fantana (Paul Rudd), ignorant Southern sportscaster Champ Kind (David Koechner)—known for his idiotic catchphrase ("Whammy!")—and semi-retarded weatherman Brick Tamland (Carell).

Up until now, all Burgundy and company have had to worry about are absurdly barbaric *Gangs of New York*-style street fights with competing news teams (featuring cameos by the likes of Vince Vaughn, Luke Wilson, and Ben Stiller). But when a new female anchor (Applegate) arrives to meet a quota, the male members of the news team feel threatened.

How many Emmys has Ron Burgundy won?

A. Four

B. Five

C. Six

D. Seven

2444. What is the name of the song that plays each and every time Bill Murray's alarm clock goes off in the comedy *Groundhog Day*?

A. "Love Will Keep Us Together"   C. "I Got You Babe"
B. "I Am . . . I Said"   D. "Three Times a Lady"

2445. Johnny Depp plays an undercover FBI agent posing as a mobster in the film *Donnie Brasco*. What is Donnie Brasco's real name?

A. Tommy Pirelli   C. Joe DeVito
B. Tommy Carello   D. Joe Pistone

2446. Harrison Ford is the president of the United States in *Air Force One*. Who's the vice-president?

A. Meryl Streep   C. William H. Macy
B. Gary Oldman   D. Glenn Close

2447. This actor once remarked, "My movies were the kind that they show in prisons and airplanes, because nobody can leave." Who said this?

A. Burt Reynolds   C. Jim Brown
B. Chuck Norris   D. Charles Bronson

2448. Bruce Nolan is an ordinary man who assumes the role of God in the 2003 comedy *Bruce Almighty*. What is Bruce's occupation?

A. Pet detective   C. Police officer
B. Reporter   D. Lawyer

2449. What author's novel served as the source material for Steven Spielberg's 1985 film *The Color Purple*?

A. Alex Haley   C. Alice Walker
B. Maya Angelou   D. James Baldwin

2450. In the action movie *Face/Off*, Sean Archer is after Castor Troy because he wants to avenge the death of his son. What was the name of his son?

A. Eric   C. Timmy
B. Sean   D. Michael

2451. What is the name of the tough-as-nails gangster played by Joe Pesci in the film *Casino*?

A. Vincent Gambini   C. Jimmy Alto
B. Nicky Santoro   D. Tommy DeVito

2452. *Airplane!* is a 1980 spoof of disaster films that centers around a commercial flight on which the captain dies. What is the destination of the airplane?

A. New York City

B. St. Louis

C. Chicago

D. Philadelphia

2453. Rick Moranis plays the character Louis Tully in the film *Ghostbusters*. What is Louis' occupation?

A. Accountant

B. IRS agent

C. Librarian

D. Scientist

2454. Forrest picks up a feather at the beginning of *Forrest Gump* and sticks it inside his book. What is the book he's holding?

A. *Cat in the Hat*

B. *Where the Sidewalk Ends*

C. *Curious George*

D. *Charlotte's Web*

2455.

2456. A noted filmmaker once remarked, "Movie directing is a perfect refuge for the mediocre." Who said this?

A. Elia Kazan

B. Anthony Mann

C. William Wellman

D. Orson Welles

2457. Dunbar spends the better half of the film *Dances with Wolves* waiting for reinforcements at an abandoned isolated military post. What is the name of this post?

A. Fort Laramie

B. Fort Totten

C. Fort Mill Ridge

D. Fort Sedgwick

2458. *All About Eve* is the story of two actresses. What is the name of the Max Fabian-produced play they are working on throughout the film?

A. *Aged in Wood*

B. *Aged in Fire*

C. *Aged in Bronze*

D. *Aged in Wine*

2459. Jim McAllister finds himself in hot water after attempting to change the election results in the film *Election*. How many votes did he throw into the trash?

A. Three

B. Two

C. Four

D. Five

2455.

The 1983 drama *Scarface* is considered a seminal film of its time. Written by Oliver Stone and directed by Brian De Palma, it is a loose remake of the 1932 Howard Hawks film of the same title. Rather than focusing on a fictionalized Al Capone, however, De Palma's film chronicles the rise and fall of a Cuban cocaine dealer in 1980s Miami.

Scarface begins with the arrival of Cuban hitman Tony Montana (Al Pacino) in the United States. Tony becomes involved in the cocaine business, working for Frank Lopez (Robert Loggia), until his ego and greed drive Tony to whack his boss and take over his business operations.

When *Scarface* was released in 1983, it was a minimal success and received negative critical attention. In the years since, however, the film has become an iconic fixture in American popular culture, spawning video games and being referenced in countless songs, movies, and television shows.

What is the name of Tony's right-hand man, who later marries his sister?

A. Manny

B. Emilio Rebenga

C. Chi-Chi

D. Sosa

2460. What song does Lloyd Dobler blast from his boombox under Diane Court's window in *Say Anything . . .*?

A. "All for Love" by Nancy Wilson   **C.** "In Your Eyes" by Peter Gabriel

B. "Stripped" by Depeche Mode   **D.** "Flower" by Soundgarden

2461. Molly Ringwald gives Judd Nelson a gift at the end of John Hughes' *The Breakfast Club*. What is this?

A. Earring   **C.** Ring

B. Necklace   **D.** None of these

2462. One contemporary actor has said, "I think it's important that you still live up to your responsibilities as a professional. We work in a business where the structure is in place to allow you to be the biggest asshole you can be." Who said this?

A. Kevin Spacey   **C.** Tom Cruise

B. Harrison Ford   **D.** Tom Hanks

2463. *Butch Cassidy and the Sundance Kid* repeatedly run into an overly loyal railroad worker who won't let them into the car holding the safe. What is this man's name?

A. Woodburn   **C.** Woodcock

B. Woodchild   **D.** Woodhouse

2464. Willard travels up the river to find Kurtz and terminate him in the film *Apocalypse Now*. What is the name of the fictional Cambodian river on which he must travel?

A. Kambuja River   **C.** Nung River

B. Chenla River   **D.** Khe Sanh

2465. In the tearjerker *Beaches*, Hillary's Aunt Vesta gives C.C. some money to "keep her honest." How much money does she give her?

A. $1   **C.** $3

B. $5   **D.** $7

2466. Writer and director Christopher Guest plays the character Harlan Pepper in the comedy *Best in Show*. What type of food does Harlan say he's obsessed with to the point that naming the varieties drove his mother crazy?

A. Berries   **C.** Nuts

B. Lettuce   **D.** Bread

2467. Annie advises Nuke to breathe in a certain way in *Bull Durham*. How is this?

A. As little as possible   **C.** Through his eyes

B. Through his ears   **D.** Backward

2468. Steve Buscemi's character warns the bartender about a mysterious man in the 1995 film *Desperado*. What is the name of Buscemi's character?

A. Gringo   C. Smith

B. Jimmy   D. Buscemi

2469. Three of these Alfred Hitchcock films have been remade by Hollywood. Which one has not?

A. *Vertigo*   C. *Rear Window*

B. *Psycho*   D. *Dial M for Murder*

2470. Three men attempt to recapture their youth by establishing a fraternity house in the comedy *Old School*. What actor plays the character known as Frank the Tank?

A. Will Ferrell   C. Jeremy Piven

B. Vince Vaughn   D. Luke Wilson

2471. Each thief is assigned a color as a code name in the film *Reservoir Dogs*. What color is Quentin Tarantino's character assigned?

A. Pink   C. Brown

B. Yellow   D. Black

2472.

2473. A popular actor once said, "I'd love to do a character with a wife, a nice little house, a couple of kids, a dog, maybe a bit of singing, and no guns and no killing, but nobody offers me those kinds of parts." Who said this?

A. Al Pacino   C. Robert De Niro

B. Joe Pesci   D. Christopher Walken

2474. Gordon Gecko shows off a .45 Luger in *Wall Street*, saying that it's the rarest gun in the world. How many does he say were manufactured?

A. 10   C. 8

B. 6   D. 3

2475. What author's novels have been adapted into the films *Jackie Brown, Get Shorty*, and *Out of Sight*?

A. Max Allan Collins   C. James M. Cain

B. Elmore Leonard   D. Ed McBain

2472.

The 1989 film *Field of Dreams*, an adaptation of the novel by W.P. Kinsella, stars Kevin Costner and combines fantastical elements with baseball to create a magical story.

Ray Kinsella (Costner) is an Iowa farmer who believes he's hearing voices telling him to plow his cornfield under and build a baseball diamond in its place. Ray believes the ghost of baseball legend "Shoeless" Joe Jackson will appear if he does this. His wife Annie (Amy Madigan) supports Ray's decision to construct the baseball diamond, but is worried when the voices return and ask Ray to travel across the country to ease the pain of reclusive author and activist Terrence Mann (James Earl Jones). In the end, the film becomes the story of Ray's last chance to reconcile with his own deceased father.

What author was the character Terence Mann loosely modeled after?

A. Kurt Vonnegut, Jr.

B. James Baldwin

C. J.D. Salinger

D. Alex Haley

2476. What name does Howard Stern give to his unborn baby in the 1997 comedy biopic *Private Parts*?

A. Bumpy

B. Lumpy

C. None of these

D. Clumpy

2477. What section of the Los Angeles area is Samuel L. Jackson's character Jules said to be from in the film *Pulp Fiction*?

A. Inglewood

B. South Central

C. Compton

D. Van Nuys

2478. This author wrote the novels that the films *Dark Blue*, *L.A. Confidential*, and *Black Dahlia* are based on. Can you name him?

A. Mickey Spillane

B. James Ellroy

C. Dashiell Hammett

D. Jim Thompson

2479. David Herman's *Office Space* character shares his name with a famous singer. Who is this?

A. Michael Bolton

B. Michael Jackson

C. Neil Diamond

D. Peter Cetera

2480. Joe and Kathleen meet and communicate via the Internet in the 1998 comedy *You've Got Mail*. What is Joe's screen moniker?

A. NY132

B. NY152

C. NY162

D. NY142

2481. *The Royal Tenenbaums* is a quirky 2001 comedy directed by Wes Anderson. What actor serves as the film's narrator?

A. Ben Stiller

B. Martin Sheen

C. Gene Hackman

D. Alec Baldwin

2482. Cole and Kathryn slip into a dark movie theater to hide in the film *12 Monkeys*. What classic film is playing in the theater?

A. *Vertigo*

B. *Casablanca*

C. *Touch of Evil*

D. *The Third Man*

2483. Val Kilmer has enjoyed a long career in which he's played a large variety of characters. He has even portrayed a few celebrities. Which of these people has not been portrayed by Kilmer?

A. Jesus Christ

B. Elvis Presley

C. Doc Holliday

D. John Holmes

2484. This famous filmmaker once said, "I have always thought that in the motion picture business the real violence was not what people do on screen, but what we do to raise the money."

A. Martin Scorsese
B. David Fincher
C. David Mamet
D. Brian De Palma

2485. John Megna plays the character Charles Baker "Dill" Harris in the film *To Kill a Mockingbird*. What real-life person was Dill based upon?

A. Truman Capote
B. Gore Vidal
C. John Steinbeck
D. Norman Mailer

2486. When *The Shawshank Redemption*'s Brooks learns that he's going to be freed, he snaps and holds a knife to someone's throat. Who is this?

A. Andy
B. Tommy
C. Red
D. Heywood

2487. Raymond, Dustin Hoffman's character in *Rain Man*, is afraid of flying but says there is one airline that has never crashed. Can you name the airline?

A. Canadian Metro
B. Qantas
C. TWA
D. China Northwest

2488. HAL sings "Daisy Bell" while being disconnected in *2001: A Space Odyssey*. At this point he says where he was created. Where was this?

A. Skokie, Illinois
B. Arlington Heights, Illinois
C. Peoria, Illinois
D. Urbana, Illinois

2489.

2490. Can you name the singer/composer responsible for the songs "I Will Go Sailing No More" and "You've Got a Friend in Me" in the film *Toy Story*?

A. Elton John
B. Bernie Taupin
C. Billy Joel
D. Randy Newman

2491. Ralph Bellamy and Don Ameche play the villainous brothers Randolph and Mortimer in the comedy *Trading Places*. The two reprise these roles in another Eddie Murphy film. What is the film?

A. *Coming to America*
B. *Another 48 Hrs.*
C. *Boomerang*
D. *Metro*

2492. In *The Wizard of Oz*, which single actor plays Professor Marvel, the Emerald City doorman, the Wizard's guard, a cabbie, and the Wizard himself?

A. Bert Lahr
B. Ray Bolger
C. Charley Grapewin
D. Frank Morgan

2489.

Although lead actor Peter O'Toole is the person most frequently remembered for David Lean's epic 70mm masterpiece *Lawrence of Arabia*, Robert Bolt's superb screenplay and Freddie Young's breathtaking cinematography could also be cited as stars.

The movie depicts the World War I exploits of the legendary Lieutenant Colonel T.E. Lawrence (O'Toole). Lawrence is dispatched by the British Army to assess and report the prospects of Bedouin Prince Faisel's (Alec Guinness) revolt against the Turks. He then recruits the powerful Howeitat tribe to assist Faisel's men, and masterminds an attack on the coastal city of Aqaba. Lawrence finally helps wage a guerrilla war against the Turks.

Lawrence of Arabia received an impressive ten Academy Award nominations. These resulted in seven Oscars, including Best Picture, Best Director, and Best Cinematography. The film went on to win prizes at virtually every other awards ceremony, and has since been ranked at number five on the American Film Institute's 1998 list of the one hundred greatest American films.

What actor appears in the film as Howeitat leader Auda abu Tayi?

A. Omar Sharif
B. Anthony Quinn
C. Jack Hawkins
D. Jose Ferrer

2493. This noted filmmaker once remarked of Sam Peckinpah, "I can shoot three people, put 'em to the burial ground, and bury 'em by the time he gets one person down to the ground." Who said this?

A. John Ford

B. Budd Boetticher

C. Howard Hawks

D. Anthony Mann

2494. Which *Seinfeld* cast member appears in the films *The Mosquito Coast*, *Brighton Beach Memoirs*, and *Pretty Woman*?

A. Jerry Seinfeld

B. Jason Alexander

C. Michael Richards

D. Julia Louis-Dreyfus

2495. What actor came to the public's attention as Falconetti on *Rich Man, Poor Man* before making movies such as *Conan the Barbarian*, *Red Dawn*, and *Zombiegeddon*?

A. Ari Bavel

B. Ben Johnson

C. Peter Strauss

D. William Smith

2496. Who is the only screenwriter in history to have written back-to-back Best Picture winners?

A. John Huston

B. William Goldman

C. Bo Goldman

D. Paul Haggis

2497. Can you name the actor who played the role of the hologram SRT in *THX 1138* before appearing in such films as *Black Caesar* and *Sugar Hill*?

A. Fred Williamson

B. Don Pedro Colley

C. D'Urville Martin

D. Glynn Turman

2498. Which of these musicals received the most Academy Award nominations?

A. *Dreamgirls*

B. *Chicago*

C. *Evita*

D. *Moulin Rouge!*

2499. Samuel L. Jackson, a self-proclaimed *Star Wars* fan, requested a certain color light saber in the film *Star Wars: Attack of the Clones*. What is this color?

A. Green

B. Purple

C. Blue

D. Orange

2500. The shower scene from the original *Psycho* is one of the most iconic scenes in motion picture history. What substance was used as blood?

A. Chocolate syrup

B. Food coloring

C. None of these

D. Ketchup

ABOUT THE AUTHOR

Andrew J. Rausch is a freelance writer and film critic whose articles, essays, reviews, and celebrity interviews have appeared in numerous publications, including *Film Threat*, *Creative Screenwriting*, *Shock Cinema*, *Bright Lights Film Journal*, *Micro-Film*, and *Images: A Journal of Film and Popular Culture*. Rausch is also the author of numerous film books including *The 100 Greatest American Films: A Quiz Book*, *Turning Points in Film History*, and *Fifty Filmmakers: Conversations with Directors from Roger Avary to Steven Zaillian*. In addition, Rausch has worked on a number of B-movies in various capacities, including producer, screenwriter, actor, composer, and cinematographer. He resides in Parsons, Kansas, with his wife Kerri and their four children.

ACKNOWLEDGMENTS

The author would like to thank the following individuals for their assistance, encouragement, and patience: God, my wife Kerri, my agent Marilyn Allen, the staff at becker&mayer!, Dan and Sherry Rausch, my mentor Steve Spignesi, Michael Dequina, Fred Rosenberg, Sean Westhoff, Chris Watson, Josh Barnett, Ryan Kasson, Ryan Robertson, Mark Gardner, Ryan Hixon, Henry Nash, Aron Taylor, Matt and Peggy Hoisington, Tim and Mary Reynolds, Norman and Marion Leistikow, Steve Harper, and Sam and Cyndee Timmerman. I would also like to thank our four children, Jordan, Jaiden, Jalyn, and Julian, for fighting quietly enough that I could complete this book with some semblance of sanity.

IMAGE CREDITS

Every effort has been made to trace copyright holders. If any unintended omissions have been made, becker&mayer! would be pleased to add appropriate acknowledgments in future editions. All photographs courtesy of MPTV.net, with the following credits:

Front Cover (left): 1971 Paramount
Front Cover (center): 1960 Paramount
Front Cover (right): © 1997 20th Century Fox
Page 2: 1942 Warner Bros.
Page 8: 1950 20th Century Fox
Page 11: © 1978 David Sutton
Page 13: © 1978 Paramount
Page 15: Anonymous
Page 16: Anonymous
Page 19: © 1978 Ned Scott Archive
Page 20: 1955 20th Century Fox
Page 23: 1935 Paramount
Page 24: 1939 Columbia
Page 26: 1930 Paramount / Photo by Eugene R. Richee
Page 28: © 1978 Ned Scott Archive
Page 31: © 1995 Warner Bros.
Page 33: Anonymous
Page 35: © 1993 TriStar / Photo by Ken Regan
Page 37: Anonymous
Page 38: 1965 20th Century Fox
Page 41: 1944 Paramount
Page 42: 1946 RKO
Page 45: 1967 Columbia
Page 47: 1950 Paramount
Page 48: 1942 Warner Bros.
Page 50: 1971 Paramount
Page 52: © 1978 John Jay
Page 55: 1960 Paramount
Page 57: © 1980 United Artists
Page 59: © 1981 Paramount
Page 61: 1970 20th Century Fox
Page 63: 1973 Universal
Page 65: 1969 Warner Bros.
Page 67: Anonymous

Page 68: 1971 Warner Bros.
Page 70: © 1988 United Artists / Photo by Stephen Vaughan
Page 73: 1953 Paramount
Page 74: 1941 RKO
Page 77: © 1990 Warner Bros.
Page 79: © 2003 Disney / Photo by Elliott Marks
Page 81: 1963 United Artists
Page 83 © 1978 John Engstead
Page 85: © 1994 Miramax
Page 87: 1961 Paramount
Page 89: 1967 Embassy
Page 90: © 1985 MGM / United Artists
Page 93: © 1994 Paramount
Page 94: © 1992 Warner Bros.
Page 97: © 1978 James Doolittle
Page 99: © 1978 Warner Bros. / Photo by Mel Traxel
Page 100: © 2000 AMPAS
Page 103: Photo by Max Munn Autrey
Page 104: © 1980 Gunther
Page 107: © 1992 Columbia / Photo by Louis Goldman
Page 108: 1952 United Artists
Page 110: 1951 MGM
Page 113: 1977 United Artists
Page 114: 1930 20th Century Fox
Page 117: Anonymous
Page 119: © 1978 David Sutton
Page 121: Photo by Vandamm
Page 123: Photo by Ted Allan
Page 124: © 2002 Glenn Weiner
Page 126: © 1997 20th Century Fox
Page 129: 1968 Warner Bros. / Photo by Mel Traxel

Page 130: © 1978 John Engstead
Page 132: © 1990 Universal / Photo by William Claxton
Page 135: © 2005 Joe Martinez
Page 137: Anonymous
Page 138: 1960 Paramount
Page 140: © 1978 Gene Trindl
Page 143: © 2006 Sony / Photo by Simon Mein
Page 145: Anonymous
Page 147: © 1987 Warner Bros.
Page 149: © 1992 Miramax / Photo by Linda R. Chen
Page 151: © 2006 Joe Martinez
Page 153: 1977 Columbia
Page 155: Anonymous
Page 157: © 1980 Paramount
Page 158: 1972 Paramount
Page 160: Photo by Wynn Hammer
Page 162: 1977 Paramount
Page 165: Anonymous
Page 167: © 2005 Columbia / Photo by Zade Rosenthal
Page 169: 1957 Columbia
Page 171: © 2004 Joe Martinez
Page 173: © 1997 Miramax / Photo by Sergio Strizzi
Page 175: © 1999 Warner Bros.
Page 177: 1972 Warner Bros.
Page 179: © 2001 Warner Bros. / Photo by Bob Marshak
Page 181: 1953 Columbia
Page 183: © 1980 Gunther
Page 185: © 2000 Glenn Weiner
Page 187: © 2006 Warner Bros. / Photo by Andrew Cooper
Page 189: 1940 20th Century Fox

Page 191: © 2006 AMPAS
Page 193: © 2000 Touchstone / Photo by Melissa Moseley
Page 194: 1939 MGM
Page 197: © 1994 Castle Rock / Photo by Michael Weinstein
Page 199: © 1993 Universal / Photo by David James
Page 200: © 1988 Warner Bros. / Photo by Etienne George
Page 203: 1946 Samuel Goldwyn Company
Page 204: © 1999 New Line Cinema / Photo by Peter Sorel
Page 206: © 1980 Warner Bros.
Page 208: © 1999 20th Century Fox / Photo by Van Redin
Page 210: 1976 MGM
Page 212: 1960 AIP
Page 214: © 1998 20th Century Fox / Photo by Merie Wallace
Page 217: © 1988 Orion
Page 219: © 2001 20th Century Fox / Photo by Sue Adler
Page 221: 1938 RKO
Page 222: Anonymous
Page 224: © 2003 DreamWorks / Photo by Darren Michaels
Page 227: © 1984 Universal
Page 229: © 1998 Universal / Photo by Sam Emerson
Page 231: © 1992 Warner Bros.
Page 233: © 1992 TriStar / Photo By Ralph Nelson
Page 235: © 1978 John Jay
Page 237: © 1990 TriStar / Photo by David Appleby
Page 239: 1977 Universal
Page 241: © 1990 Paramount
Page 243: © 1986 20th Century Fox / Photo by Bruce McBroom
Page 245: © 1995 United Artists / Photo by Douglas Kirkland
Page 247: © 1985 TriStar
Page 249: © 1990 Universal / Photo by Henny Garunkel

Page 251: 1968 20th Century Fox
Page 253: © 1987 Vestron
Page 255: © 1990 Warner Bros.
Page 256: © 1998 Gramercy
Page 259: 1973 Warner Bros.
Page 261: 1976 Warner Bros.
Page 263: © 1979 United Artists / Photo by Chas Gerretsen
Page 265: © 1984 Orion
Page 267: © 1988 Universal
Page 269: © 2006 20th Century Fox
Page 271: © 1994 Hollywood Pictures / Photo by Barry Wetcher
Page 272: © 1995 Gramercy / Photo by Linda R. Chen
Page 274: © 1984 Paramount
Page 277: 1971 MGM
Page 279: © 1992 Warner Bros.
Page 281: 1970 20th Century Fox
Page 283: 1976 MGM
Page 285: © 1999 DreamWorks / Photo by Lorey Sebastian
Page 286: © 1982 Universal
Page 289: © 1998 DreamWorks / Photo by David James
Page 291: © 2003 Miramax / Photo by Andrew Cooper
Page 293: © 1978 David Sutton
Page 295: © 2004 20th Century Fox
Page 297: © 1989 Castle Rock
Page 299: © 2004 Icon Prod.
Page 301: © 1980 Universal
Page 303: © 1999 20th Century Fox / Photo by Merrick Morton
Page 305: Anonymous
Page 307: 1954 Paramount
Page 309: © 2000 Newmarket Films / Photo by Danny Rothenberg
Page 311: © 2004 DreamWorks / Photo by Darren Michaels
Page 313: 1983 Universal
Page 315: © 1989 Universal / Photo by Melinda Sue Gordon
Page 317: 1962 Paramount